Advanced Algebra Through Data Exploration

A Graphing Calculator Approach

SOLUTIONS MANUAL

KEY CURRICULUM PRESS
Innovators in Mathematics Education

Project Editor	Crystal Mills
Production Editor	Deborah Cogan
Copy Editor	Margaret Moore
Editorial Assistant	Jeff Gammon
Production Coordinator	Diana Krevsky
Art and Layout	Ann Rothenbuhler
Cover Design	Dennis Teutschel
Contributors	Judy Cubillo, Ellen Kamischke, Jerald Murdock

Publisher

Steven Rasmussen

Editorial Director

John Bergez

This material is based upon work supported by the National Science Foundation under award number MDR9154410. Any opinions, findings, and conclusions or recommendations expressed in this publication are those of the authors and do not necessarily reflect the views of the National Science Foundation.

Key Curriculum Press
P.O. Box 2304
Berkeley, CA 94702
editorial@keypress.com
http://www.keypress.com

Printed in the United States of America   10 9 8 7 6 5 4 3 2   01 00 99 98   ISBN 1-55953-227-0

Contents

Advanced Algebra Through Data Exploration
Teacher's Support Materials

Teacher's Guide and Answer Key

- Overview and philosophy
- Course outlines
- Cooperative learning suggestions
- Assessment suggestions
- Section guides
- Answers for Problem Sets

Teacher's Resource Book

- Transparency and worksheet masters
- Extra projects
- Extra Take Another Looks
- Extra assessment problems
- Data and programs disk for popular calculator models with linking capabilities

Quizzes, Tests, and Exams

- Two quizzes per chapter
- Form A and Form B chapter tests
- Form A and Form B exams (midyear and final) for three different course plans
- CD-ROM with quizzes, tests, and exams formatted for Microsoft Word® for Windows® and Macintosh® computers
- Answers to quizzes, tests, and exams

Solutions Manual

- Complete solutions for Problem Sets
- Project hints and answers
- Take Another Look answers

Blackline Masters for Calculator Notes

- Separate volumes for popular calculator models, keyed to the text

Constructive Assessment in Mathematics
Practical Steps for Classroom Teachers
by David Clarke

- Guide to implementing assessment strategies, including observational assessment, student-constructed tests, group assessment, student self-assessment, student journals, and portfolios
- Tips for recording, interpreting, and communicating assessment information
- Annotated bibliography of assessment resources

Suggested Supplemental Resources

The Geometer's Sketchpad®

- Dynamic geometry software for Windows and Macintosh computers

Exploring Trigonometry with The Geometer's Sketchpad

- Add-on module for The Geometer's Sketchpad that teaches students to actively explore trigonometry
- Includes sample activity disks for Windows and Macintosh computers and a book of blackline activity masters

Exploring Conic Sections with The Geometer's Sketchpad

- Add-on module for The Geometer's Sketchpad that deepens students' understanding of the conic sections
- Includes sample activity disks for Windows and Macintosh computers and a book of blackline activity masters

Introduction

This *Solutions Manual* for *Advanced Algebra Through Data Exploration: A Graphing Calculator Approach* contains solutions to all problems in the Problem Sets, hints and solutions for the Projects, and solutions to the Take Another Look activities. Solutions for the Investigations in the student text can be found in the *Teacher's Guide and Answer Key*. Although complete solutions for the problems are provided, you should keep in mind that often there is more than one method that students might use to solve a particular problem. Also, their answers may vary on some problems depending on assumptions they make. Refer to these solutions when you or the students have difficulty solving a problem and need some assistance in determining a possible approach toward solving it. You might also want to provide a copy of certain solutions for students who have been absent for an extended period of time.

Chapter 0

Problem Set 0.1

1. **a.** $\sqrt{(7^2 + 8^2)} \approx 10.63014581$ **b.** $(2(18 - 2) + 7)/(14 + 2 \cdot 3) = 1.95$

   c. $\sqrt{(12(32 + 43))} = 30$ **d.** $\pi(1/2)12.6^2 \approx 249.3796248$

2. **a.** $(-4)^2 = 16$; $-4^2 = -16$. In the first expression -4 is being squared. In the second, only the 4 is being squared. The squaring is done first (the order of operations), and then the multiplication by -1 causes the sign change.

   b. $17^2 = 289$ **c.** $-24^2 = -576$ **d.** $17 \boxed{\text{STO}}\; x; x \boxed{x^2}; -x \boxed{x^2}$

```
17→X
             17
X²
            289
-X²
           -289
```

3. **a.** i.   8
       ii.   4/5 or 0.8

   b. $12 + \dfrac{3 - \sqrt{169 - 2^3(6)}}{2}$ $\dfrac{2 + \frac{11 - \sqrt{25}}{3}}{\sqrt{6^3 - 20} - \frac{18}{2}}$

   $12 + \dfrac{3 - \sqrt{169 - 8(6)}}{2}$ $\dfrac{2 + \frac{11 - 5}{3}}{\sqrt{216 - 20} - 9}$

   $12 + \dfrac{3 - \sqrt{169 - 48}}{2}$ $\dfrac{2 + \frac{6}{3}}{\sqrt{196} - 9}$

   $12 + \dfrac{3 - \sqrt{121}}{2}$ $\dfrac{2 + 2}{14 - 9}$

   $12 + \dfrac{3 - 11}{2}$ $\dfrac{4}{5}$

   $12 + \dfrac{-8}{2}$

   $12 + -4$

   8

   c. i. $12 + \left(3 - \sqrt{(169 - 2^3(6))}\right)/2$

   ii. $\left(2 + \frac{(11 - \sqrt{25})}{3}\right) / \sqrt{(6^3 - 20 - 18/2)}$

   d. Answers will vary.

4. **a.** Area of a triangle; $(1/2)(12.3) \cdot 43.7$
       i.   268.755   ii.   1.70154   iii.   6.8385
   b. Height of an object in free fall; $-16 \cdot 3.6^2 + 75 \cdot 3.6 + 24.75$
       i.   87.39   ii.   1358.8416   iii.   12.68
   c. Slope of a line given two points; $(11.8 - -5.3)/(-7 - 7)$
       i. -1.221428571 ii.   Value not defined because of division by zero.
       iii. -0.5423728814

5. **a.** $(5 + 3)8/4 = 16$; Add 5 and 3, then multiply by 8 and finally divide by 4.
   b. $7(5 + 3^4) = 602$; Raise 3 to the fourth power and add 5, then multiply by 7.
   c. $(1 + 2(3))4 = 28$; Multiply 2 by 3 and add 1, then multiply by 4.
   d. $(7 - 3 - 2)9 = 18$; Subtract 3 from 7, then subtract 2 and finally multiply by 9.
   e. $15 - 3(7 - 12) = 30$; Subtract 12 from 7, multiply by 3 and then subtract that answer from 15.

6. a. 0.4444444444; The display shows a decimal point followed by ten 4's. This is an exact decimal value.

   b. .4444444444666 ENTER ; The display shows a decimal point followed by ten 4's.
This is an exact decimal value.

   c. A sample answer might be that the calculator displays 10 digits, but works internally with 13.

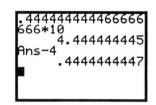

Problem Set 0.2

1. a. i. $12{,}345{,}678\sqrt{(1 - 5{,}000{,}000^2/300{,}000{,}000^2)} = 1.23439632\text{E7}$ or $1.23439632 \cdot 10^7$

     ii. $8.164967851 \cdot 10^{-5}$
Be sure the calculator is set in scientific (SCI) mode.

   b. i. $(1.6 \cdot 10^{-19} \cdot 40{,}000 \cdot 3.11 \cdot 10^{-11})/3 \cdot 10^8 = 6.63466667 \cdot 10^{-34}$

     ii. $1.116 \cdot 10^{-33}$

2. a. 347,895,000
Be sure the calculator is in Normal mode.

   b. 0.000 000 000 008 247

   c. 140,000

3. Answers will vary. The exponent will be positive when the original number is greater than or equal to 10 and will be negative when the original number is less than 1.

4. $(8 \cdot 10^9)(2.5 \cdot 10^8) = 2 \cdot 10^{18}$

5. The first person takes 1/9, so 8/9 remains. The second person takes 1/8, so 1/8 of 8/9 = 1/9 is taken, so 7/9 remains. The next person takes 1/7 of 7/9 = 1/9, so 6/9 remains, and so on.

   a. Each person will take 1/9 of the pizza, so the pizza is divided fairly.

   b. The last person to select will also get 1/9 of the pizza.

6. a. $\dfrac{60 \text{ ft}}{\text{sec}} \cdot \dfrac{1 \text{ mi}}{5280 \text{ ft}} \cdot \dfrac{60 \text{ sec}}{1 \text{ min}} \cdot \dfrac{60 \text{ min}}{1 \text{ hr}} = 40.9$ mi/hr. This answer is highly unlikely because the winner of the Tour de France in 1993 averaged 24.08 mi/hr.

   b. The distance between bases on a baseball field is 90 ft, so $90 \cdot 4 = 360$ ft traveled in 10 sec, or 36 ft/sec. $\dfrac{36 \text{ ft}}{1 \text{ sec}} \cdot \dfrac{1 \text{ mi}}{5280 \text{ ft}} \cdot \dfrac{60 \text{ sec}}{1 \text{ min}} \cdot \dfrac{60 \text{ min}}{1 \text{ hr}} = 24.54545455$ mi/hr. He was wrong. (Note: Carl Lewis set a world record of 100 m in 9.86 sec. 100 m is approximately 328 ft. So the average player would have to be able to run faster than the world record holder!)

   c. i. $65 \cdot 4 = 260$ km   ii. Actual distance: $65 \cdot 3.9 = 253.5$ km

   Error: $\dfrac{(260 - 253.5)}{253.5} = 0.026$, which is approximately a 3% error.

7. a. 1 sq mi $\cdot 5280^2 \cdot 12^2 = 4{,}014{,}489{,}600$ sq in.
Rain = $(0.1)\ 4{,}014{,}489{,}600 = 401{,}448{,}960$. There are 12^3 in.³ in a cubic foot, so there would be $401{,}448{,}960/12^3 = 232{,}320$ ft³ of rain. $232{,}320 \cdot 62.4 = 14{,}496{,}768$ lb of water fell on the farm. $(14{,}496{,}768/2000 = 7{,}248.384$ T of water.)

   b. The water will weigh ten times as much as in part a because you will have ten times as much water covering the farm uniformly.

8. The hydrogen atom has about $\dfrac{1.7 \cdot 10^{-24}}{9.1 \cdot 10^{-28}} \approx 1868$ times the mass of the electron. Look up the atomic weight of each.

9. Answers will vary.

Problem Set 0.3

1. **a.** Answers will vary. Xmin = ⁻2 or less, Xmax = 3 or more, Xscl = 1 or less, Ymin = 5 or less, Ymax = 21 or more, Yscl = 1 or more. Values slightly less and more for the minimum and maximum values create an envelope on the screen to better see the points.
    b. Xmin = 0 or less, Xmax = 4 or more, Xscl = 1 or less, Ymin = ⁻4 or less, Ymax = 12 or more, Yscl = 1 or more.

2. $20 \cdot 1.5^h$

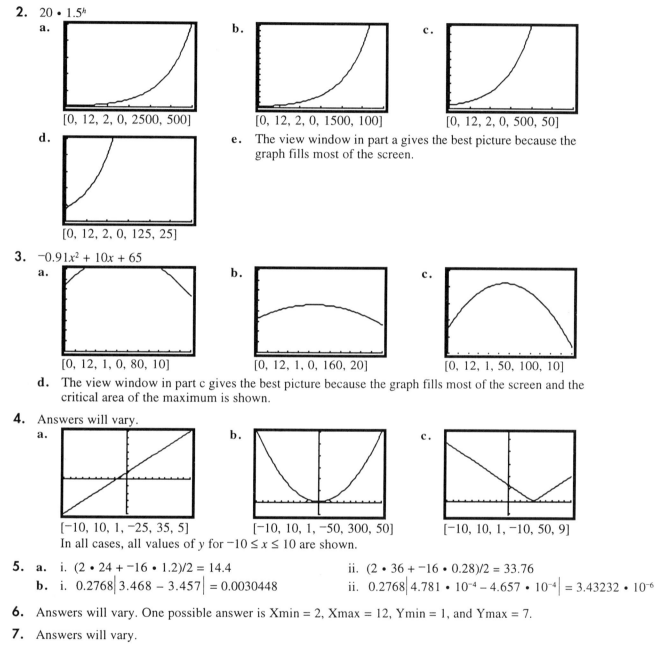

    a.

    [0, 12, 2, 0, 2500, 500]

    b.

    [0, 12, 2, 0, 1500, 100]

    c.

    [0, 12, 2, 0, 500, 50]

    d.

    [0, 12, 2, 0, 125, 25]

    e. The view window in part a gives the best picture because the graph fills most of the screen.

3. $-0.91x^2 + 10x + 65$

    a.

    [0, 12, 1, 0, 80, 10]

    b.

    [0, 12, 1, 0, 160, 20]

    c.

    [0, 12, 1, 50, 100, 10]

    d. The view window in part c gives the best picture because the graph fills most of the screen and the critical area of the maximum is shown.

4. Answers will vary.

    a.

    [⁻10, 10, 1, ⁻25, 35, 5]

    b.

    [⁻10, 10, 1, ⁻50, 300, 50]

    c.

    [⁻10, 10, 1, ⁻10, 50, 9]

    In all cases, all values of y for $-10 \le x \le 10$ are shown.

5. **a.** i. $(2 \cdot 24 + {}^-16 \cdot 1.2)/2 = 14.4$ ii. $(2 \cdot 36 + {}^-16 \cdot 0.28)/2 = 33.76$
    b. i. $0.2768|3.468 - 3.457| = 0.0030448$ ii. $0.2768|4.781 \cdot 10^{-4} - 4.657 \cdot 10^{-4}| = 3.43232 \cdot 10^{-6}$

6. Answers will vary. One possible answer is Xmin = 2, Xmax = 12, Ymin = 1, and Ymax = 7.

7. Answers will vary.

8. Answers will vary.

Chapter 1

Problem Set 1.1

1. The first screen pictures the first five sequence terms. This sequence is geometric because each term is **multiplied** by 1.5 to produce the next term. The tenth term, $u_{10} = 230.6601563$.

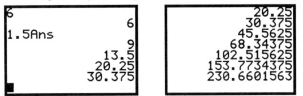

```
6                    6
1.5Ans
           9
        13.5
       20.25
      30.375
```
```
              20.25
             30.375
             45.5625
            68.34375
          102.515625
         153.7734375
         230.6601563
```

2. 6 ENTER

   3.2 + Ans ENTER. Continue pressing ENTER to generate more terms.

   The first screen shows the initial or seed value of 6. Each term after the first term is 3.2 larger than the previous term; $u_{10} = 34.8$.

3. **a.** 2 ENTER seeds the sequence. Ans • 3 ENTER ...; $u_{15} = 9,565,938$

   b. 10 ENTER Ans • 0.5 ENTER ...; $u_{12} = 0.004\ 882\ 812\ 5$

   c. 0.4 ENTER Ans • 0.1 ENTER ...; $u_{10} = 4\text{E}{-}10$ (or $4 \cdot 10^{-10}$)

   d. 2 ENTER Ans + 6 ENTER ...; $u_{30} = 176$

   e. 1.56 ENTER Ans + 3.29 ENTER ...; $u_{14} = 44.33$

   f. 6.24 ENTER Ans • -2.5 ENTER ...; $u_{20} = {-}227,009,877.6$

4. **a.** 20 ENTER Ans + 2.4 ENTER .... After 4 min there are 29.6 gal in the tub. The tub fills somewhere between 12 and 13 min.

   b. Press 20 ENTER Ans + 2.4 − 3.1 ENTER and so on. The first screen pictures the amount of water in the tub after the first four minutes. The tub continues to empty until somewhere between 28 and 29 min.

   c. 20 ENTER Ans + 2.4 − 3.1 ENTER and so on.

5. **a.** The car will have traveled 57 km/hr • 7 hr = 399 km.

   b. The second car will pass the first during the eighth hour after the second car leaves.

Time	0	1	2	3	4	5	6	7	8	9	10
At 57 mph	0	57	114	171	228	285	342	399	456	513	570
At 72 mph	0	0	0	72	144	216	288	360	432	504	576

6. **a.** After 1 min, 10 gal are left.

   b. After 5 min, 0.625 gal remains.

   c. In theory, never. However, only about 0.0006 gal remains after 15 min.

7. **a.** 80 ENTER Ans(1 − 0.25) ENTER .... $60.00 is the price during the second week.

   b. $33.75 is the price during the fourth week.   **c.** The price is less than $10 during the ninth week.

8. **a.** 20 ENTER Ans(1 − 0.5) + 2.4 ENTER ...   **b.** After 1 min, 12.4 gal remain.

   c. After 5 min, 5.275 gal remain.   **d.** After pressing ENTER many times, 4.8 gal remain.

Problem Set 1.2

1.

Generations back	0	1	2	3	4	17	n
Ancestors within a generation	$u_0 = 1$	$u_1 = 2$	$u_2 = 4$	$u_3 = 8$	$u_4 = 16$	$u_{17} = 131{,}072$	$u_n = 2u_{(n-1)}$

a. 1 $\boxed{\text{ENTER}}$ 2 Ans $\boxed{\text{ENTER}}$ and so on until you reach 131,072.

b. Multiply the number in the preceding generation by 2.

c. Continue pressing $\boxed{\text{ENTER}}$ from the recursive routine in part a until you reach 4,194,304.
About 22 generations back, Jill would have almost 5 million ancestors.

d. $22 \cdot 25 = 550$ yr ago

e. Answers will vary. By going back a few more generations, Jill would soon have more ancestors than the population of the earth at the time. For example, going back 25 generations based on this model, Jill would have 536,870,912 ancestors, but the population of the world in 1250 was only about 400,000,000.

2.

Round number	1	2	3	4	5	6
Letters sent	400	9600	230,400	5,529,600	132,710,400	3,185,049,600
Responded	24	576	13,824	331,776	7,962,624	191,102,976

For the fifth round you will receive $5 from each of the 7,962,624 respondents, so you will hypothetically receive $39,813,120 in this round. In the original activity, you would have received $1,244,160 in the fifth round, so your income in this case would be 32 times as great as it was in the original scenario. In each round of the process, your profit would be double that of the original plan, so by the fifth round, your hypothetical income would increase by 2^5, or 32 times.

3. 100 $\boxed{\text{ENTER}}$ Ans $\cdot$ 0.8855 $\boxed{\text{ENTER}}$ .... Less than 5% remains after about 25 time periods or between 24,000 and 25,000 yr.

4. a. $\frac{0.065}{12} = 0.0054166667$, or 0.54% b. $\left(1 + \frac{0.065}{12}\right)500 = \$502.71$

c. 500 $\boxed{\text{ENTER}}$ $\left(1 + \frac{0.065}{12}\right)$ Ans $\boxed{\text{ENTER}}$ .... After 1 yr, the balance is $533.49.

d. After 29 mo, the balance is $584.80.

e. Use guess-and-check, increasing the interest rate, until the balance equals $600 after 29 mo. The interest rate is approximately 7.568%.

5. a. $64{,}273 - 39{,}175 = 25{,}098$ b. $25{,}098/39{,}175 = 0.6406636886 \approx 64.07\%$

c. $64.07/20 = 0.0320331844 \approx 3.2\%$ annual growth

d. 39,175 $\boxed{\text{ENTER}}$ $(1 + 0.032)$Ans $\boxed{\text{ENTER}}$ .... Using 0.032 as the rate, you get a population of 73,553, which is too large. You need to find a smaller rate than 3.2% to compensate for the compounding effect.

e. Use trial and error, decreasing the percentage rate, until you get approximately 64,273 people in 20 yr. The rate would be close to 2.5%.

f. 39,175 $\boxed{\text{ENTER}}$ $(1 + 0.025)$Ans $\boxed{\text{ENTER}}$ .... The average population is $(39{,}175 + 64{,}273)/2 = 51{,}724$. The average is less than half the 1980 population because the relationship is nonlinear.

6. Answers will vary.

Problem Set 1.3

1. a. 747.45, 818.04 b. Answers will vary. c. The sequence levels out at 840.

2. a. 1, 2, 6, 24, 120, 720 b. $u_7 = 5040$, $u_{14} \approx 8.7 \cdot 10^{10}$

3. a. $u_n = \begin{cases} 49.06 & \text{if } n = 1 \\ 1.18 + u_{(n-1)} & \text{if } n > 1 \end{cases}$ b. $u_n = \begin{cases} -4.24 & \text{if } n = 1 \\ 5 \cdot u_{(n-1)} & \text{if } n > 1 \end{cases}$

4. a. $u_1 = 24{,}000$ and $u_n = \left(1 + \frac{0.064}{12}\right) \cdot u_{(n-1)} - 100$

b. The first five terms are $24,000; $24,028; $24,056.15; $24,084.45; $24,112.90.

c. The fifth term represents the balance after 4 mo.

d. The balance after one year is $24,346.03; after three years, the balance is $25,108.03.

5. a. $u_1 = 7000$ and $u_n = (1 - 0.12) \cdot u_{(n-1)} + 600$; after 10 yr there are 5557 trees.

b. In the long run, there will be 5000 trees. 12% of 5000 is 600 trees sold in a year, which will balance out the 600 new trees planted each year.

c. There are no changes in the long-run totals.

d. Answers will vary.

e. There are no changes in the long-run totals. The change occurs only in the time it takes to reach the limit.

6. $u_1 = 20$ and $u_n = (1 - 0.25) \cdot u_{(n-1)}$; there will be less than 1 mg of the drug in his body between 10 and 11 days.

7. $u_1 = 20$ and $u_n = (1 - 0.25) \cdot u_n + 20$; the drug will accumulate to 80 mg.

8. For the colored water, $u_1 = 16$ and $u_n = (1 - 0.25) \cdot u_{(n-1)} + 32$. The final concentration of colored water will double because the amount approached 64 mL in the Color Concentration Investigation and approaches 128 mL when you double the amount added.

9. a. $u_1 = 11{,}000$ and $u_n = \left(1 + \frac{0.096}{12}\right) \cdot u_{(n-1)} - 274$

b. $11{,}000$; $10{,}814$; $10{,}626.51$; $10{,}437.52$; $10{,}247.02$

c. The loan is paid off in 49 mo.

d. $48 \cdot \$274 + \$167.73 = \$13{,}319.73$

10. a. The balance will continue to increase.

b. Because $\$24{,}000 \cdot 0.064/12 = \$128$, a withdrawal of $\$128$ will maintain a constant balance.

Take Another Look 1.3

1. Answers will vary.

2. Answers will vary.

Project: Automobile Depreciation

The results for this project will depend greatly on the type and price range of the car. Expensive cars will tend to depreciate slightly slower. The depreciation is greatest in the first couple of years.

Problem Set 1.4

1. a.

1st coordinate	1	2	3	4	5	6
2nd coordinate	2.5	4	5.5	7	8.5	10

b. Answers will vary. One possible window is [0, 7, 1, 0, 11, 1].

c.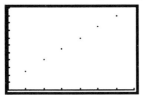

d. The sketch will look like the graph for part c.

2. a.

n (decades)	0	1	2	3	4	5
u_n	3,929,000	4,871,960	6,041,230	7,491,126	9,288,996	11,518,355

b. 3,929,000 is the initial population.

c. The growth rate is 24%.

d. The sequence is geometric because each term is multiplied by $(1 + 0.24)$ to obtain the next term.

e.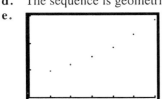

[0, 6, 1, 0, 15000000, 5000000]

3. a.

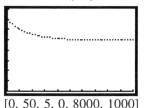

[0, 20, 2, 0, 290000000, 100000000]

b. The graph is nonlinear.

c. $(u_{20} - u_0)/u_0 = (290,212,244.5 - 3,929,000)/$
$3,929,000 = 72.86 = 7286\%$ growth rate.

4. No, because the points representing the sequence of balances do not lie on a line. When you withdraw 20% of the doubled investment, your investment will decrease more rapidly than the original investment. It will not take double the time to withdraw it all. In fact, it will take only about four years longer to withdraw all of the money.

5. $u_0 = 7000$; $u_{(n-1)}(1 - 0.12) + 600$

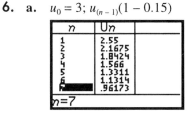

[0, 50, 5, 0, 8000, 1000]

6. a. $u_0 = 3$; $u_{(n-1)}(1 - 0.15)$

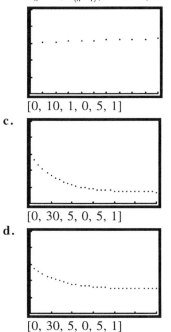

n=7

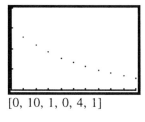

[0, 10, 1, 0, 4, 1]

From the table or the graph, you can see that the slime takes over during the seventh day.

b. $u_0 = 3$; $u_{(n-1)}(1 - 0.15) + 0.5$

[0, 10, 1, 0, 5, 1]

From the graph, you can see that the concentration is increasing. It will never be 100% chlorine, but appears to establish equilibrium at 3.33333 ppm.

c.

[0, 30, 5, 0, 5, 1]

From a table or a graph, you will see that the concentration is decreasing and appears to establish equilibrium at 0.66667 ppm.

d.

[0, 30, 5, 0, 5, 1]

Use trial and error, changing the amount of chlorine you add. You need to add 0.225 ppm to stabilize at 1.5 ppm.

Take Another Look 1.4

1. **a.** Answers will vary. If you know u_n and $u_{(n-1)}$, you could solve the equation

   $u_n = (1 + r)u_{(n-1)}$, for r. $r = \dfrac{u_n - u_{(n-1)}}{u_{(n-1)}}$.

   b. Solve $u_3 = (1 + 0.07)2289.8 = 2450.09$.

   c. You could solve the equation $2450.09 = (1 + 0.07)u_{(n-1)}$.

   d.

Elapsed time (mo)	0	1	2	3	4	5
Balance ($)	2,000	2,014.67	2,028.43	2,042.80	2,057.27	2,071.84

$$u_{(n-1)} = \begin{cases} 2071.84 & \text{if } n = 5 \\ u_n(1 + 0.085/12) & \text{if } n < 5 \end{cases}$$

2. Answers will vary. $u_{(n-1)} = \dfrac{u_n - 210}{0.75}$

Project: The Gingerbread Man

a. $(0, 0)$; $(1, 0)$; $(2, 1)$; $(2, 2)$; $(1, 2)$; $(0, 1)$ repeat . . . .

b. $(3, -1)$; $(5, 3)$; $(3, 5)$; $(-1, 3)$; $(-1, -1)$; . . . ; period 5.

c. period 30

d.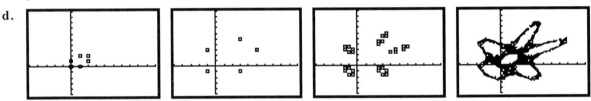

e. This figure is a more complete representation of what was seen in parts a, b, and c. In part a, the outside of the "belly" region was marked. In part b, the centers of the limbs were marked. Part c showed the outlines of the open regions in the head and limbs. Adding more initial points would just fill in the darkened regions more completely and further define the edges of the open spaces.

f. All points within the belly have a period of 6 except the center point, which is fixed. The periodic points form hexagons around the center.

g. The centers of these regions iterate with period 5 as seen in part b. All other points have period 30, forming hexagons in each of the open regions.

h. Iterating points that lie just outside of the gingerbread man causes a lacy network to form. Increase the viewing window size and try many points to see the complexity of this new region. The gingerbread man lies inside the region shown at right. (All values for Xmin, Xmax, Ymin, and Ymax were doubled.)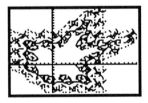

Problem Set 1.5

1. $u_1 = 2$; $u_n = u_{(n-1)} + 6$

   The 10th term is 56, the 20th term is 116, and the 30th term is 176. An alternative solution is to use the recursive routine. 2 ENTER Ans + 6 ENTER ENTER and so on.

2. $u_0 = 1000$; $u_n = (1 + 0.065/4)u_{(n-1)}$

   a. In 10 years (40 quarters), the value is $1,905.56.

   b. In 20 years (80 quarters), the value is $3,631.15.

   c. In 30 years (120 quarters), the value is $6,919.38. An alternative solution is to use the recursive routine. 1000 ENTER Ans (1 + .065/4) ENTER ENTER and so on.

3. $u_0 = 7000$; $u_n = (1 - 0.12)u_{(n-1)} + 600$

a.

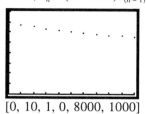

[0, 10, 1, 0, 8000, 1000]

b. 20 yr   30 yr

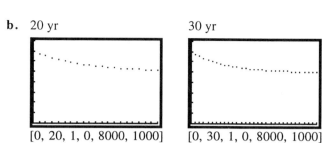

[0, 20, 1, 0, 8000, 1000]   [0, 30, 1, 0, 8000, 1000]

c. 75 yr

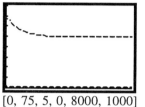

[0, 75, 5, 0, 8000, 1000]

In the long run, the number of trees stabilizes at 5000. An alternative solution is to use the recursive routine.
7000 [ENTER] Ans (1 − 0.12) + 600 [ENTER] [ENTER]
and so on.

4. **a.** $u_0 = 14.7$, $u_n = (1 - 0.20)u_{(n-1)}$
c. (7, 3.1). You can trace the graph to find these coordinates. You could also look at the table.
d. At an altitude of 11 mi, the pressure is less than 1.5 psi.

b.

[0, 12, 1, 0, 15, 3]

5. **a.** $u_0 = 5000$; $u_n = (1 + 0.085/12)u_{(n-1)}$ + *monthly deposit*. Use guess-and-check to find the monthly deposit so that the account will be worth $1,000,000 by the time the child is 55 yr old, which is in 45 yr (55 − 10 = 45). Multiply 45 • 12 to get 540 mo of deposits. The monthly deposit should be $123.98.

b.

[0, 550, 50, 0, 1100000, 100000]

6. **a.** $u_0 = 60,000$; $u_n = (1 + 0.096/12)u_{(n-1)}$ − *monthly deposit*. Use guess-and-check to find the monthly payment needed in order to pay off the loan in 25 yr, or 25 • 12, or 300 payments. The payments should be $528.40 for the first 299 and one payment of $528.40 − 6.42, or $521.98.

b.

[0, 300, 50, 0, 60000, 10000]

7. **a.** 20 • 0.10 = 2 million people left California.   **b.** 220 • 0.05 = 11 million people moved into California.
c. The population of California in 1987 would have been 20 − 2 + 11 = 29 million.
d. The population outside of California in 1987 would have been 240 − 29 = 211 million.
e. 240 − California population = population outside California.
f. $u_0 = 20$; $u_n = (1 - 0.10)u_{(n-1)} + 0.05(240 - u_{(n-1)})$
1990 − 1986 = 4 yr; the population of California in 1990 would be approximately 48.68 million.
1995 − 1986 = 9 yr; the population of California in 1995 would be approximately 66.10 million.
The long-term equilibrium is 80 million people in California.

8. **a.** 1, 1, 2, 3, 5, 8, 13, 21, 34, 55; (the third term is 1 + 1, the fourth term is 1 + 2, the fifth term is 2 + 3, and so on).
b. 1/1 = 1, 2/1 = 2, 3/2 = 1.5, 5/3 = 1.6 . . . , 8/5 = 1.6, 13/8 = 1.625, 21/13 = 1.615384615, 34/21 = 1.619047, 55/34 = 1.617647. The ratios are approaching 1.618033989.

9. Answers will vary.

Take Another Look 1.5

a. The ninth balance takes into account the 9.5% interest.

b. This equation shows how the tenth month balance is calculated by adding 9.5% interest that is compounded monthly and subtracting the payment of $294.03.

$$u_9 \cdot \left(1 + \frac{0.095}{12}\right) - 294.03 = 12,101.37$$

c. $u_n = \dfrac{u_{n-1} + 294.03}{\left(1 + \dfrac{0.095}{12}\right)}$

d. $12,298.04

e. $14,000.00

f. She can start with the initial amount and find the balance at the end of each year.

g. $1,041.67

In sequence mode: $u_0 = 14,000$; $u_n = u_{n-1}\left(1 + \frac{0.095}{12}\right) - 294.03$: $v_0 \neq \phi$; $v_n = u_{n-1}\left(1 + \frac{0.095}{12}\right) + v_{n-1}$

Project: Recursive Midpoint Games

The resulting figure for Game 1 eventually becomes a solid triangle. Below is a Sketchpad drawing showing 100 iterations and a calculator graph of 300 iterations. The same Sketchpad drawing without the segments is also shown. You can start to see the pattern. On the calculator the game is continued for 30 iterations.

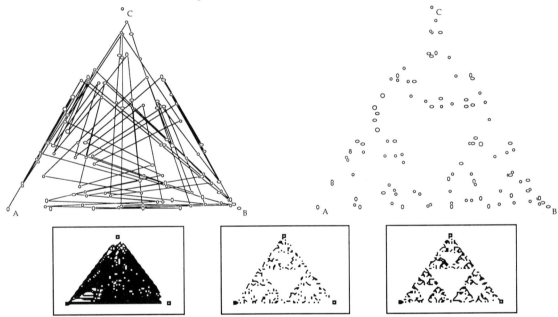

The first game shows no pattern, but the second game creates a picture with self-similarity. Each vertex of each triangle is identical to the whole picture.

Problem Set 1.6

1. $S_1 = 2, S_2 = 8, S_3 = 18, S_4 = 32, S_5 = 50$

2. a. Modify the Series program in Calculator Note 1D with $2 \to u$ for the first term, $u \cdot 3 \to u$ for the next term, and FOR(N, 1, 15) for summing 15 terms. The sum is 14,348,906. Or use Sequence mode and let u_nStart $= 2$, v_nStart $= 2$, $u_n = 3u_{(n-1)}$, and $v_n = v_{(n-1)} + 3u_{(n-1)}$. The table entry for v_{15} will represent the sum.

b. It is probably impossible to find a graphing window that pictures the initial small sums and the eventual gigantic sums.

3. a. Modify the Series program with $1 \to u$ for the first term, $u \cdot 0.1 \to u$ for the next term, and FOR(N, 1, 10) to sum 10 terms. The sum is 0.3333333333. Or use the Sequence mode and let u_nStart $= 0.3$, v_nStart $= 0.3$, $u_n = 0.1u_{(n-1)}$, and $v_n = v_{(n-1)} + 0.1u_{(n-1)}$. The table entry for v_{10} will represent the sums.

b. Modify the program with FOR(N, 1, 15) to sum 15 terms. The sum is 0.333333333333333. The sum is the same as for ten terms because the calculator cannot display more digits.

c. $0.\overline{3}$ or 1/3

4. a. Modify the Series program with $1 \to u$ for the first term, $u + 2 \to u$ for the next term, and FOR(N, 1, 12) to sum 12 terms. Or use the Sequence mode and let u_nStart $= 1$, v_nStart $= 1$, $u_n = u_{(n-1)} + 1$, and $v_n = v_{(n-1)} + u_{(n-1)} + 1$. The table entry for v_{12} will represent the sums. The sum of the first 12 odd positive integers is 144. (If you use v_n and look at the table, you will see the sequence of square numbers.)

b. Modify the Series program with FOR(N, 1, 20) to sum 20 terms. The sum of the first 20 odd integers is 400.

c. The sum for the first n odd integers is n^2.

5. Modify the Series program with $45 \to u$ for the first term, $u + 5 \to u$ for the next term, and FOR(N, 1, 15) to sum 15 days. Or use the Sequence mode and let u_nStart $= 45$, v_nStart $= 45$, $u_n = u_{(n-1)} + 5$, and $v_n = v_{(n-1)} + u_{(n-1)} + 5$. The table entry for v_{15} will represent the sum. The sum is 1200 min, or 20 hr. For 35 days, change to FOR(N, 1, 35). The sum is 4550 min, or 78.5 hr.

6. a. Modify the Series program with $1 \to u$, $u + 1 \to u$, and FOR(N, 1, 1000). Or use the Sequence mode and let u_nStart $= 1$, v_nStart $= 1$, $u_n = u_{(n-1)} + 1$, and $v_n = v_{(n-1)} + u_{(n-1)} + 1$. The table entry for v_{1000} will represent the sum. The sum is 500,500.

b. Modify the Series program with $1001 \to u$. The sum is 1,500,500.

c. Answers will vary.

d. Modify the Series program with $2001 \to u$. The sum is 2,500,500.

e. $2(1000)^2 + S(1000)$, or put the leftmost digit of the initial term in front of $S(1000)$.

7. For the first plan, modify the Series program with $1000 \to u$, $u + 1000 \to u$, and FOR(N, 1, 8760). (Note: 365 days $\cdot$ 24 hr = 8760 hr.) The program will take a long time to run. You might instead use what you learned in Problem 6e to shorten the work. You could also use the Sequence mode. Let u_nStart $= 0$, v_nStart $= 0$, $u_n = u_{(n-1)} + 1000$, and $v_n = u_{(n-1)} + u_{(n-1)} + 1000$. The table entry for v_{8760} will represent the sum. The sum is \$38,373,180,000. For the second plan, modify the program with $0.01 \to u$, $u \cdot 2 \to u$, and FOR(N, 1, 52). Or in Sequence mode, let u_nStart $= 0.01$, v_nStart $= 0.01$, $u_n = 2u_{(n-1)}$, and $v_n = v_{(n-1)} + 2u_{(n-1)}$. The table entry for v_{52} will represent the sum. The sum is \$45,035,996,273,704. The second plan is more profitable by \$44,997,623,093,704.

8. Modify the Series program with $0.39 \to u$, $u \cdot 0.01 \to u$, and FOR(N, 1, 6). Or use the Sequence mode and let u_nStart $= 0.39$, v_nStart $= 0.39$, $u_n = 0.01u_{(n-1)}$, and $v_n = v_{(n-1)} + 0.01u_{(n-1)}$. The table entry for v_6 will represent the sum. The sum is 0.3939393939.

9. a. Modify the Series program with $650{,}000 \cdot 0.42 \to u$, $(650{,}000 - u)(0.42) \to u$, and FOR(N, 1, 4). (Note: Use 4 because 1 hour has four 15 min time periods.) Or use the Sequence mode and let u_nStart $= 0$, v_nStart $= 0$, $u_n = 0.42(650000 - u_{(n-1)})$, and $v_n = v_{(n-1)} + 0.42(650000 - u_{(n-1)})$. The table entry for v_4 will represent the sum. After one hour, 576,443 people will have heard the news. Now change to FOR(N, 1, 8). After two hours, 641,676 people will have heard the news.

b. Answers will vary.

10. Answers will vary.

Chapter Review

Problem Set 1.7

1. a. 3, 6, 9, 12, 15, 18, 21, 24, 27, 30

b. $u_n = \begin{cases} 3 & \text{if } n = 1 \\ u_{(n-1)} + 3 & \text{if } n > 1 \end{cases}$

c. Use the Series program with $3 \to u$ for the first term, $u + 3 \to u$ for the next term, and FOR(N, 1, 47) for 47 layers. Or use the Sequence mode and let u_nStart $= 3$, v_nStart $= 3$, $u_n = u_{(n-1)} + 3$, and $v_n = v_{(n-1)} + u_{(n-1)} + 3$. The table entry for v_{47} will represent the sum. He would need 3384 cans.

d. Use guess-and-check, changing the number of rows in FOR(N, 1, _). Or, if you're using Sequence mode, look at the table entries for v^n. A 13-row structure uses 273 cans and 14 rows uses 315 cans. If he must use 288 cans, he can complete 13 rows and start on the 14th row.

2. a. 3 |ENTER| Ans + 4 |ENTER| . . . , or use Sequence mode and look at the table. The 128th term is 511.

b. Count the number of |ENTER|s you press or use Sequence mode and look at the table. The 40th term is 159.

c. $u_{20} = 79$

d. Use the Series program with $3 \to u$, $u + 4 \to u$, and FOR(N, 1, 20). Or use the Sequence mode and let u_nStart $= 3$, v_nStart $= 3$, $u_n = u_{(n-1)} + 4$, and $v_n = v_{(n-1)} + u_{(n-1)} + 4$. The table entry for v_{20} will represent the sum. The sum is 820.

3. a. 256 |ENTER| Ans • 0.75 |ENTER| . . . . The eighth term is 34.171875.

b. The tenth term is smaller than 20. (To see this, continue pressing |ENTER|.)

c. $u_7 = 45.5625$

d. Use the Series program with $256 \to u$, $u • 0.75 \to u$, and FOR(N, 1, 7). Or use the Sequence mode and let u_nStart $= 256$, v_nStart $= 256$, $u_n = 0.75u_{(n-1)}$, and $v_n = v_{(n-1)} + 0.75u_{(n-1)}$. The table entry for v_7 will represent the sum. The sum is 887.3125.

4. a. 500 |ENTER| Ans(1 + 0.055/4) |ENTER| . . . for 5 • 4 = 20 quarters or in Sequence mode, enter $u_n = u_{(n-1)}(1 + 0.055/4)$. Set u_nStart $= 500$. The balance after five years is \$657.03.

b. 500 |ENTER| Ans(1 + 0.055/4) + 50 |ENTER| . . . for 20 quarters or in Sequence mode, enter $u_n = u_{(n-1)}(1 + 0.055/4) + 150$. The balance after five years is \$4,083.21.

5. In Sequence mode, enter $u_n = u_{(n-1)}(1 - 0.24) + 1250$. Set u_nStart $= 5678$. The enrollment during the sixth year will be 5299 students. In the long run, the enrollment will be 5208 students.

6. In Sequence mode, enter $u_n = u_{(n-1)}(1 + 0.089/12) - $ *monthly payment*. Set u_nStart $= 80,000$. Use guess-and-check for the monthly payment so that after 360 payments the balance will be 0 or close to 0. There will be 359 payments of \$637.96 and one payment of \$620.46.

7. a. −3 |ENTER| 1.5 + Ans |ENTER| . . . . The first five terms are −3, −1.5, 0, 1.5, and 3.

b. 2 |ENTER| 3Ans − 2 |ENTER| . . . . The first five terms are 2, 4, 10, 28, and 82.

Chapter 2

Problem Set 2.1

1. a. Substitute $n = 1$ into $u_n = \frac{n(n+1)(2n+3)}{6}$ to get $\frac{5}{3}$; when $n = 2$, $u_2 = 7$, $u_3 = 18$, $u_4 = 36\frac{2}{3}$, and $u_5 = 65$.

b. Neither. It is not arithmetic because there is not a common difference, and it is not geometric because there is not a common ratio.

2.

n	1	2	3	4	5	6	. . .	15	n
u_n	1	1.41	1.73	2	2.24	2.45	. . .	3.87	$\sqrt{n}$

$u_n = \sqrt{n}$ (rounded to two decimal places)

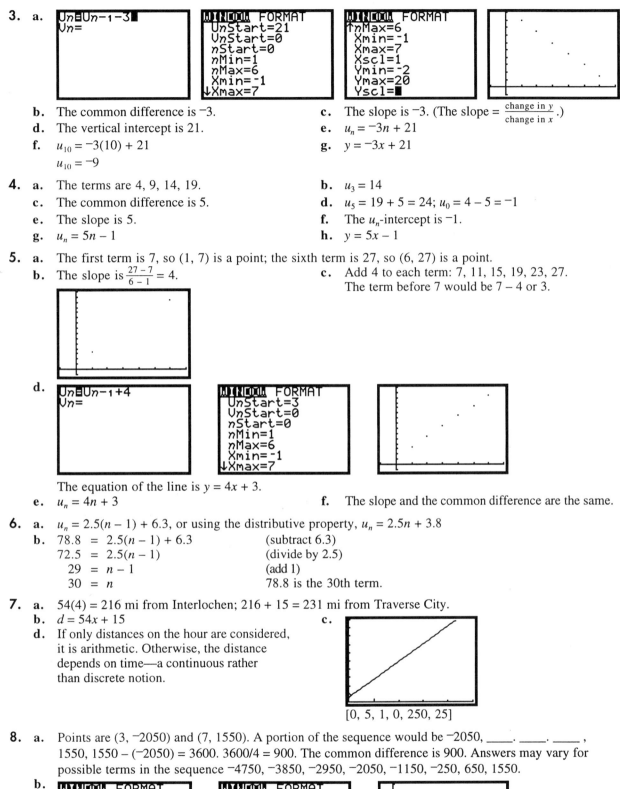

3. **a.**
   (calculator screens)
   b. The common difference is $^{-}3$.
   c. The slope is $^{-}3$. (The slope $= \frac{\text{change in } y}{\text{change in } x}$.)
   d. The vertical intercept is 21.
   e. $u_n = ^{-}3n + 21$
   f. $u_{10} = ^{-}3(10) + 21$
   $u_{10} = ^{-}9$
   g. $y = ^{-}3x + 21$

4. **a.** The terms are 4, 9, 14, 19.
   b. $u_3 = 14$
   c. The common difference is 5.
   d. $u_5 = 19 + 5 = 24;\ u_0 = 4 - 5 = ^{-}1$
   e. The slope is 5.
   f. The u_n-intercept is $^{-}1$.
   g. $u_n = 5n - 1$
   h. $y = 5x - 1$

5. **a.** The first term is 7, so (1, 7) is a point; the sixth term is 27, so (6, 27) is a point.
   b. The slope is $\frac{27 - 7}{6 - 1} = 4$.
   c. Add 4 to each term: 7, 11, 15, 19, 23, 27. The term before 7 would be $7 - 4$ or 3.

   d.
   (calculator screens)
   The equation of the line is $y = 4x + 3$.
   e. $u_n = 4n + 3$
   f. The slope and the common difference are the same.

6. **a.** $u_n = 2.5(n - 1) + 6.3$, or using the distributive property, $u_n = 2.5n + 3.8$
   b.
78.8	$= 2.5(n - 1) + 6.3$	(subtract 6.3)
72.5	$= 2.5(n - 1)$	(divide by 2.5)
29	$= n - 1$	(add 1)
30	$= n$	78.8 is the 30th term.

7. **a.** $54(4) = 216$ mi from Interlochen; $216 + 15 = 231$ mi from Traverse City.
   b. $d = 54x + 15$
   c.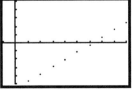
   $[0, 5, 1, 0, 250, 25]$
   d. If only distances on the hour are considered, it is arithmetic. Otherwise, the distance depends on time—a continuous rather than discrete notion.

8. **a.** Points are (3, $^{-}2050$) and (7, 1550). A portion of the sequence would be $^{-}2050$, ____. ____. ____ , 1550, $1550 - (^{-}2050) = 3600$. $3600/4 = 900$. The common difference is 900. Answers may vary for possible terms in the sequence $^{-}4750, ^{-}3850, ^{-}2950, ^{-}2050, ^{-}1150, ^{-}250, 650, 1550$.
   b.
   (calculator screens)
   c. The common difference, $900, is the profit per car sold.
   d. The slope, 900, represents the profit per car sold.

e. The vertical intercept (or y-intercept) of -4750 represents the expenses even if no cars are sold. The horizontal intercept (or x-intercept) of 5.27 represents the number of cars that must be sold to break even. (Six cars must be sold to make a profit.)

f. $d = 900c - 4750$

9. a. $u_0 = 3 - 5 = -2$ **b.** 5 (count from the graph)   **c.** 7

     d. The height can be found from the equation because you need to add seven heights of d to the original height of u_0.

     e. $u_{13} = u_0 + 13d$ **f.** $u_n = u_0 + nd$

10. a. They are the same and will always be the same.

     b. The trick is to look at the total income at the end of each six-month period. Assume that the raise goes into effect at the beginning of the next time period. Although the total earnings are different at the end of the odd-numbered six-month periods, at the end of each year the total income is always the same.

	Case 1	Total earnings	Case 2	Total earnings
First 6 mo	9,200	9,200	8,950	8,950
First yr	9,200	18,400	8,950 + 500 = 9,450	18,400
Third 6 mo	(18,400 + 2,000) ÷ 2 = 10,200	28,600	9,450 + 500 = 9,950	28,350
Second yr	10,200	38,800	9,950 + 500 = 10,450	38,800
Fifth 6 mo	(20,400 + 2,000) ÷ 2 = 11,200	50,000	10,450 + 500 = 10,950	49,750
Third yr	11,200	61,200	10,950 + 500 = 11,450	61,200

Take Another Look 2.1

a. Find u_n for $u_{(n-1)}\left(1 - \frac{0.074}{12}\right) - p$ by guessing values for the payment.

b. Check to see if $u_{3000} = 0$ or is very close to zero.

c. Multiply the initial balance by the interest rate and divide by 12.

d. After 25 yr they would still owe \$84,000.

e. After 25 yr they would owe more than \$84,000.

f.

Monthly payment	Final balance after 25 yr	Common difference
\$518	\$84,000.00	
\$519	\$83,142.97	\$857.03
\$520	\$82,285.93	\$857.04
\$521	\$81,428.90	\$857.03
\$522	\$80,571.86	\$857.04

g. The common difference is almost the same.

h. Each \$1 in the payment amount reduces the balance by \$857. Divide \$84,000 by \$857 to get \$98.02, the amount you add to \$518 to get the payment.

i. \$616.02. Check that u_{300} for $u_{(n-1)}\left(1 - \frac{0.074}{12}\right) - 616.02 = 0$.

j. You need only two rows to find the common difference.

k. The "interest only" payment is \$593.33. The common difference is \$1,778.85. The amount to be added to the "interest only" payment is 80,000/1778.85 = 44.37. The payment required is \$593.33 + \$44.97 = \$638.30.

Problem Set 2.2

1. $d = 6$; $u_{50} = 49(6) + 6 = 300$;

$u_1 + u_{50} = 6 + 300 = 306$

$S_{50} = \frac{50(306)}{2} = 7650$, or use the Series program from Calculator Note 2A.

```
PROGRAM:SERIES
:For(N,1,50)
:6N→U
:S+U→S
:Disp N,U,S,"  "
:End
```

```
                    7350

                      50
                     300
                    7650

                    Done
```

2. $2, 4, 6, \ldots$; $u_{75} = 74(2) + 2 = 150$;

$u_1 + u_{75} = 2 + 150 = 152$

$S_{75} = \dfrac{75 \cdot 152}{2} = 5700$, or use the Series program.

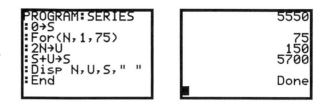

```
PROGRAM:SERIES
:0→S
:For(N,1,75)
:2N→U
:S+U→S
:Disp N,U,S," "
:End
```

```
                    5550
                      75
                     150
                    5700
                    Done
```

3. a. $u_{75} = 2(75) - 1 = 149$

   b. $u_1 = 2(1) - 1 = 1$; $u_1 + u_{75} = 1 + 149 = 150$; $S_{75} = \dfrac{75 \cdot 150}{2} = 5625$, or use the Series program.

   c. $u_{20} = 2(20) - 1 = 39$; $u_{20} + u_{75} = 39 + 149 = 188$

      There are 56 terms in the series. $(75 + 20 + 1 = 56)$; $S = \dfrac{56 \cdot 188}{2} = 5264$

      Another alternative is to find the sum of the first 19 terms (361) and subtract this sum from the sum of 75 terms $(5625 - 361 = 5264)$.

4. a. $118.5 - 125.3 = {}^-6.8$; $111.7 - 118.5 = {}^-6.8$; the common difference is $^-6.8$.

      $u_{67} = 66({}^-6.8) + 125.3 = {}^-323.5$

      $u_1 + u_{67} = 125.3 + ({}^-323.5) = {}^-198.2$

      $S_{67} = \dfrac{678({}^-198.2)}{2} = {}^-6639.7$

      Or use the Series program.

   b. $\displaystyle\sum_{n-1}^{64} 132.1 - 6.8n$

5. a. $u_1 = 4$; the common difference $d = 5$

      so $u_{46} = 45(5) + 4 = 229$

      Or use the Recur program.

   b. $u_n = 4 + (n - 1)5$

      $u_n = 4 + 5n - 5$

      $u_n = 5n - 1$

   c. $u_1 + u_{46} = 4 + 229 = 233$

      $S_{46} = \dfrac{46(233)}{2} = 5359$

      Or use the Series program.

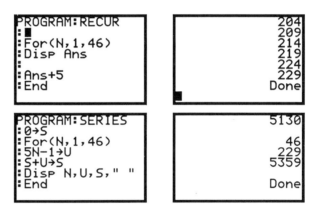

```
PROGRAM:RECUR
:
:For(N,1,46)
:Disp Ans
:
:Ans+5
:End
```

```
                     204
                     209
                     214
                     219
                     224
                     229
                    Done
```

```
PROGRAM:SERIES
:0→S
:For(N,1,46)
:5N-1→U
:S+U→S
:Disp N,U,S," "
:End
```

```
                    5130

                      46
                     229
                    5359

                    Done
```

6. $12.4 + 18(4.2) = 88$ gal were in the barrel initially.

7. There are three possibilities: a sequence with positive slope (line a), a sequence with negative slope (line b), a sequence with zero slope (line c).

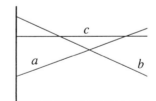

8. a. $u_1 = 65$; the common difference is 2 so $u_{40} = 39(2) + 65 = 143$ seats.

   b. $u_1 + u_{40} = 65 + 143 = 208$

      $S_{40} = \dfrac{40(208)}{2} = 4160$ seats

      Or use the Series program.

```
PROGRAM:SERIES
:0→S
:For(N,1,40)
:2(N-1)+65→U■
:S+U→S
:Disp N,U,S," "
:End
```

```
                    4017

                      40
                     143
                    4160

                    Done
```

   c. Use guess-and-check. $u_{13} = 65 + 12(2) = 208$

      $S_{13} = \dfrac{13(154)}{2} = 1001$, which is close to your seat #995.

      $1001 - 995 = 6$; your seat is 6 seats from the 1001st seat or the 7th seat from the right aisle.

9. a. 12.5   **b.** 116   **c.** Add the areas of the ten trapezoids formed at consecutive integers. $3.5 + 5.3 + \cdots + 19.7 = 116$

Problem Set 2.3

1. $\frac{6}{2} = 3$; $u_{15} = 2(3^{14}) = 9{,}565{,}938$

2. The common ratio $r = (1 + 0.055) = 1.055$; $u_9 = 1500(1.055^8) = \$2{,}302.03$. Use guess-and-check to find a balance of at least \$5,000. Note: Pressing $\boxed{\text{2nd}}$ $\boxed{\text{ENTER}}$ allows you to quickly change your guess. After 23 yr the balance is \$5,139.23.

3. a. The value of \$4,000 after 10 yr of compounded interest at 7.2%.
   b. The value of \$4,000 after 4 yr of interest compounded monthly. (The expression $\frac{0.072}{12}$ tells you the interest is compounded 12 times a year, and the 48th power tells you the number of months it has been compounding (48 mo = 4 yr).
   c. $1500(1 + 0.055)^8$

4. a. iv   b. iii   c. ii   d. i

5. Answers will vary. When $r > 1$, the graph slopes up to the right. The larger r is, the more quickly the graph goes up. When $r = 1$, the graph is a horizontal line at $y = 60$. When $0 < r < 1$, the graph slopes down to the right. When $r = 0$, the graph is a horizontal line at $y = 0$. When $r < 0$, the values alternate between positive and negative, with both the positive and negative sequence of numbers approaching 0.
   $r \approx 1.15$ (graph a)
   $r = 1$ (graph b)
   $r \approx 0.85$ (graph c)

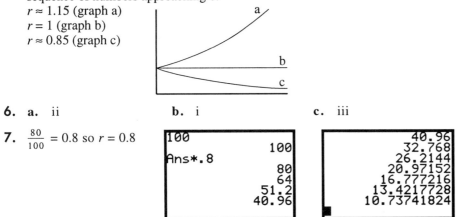

6. a. ii   b. i   c. iii

7. $\frac{80}{100} = 0.8$ so $r = 0.8$

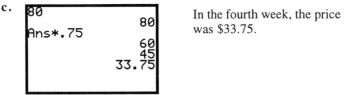

   a. The height is 10.74 inches on the tenth rebound.
   b. Continue pressing $\boxed{\text{ENTER}}$. On the 21st rebound, the height is less than 1 in. Continue pressing $\boxed{\text{ENTER}}$. On the 31st rebound, the height is less than 0.1 in.

8. a. $u_n = 80(1 - 0.25)^{(n-1)}$ or $u_n = 80(0.75)^{(n-1)}$
   b. $80(0.75)^{(2-1)} = \$60$
   c.

   In the fourth week, the price was \$33.75.

   d. Continue pressing $\boxed{\text{ENTER}}$. In the ninth week, the price will be less than \$10.00 (\$8.01).

9. $0.39 + 0.0039 + \cdots + 0.0000000000039 = 0.393939393939$

10. Answers will vary.

Project: Instant Money

The loan balance actually drops by only 0.175% each month. Also, since the payment drops each month, you are paying less on the principal each month. It takes about 395 mo to cut the balance in half, regardless of the initial loan. You actually pay the amount of the principal in a little more than two years. Since this is an example of exponential decay, the balance will never reach 0. This is not a good deal for the consumer; it is a great deal for the lender.

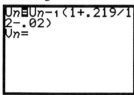

```
Un=Un-1(1+.219/1
2-.02)
Un=
```

```
WINDOW FORMAT
 UnStart=5000
 VnStart=0
 nStart=0
 nMin=0
 nMax=120
 Xmin=0
↓Xmax=120
```

n	Un
0	5000
12	4896
24	4794.2
36	4694.5
48	4596.8
60	4501.2
72	4407.6

n=0

Problem Set 2.4

1. **a.** $S_{10} = \frac{3(1 - 2^{10})}{1 - 2} = 3069$

   b. $9.999868378 = \frac{4(1 - 0.6^n)}{1 - 0.6}$

   $= \frac{4(1 - 0.6^n)}{0.4}$

   $= 10(1 - 0.6^n)$

   $0.9999868378 = 1 - 0.6^n$

   $-0.000013622 = -0.6^n$

   Now use guess-and-check. $n = 22$ so $S_{22} = 9.999868378$

   c. $1081.976669 = \frac{u_1(1 - 1.4^{15})}{1 - 1.4}$

   $= \frac{u_1(-154.5680956)}{-0.4}$

   $= u_1(386.4202389)$

   $2.8 = u_1$

   d. Use guess-and-check to find r. $r = 0.95$

   ```
   (5.5(1-.95^18))/
   (1-.95)
             66.30642497
   ```

2. Use guess-and-check to find r. The percentage raise is 21.4%. $r = 1.214$. (Note: A multiplier of 1 keeps the same salary and a multiplier of 1.214 increases the salary by 21.4%.)

   ```
   (200000(1-1.214^
   7))/(1-1.214)
             2697430.51
   ```

3. **a.** $S_1 = 5, S_2 = 5 + 10 = 15, S_3 = 5 + 10 + 20 = 35, S_4 = 5 + 10 + 20 + 40 = 75, \ldots$

n	1	2	3	4	5	6	7
S_n	5	15	35	75	155	315	635

   b. No, the partial sums are not geometric. $\frac{15}{5} \neq \frac{35}{15}$

   c. The terms will form a geometric sequence if $r = 0$.

4. **a.** $S_5 = \frac{40(1 - 0.60^5)}{1 - 0.60} = 92.224$

   b. $S_{15} = \frac{40(1 - 0.60^{15})}{1 - 0.60} = 99.9529815$ (Note: Press 2nd ENTER to quickly change from the fifth to the fifteenth power.)

   c. $S_{25} = 99.9997157$

5. a. Neither. It is not arithmetic because there is not a common difference. It is not geometric because there is not a common ratio.

b. $\frac{1}{1} + \frac{1}{2} + \frac{1}{3} + \frac{1}{4} + \cdots + \frac{1}{8} = \frac{761}{280}$ or about 2.718

6. a. $1^2 + 2^2 + 3^2 + 4^2 + 5^2 + 6^2 + 7^2 = 140$ **b.** $3^2 + 4^2 + 5^2 + 6^2 + 7^2 = 135$

7. a. $u_1 = 1, u_2 = 2, u_3 = 4, r = 2; u_{64} = 1 \cdot 2^{63} \approx 9.22 \cdot 10^{18}$

b. $S_{64} = \frac{1(1 - 2^{64})}{1 - 2} \approx 1.84 \cdot 10^{19}$ **c.** $\displaystyle\sum_{1}^{64} 2^{(n-1)}$

8. a. $S_{10} = 15.984375$ **b.** $S_{20} = 15.99998474$ **c.** $S_{30} = 15.99999999$ **d.** The partial sums approach 16.

Project: Living in the City

One true relationship is that 1.4 billion growing at 3.8% will increase by 1 million in the first week. But the article must also have other information that is not given. If the growth rate of 3.8% was constant, then in 30 years (in 2020) the urban population would be 4.3 billion. In order to reach 3.6 billion, the average annual growth rate would have to be 3.2%.

A constant linear rate of 1 million per week would mean a population of only 3 billion in 2020. The average growth rate would have to be 1.4 million per week to reach 3.6 billion in 2020.

Problem Set 2.5

1. The explicit formula for the sum of a geometric series does not apply when $r = 1$. The sequence is 6, 6, 6, 6 . . . . $S_{10} = 6(10) = 60$. $S_n = 6 \cdot n$. The sum of the infinite series is infinity.

2. a. $S_{10} = \frac{4(1 - 0.7^{10})}{1 - 0.7} \approx 12.96$

$S_{40} = \frac{4(1 - 0.7^{40})}{1 - 0.7} \approx 13.33$

b. $S_{10} = \frac{4(1 - 1.3^{10})}{1 - 1.3} \approx 170.48$

$S_{40} = \frac{4(1 - 1.3^{40})}{1 - 1.3} \approx 481{,}572$

c. (See note for Problem 1 when $r = 1$.) $S_{10} = 4(10) = 40$; $S_{40} = 4 \cdot 40 = 160$.

d. A value of $r > 1$ gives the top graph; $r = 1$ gives the middle graph; $0 < r < 1$ gives the bottom graph.

e. The sum appears to approach a limiting value when $|r| < 1$. When $|r| \geq 1$, the graph of the partial sums continues to increase and not approach a limit.

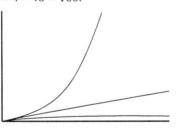

3. When the amount added and the amount taken away are equal, the problem has reached the limiting value. For the white pine tree problem, the limiting value is $\frac{600}{0.12}$ or 5000 trees.

4. a. $u_1 = \frac{1}{10}; r = \frac{1}{3}; S_5 = \dfrac{\frac{1}{10}\left(1 - \left(\frac{1}{3}\right)^5\right)}{1 - \frac{1}{3}} = 0.149382716$

b. $S_{10} = \dfrac{\frac{1}{10}\left(1 - \left(\frac{1}{3}\right)^{10}\right)}{1 - \frac{1}{3}} = 0.1499974597$

c. $S = 0.15$

d. Answers will vary. In the explicit formula, $S_n = \frac{u_1(1 - r^n)}{1 - r}$, as n gets extremely large, when the value of r is a fraction between 1 and -1, r^n becomes extremely small and in fact becomes negligible.

5. $u_1 = 1{,}000{,}000; r = 0.9; S = \frac{1000000}{1 - 0.9} = 10{,}000{,}000$

6. a.

1	2	3	4	5	6	7
R 1/2	L 1/4	R 1/8	L 1/16	R 1/32	L 1/64	R 1/128

The seventh jump is to the right $\frac{1}{128}$ ft. (Note: Odd jumps are to the right and even jumps are to the left.)

b. Think of movement to the right as positive and to the left as negative.

$u_1 = \frac{1}{2}$; $r = \frac{-1}{2}$; $u_{18} = \frac{1}{2}\left(\frac{-1}{2}\right)^{17}$ or $\frac{-1}{262144}$, which is to the left.

c. $S = \dfrac{\frac{1}{2}}{1 - \frac{-1}{2}} = \dfrac{\frac{1}{2}}{\frac{3}{2}} = \frac{1}{3}$

7. If the trains are 60 mi apart and they are both traveling at 30 mi/hr, they will meet in 1 hr. The bee is traveling at 50 mi/hr, so in one hour it will have traveled 50 mi.

8. At age 30 (10 yr later), Prudence has \$35,120.59 ($u_0 = 2000$ and $u_n = u_{(n-1)} \cdot 1.09 + 2000$). At age 30, Charity has \$2,000.

At age 65 (35 yr later), Prudence has \$716,950.60 ($u_0 = 35120.59$ and $u_n = u_{(n-1)} \cdot 1.09$).

At age 65, Charity has \$472,249.45 ($u_0 = 2000$ and $u_n = u_{(n-1)} \cdot 1.09 + 2000$).

9. a. $u_1 = 8 \cdot 4 = 32$ in.; $u_2 = 4\sqrt{2} \cdot 4 = 16\sqrt{2}$ in. $u_3 = 4 \cdot 4 = 16$ in. $r = \frac{\sqrt{2}}{2}$; $u_{10} = 32\left(\frac{\sqrt{2}}{2}\right)^9 \approx 1.414$, which is the perimeter of the tenth square.

b. $A_{10} = \left(\frac{1.414}{4}\right)^2 \approx 0.125$, which is the area of the tenth square.

c. $S = \dfrac{32}{1 - \frac{\sqrt{2}}{2}} \approx 109.25$, so the total perimeter of all the squares approaches 109.25. $A = \dfrac{64}{1 - \frac{1}{2}} = 128$, so the total area of all the squares approaches 128.

10. a. Substitute 1 through 12 for n: $96 + 24 + 6 + 1.5 + 0.375 + 0.09375 + 0.0234375 + 0.005859375 + 0.0014648438 + \cdots + 3.662109375 \cdot 10^{-4}$.

b. $S_{10} = \dfrac{96(1 - 0.25^{12})}{1 - 0.25} = 127.9999924$

c. $S = \dfrac{96}{1 - 0.25} = 128$

d.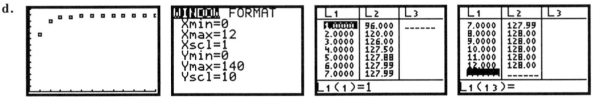

11. Answers will vary.

Take Another Look 2.5

a. After the second bounce, the ball will rebound to a height of 128 units.

b. The 488 represents the sum of the falling distances when the ball bounces the third time. An equation that would work is $y_2 = \dfrac{200(1 - 0.8^x)}{(1 - 0.8)}$.

c. The rebound height gets closer and closer to zero. The sum of the falling heights approaches 1000 units.

d. One possibility is $y_1 = 160(0.80)^x$.

e. $u_n = y_1 = 2(x - 1) + 65$; $S_n = y_2 = \dfrac{x(65 + 2(x - 1)) + 65}{2}$ or $y_2 = \dfrac{x(y_1(x)) + 65}{2}$

For $x = 40$, $y_1 = 143$ (the number of seats in row 40) and $y_2 = 4160$ (the number of seats in the concert hall). Row 12 ends with seat 912. Calculate $995 - 912 = 183$. Thus you are 83 seats from the left-hand side or, since row 13 has 89 seats, you have the seventh seat from the right-hand side.

f. $y_1 = 4(x - 1) + 25$; $y_2 = \dfrac{x(25 + 4(x - 1)) + 25}{2}$ or $y_2 = \dfrac{x\left(y_1(x)\right) + 25}{2}$. The last row has 165 seats. There are 3420 seats in the concert hall. Your seats are in the sixteenth row. Row 16 ends with seat 880, so you have the first two seats on the right-hand side.

Problem Set 2.6

1. Geome tree

		1	2	3	4	n	∞
a.	Length of the last segment	1	0.5	0.25	0.125	$1\left(\frac{1}{2}\right)^{(n-1)}$	0
b.	Length of the path	1	1.5	1.75	1.875	$\dfrac{1\left(1 - \left(\frac{1}{2}\right)^n\right)}{1 - \frac{1}{2}}$	2
c.	Total number of segments	1	3	7	15	$2^n - 1$	∞
d.	Sum of the lengths of all segments	1	2	3	4	n	∞
e.	Height of the tree	1	1.354	1.604	1.692		1.8047
f.	Width of the tree	0	0.707	1.207	1.384		1.609

Draw each tree branch carefully. For branches going up at a 135° angle, the triangle formed is a 45–45–90 triangle. The height and width are both the length of the segment divided by $\sqrt{2}$. For branches going straight up, both the height and width are the length of the segment. When computing the width, the length of the width segment must be doubled. For example, for $n = 3$, the height is $1.354 + 0.25$ and the width is $0.707 + 0.25(2)$. For $n = 4$, the height is $1.604 + \dfrac{0.125}{\sqrt{2}}$ and the width is $1.604 + \dfrac{0.125}{\sqrt{2}}(2)$.

2. Koch snowflake

		1	2	3	4	n	∞
a.	Length of each segment	1	$\frac{1}{3}$	$\frac{1}{9}$	$\frac{1}{27}$	$\left(\frac{1}{3}\right)^{(n-1)}$	0
b.	Total number of segments	3	12	48	192	$3 \cdot 4^{(n-1)}$	∞
c.	Perimeter	3	4	$5\frac{1}{3}$	$\frac{64}{9}$	$\dfrac{3 \cdot 4^{(n-1)}}{3^{(n-1)}}$	∞
d.	Area	0.43301	0.577	0.641	0.67001		0.69282

The area of a triangle is $\frac{1}{2}bh$. For an equilateral triangle, $h = \frac{1}{2}b\sqrt{3}$ so the area of a triangle is $\frac{1}{4}b^2\sqrt{3}$.
$A_1 = \frac{\sqrt{3}}{4}$; $A_2 = A_1 + \frac{\sqrt{3}}{12}$; $A_3 = A_1 + A_2 + \frac{\sqrt{3}}{27}$; $A_4 = A_1 + A_2 + A_3 + \frac{4\sqrt{3}}{243}$

3. Sierpiński triangle

		1	2	3	4	n	∞
a.	Length of last side	1	$\frac{1}{2}$	$\frac{1}{4}$	$\frac{1}{8}$	$\left(\frac{1}{2}\right)^{(n-1)}$	0
b.	Number of triangles	1	3	9	27	$3^{(n-1)}$	∞
c.	Perimeter of each	3	$\frac{3}{2}$	$\frac{3}{4}$	$\frac{3}{8}$	$\frac{3}{2^{n-1}}$	0
d.	Area of each	$\frac{\sqrt{3}}{4}$	$\frac{\sqrt{3}}{16}$	$\frac{\sqrt{3}}{64}$	$\frac{\sqrt{3}}{256}$	$\frac{\sqrt{3}}{4^n}$	0
e.	Sum of perimeters	3	4.5	6.75	10.125	$\frac{3^n}{2^{(n-1)}}$	∞
f.	Sum of areas	$\frac{\sqrt{3}}{4}$	$\frac{3\sqrt{3}}{16}$	$\frac{9\sqrt{3}}{64}$	$\frac{27\sqrt{3}}{256}$	$\frac{3^{(n-1)}\sqrt{3}}{4^n}$	0

a. The length of the last side is one-half the length of the previous side.
b. The number of triangles is three times the previous number of triangles.
c. The perimeter is three times the length of each side.
d. The area of a triangle is $\frac{1}{2}bh$. For an equilateral triangle, $h = \frac{1}{2}b\sqrt{3}$ so the area of a triangle is $\frac{1}{4}b^2\sqrt{3}$.
e. Multiply number of triangles (b) by their perimeter (c).
f. The area decreases by 3/4 each time.

4. Answers will vary.

Take Another Look 2.6

a. Answers will vary on which strategy to use. It is a geometric jumping flea with a common ratio of 1/2.

b. The eighth jump is 0.0039 ft. The flea is 0.996 ft to the right of where it started.

c. The twentieth jump is $9.5 \cdot 10^{-7}$ ft long. The flea is 1 ft to the right of where it started.

d. $y_1 = 0.5x$; $y_2 = \frac{0.5(1 - 0.5x)}{1 - 0.5}$

e. The flea is zooming in on the 1 ft mark.

Project: Sierpiński Carpet

This figure, like the Sierpiński triangle (Problem 3 in Problem Set 2.6), is full of self-similarity. It holds a couple of surprises when you look at area and perimeter. The number of squares forms a geometric sequence with ratio 8. The remaining areas form a geometric sequence with ratio 8/9. The perimeters form a geometric sequence with ratio 8/3. The removed areas are the differences between 1 and the areas. In the long run, the carpet will be all holes bounded by an infinitely thin mesh. This will create a figure with an infinite perimeter and no area.

Stage	Number of squares	Remaining area	Removed area	Perimeter of removed area
0	1	1	0	0
1	8	8/9	1/9	4/3
2	64	64/81	17/81	44/9
3	512	512/729	217/729	388/27
n	8^n	$(8/9)^n$	$1 - (8/9)^n$	$\frac{4}{3}\left(\dfrac{1 - \left(\frac{8}{3}\right)^n}{1 - \frac{8}{3}}\right)$
Long run	∞	0	1	∞

Chapter Review
Problem Set 2.7

1. a. 3, 6, 9, 12, 15, 18, 21, 24, 27, 30
   b. $u_n = \begin{cases} 3 & \text{if } n = 1 \\ u_{(n-1)} + 3 & \text{if } n > 1 \end{cases}$

   c. $u_n = 3n$
   d. $u_{47} = 3 \cdot 47 = 141$; $u_1 + u_{47} = 3 + 141 = 144$; $S_{47} = \frac{47(44)}{2} = 3384$ cans

   e. Use guess-and-check. $u_{13} = 3 \cdot 13 = 39$; $u_1 + u_{13} = 3 + 39 = 42$; $S_{13} = \frac{13(42)}{2} = 273$ cans
   $u_{14} = 3 \cdot 14 = 42$; $u_1 + u_{14} = 3 + 42 = 45$; $S_{14} = \frac{14(45)}{2} = 315$
   You can make 13 complete rows with 288 cans.

2. a. $u_1 = 3$; $d = 4$; $u_{128} = 3 + 127(4) = 511$
   b. $\begin{aligned} 159 &= 3 + (n-1)4 \\ 156 &= (n-1)4 \\ 39 &= n - 1 \\ 40 &= n, \text{ so 159 is the 40th term.} \end{aligned}$
   c. $u_{20} = 3 + 19(4) = 3 + 76 = 79$
   d. $u_1 + u_{20} = 3 + 79 = 82$; $S_{20} = \frac{20(82)}{2} = 820$

3. a. $r = 12; u_1 = 12$

```
12
              12
Ans*12
             144
            1728
           20736
          248832
■
```

In 5 days, there will be $6(24) = 144 = 12(12)$ bugs.
In 10 days, there will be $72(24) = 1728 = 12(12)^2$ bugs.
In 15 days, there will be $864(24) = 20,736 = 12(12)^3$ bugs.
In 35 days, there will be 429,981,696 or $4.3 \cdot 10^8$ bugs.

b. $u_n = \begin{cases} 12 & \text{if } n = 1 \\ 12 \cdot u_{(n-1)} & \text{if } n > 1 \end{cases}$

c. $u_n = 12^n$ **d.** 60 days = 12 time periods

$u_{12} = 12^{12} \approx 8.9 \cdot 10^{12}; S_{12} = \frac{12(1 - 12^{12})}{1 - 12} \approx 9.7 \cdot 10^{12}$ bugs

4. a. $\frac{192}{256} = 0.75 = r; u_8 = 256(0.75)^7 = 34.171875$

b. $256(0.75)^8 = 25.62890625$
$256(0.75)^9 = 19.22167969$
Therefore, the tenth term is the first term less than 20.

c. $u_7 = 256(0.75)^6 = 45.5625$ **d.** $S_7 = \frac{256(1 - 0.75^7)}{1 - 0.75} = 887.3125$

e. $S_n = \frac{256}{1 - 0.75} = 1024$; as n gets very large, the sum approaches 1024.

5. a. The explicit formula is $u_n = 500\left(1 + \frac{0.055}{4}\right)^{20} = \$657.03$ (Note: Use 20 because 5 yr compounded quarterly is 20 terms.)

b. Using Sequence mode, define $u_n = u_{(n-1)}\left(1 + \frac{0.055}{4}\right) + 150$ with $u_0 = 500$. You will have $4,083.21 after 5 yr.

6. a. Using Sequence mode, define $u_n = u_{(n-1)}(1 - 0.24) + 1250$ with $u_0 = 5678$. After 5 yr there will be 5327 students.

b. In the long run, there will be 5208 students.

7. a. $u_n = 200(0.95)^7 \approx 139.67$ cm. **b.** $u_1 = 200, r = 0.95, S_7 = \frac{200(1 - (0.95)^7)}{1 - 0.95} \approx 1206.65$ cm

c. Try larger and larger values for n. In the long run, the total falling distance will be 4000 cm.

8. $u_1 = 20; r = \frac{2}{3}; S_7 = \dfrac{20\left(1 - \left(\frac{2}{3}\right)^7\right)}{1 - \frac{2}{3}} \approx 56.488$ ft in seven strokes.

The ball travels a total of 20 ft on the first putt, and the distance traveled for each successive putt is 2/3 the previous distance.

$S = \dfrac{20}{1 - \frac{2}{3}} = 60$ ft in the long run.

9. Use guess-and-check. $u_0 = 80,000; u_n = u_{(n-1)}\left(1 + \frac{0.089}{12}\right) - p$ where p is the monthly payment. If $n = 360$ (30 years of monthly payments), we want the balance to be 0 or close to 0. There would be 359 payments of \$637.96 and 1 payment of \$637.96 – \$17.50 or \$620.46.

10. a. $\left(\frac{2}{3}\right)^0, \left(\frac{2}{3}\right)^1, \left(\frac{2}{3}\right)^2, \left(\frac{2}{3}\right)^3$, and so on. **b.** The sum $C_n \to 0$

11. a. $u_n = \frac{1}{n}; v_n = v_{(n-1)} + \frac{1}{n}; u_1 = 1, v_1 = 1$. The partial sums are 2.929, 3.598, 3.995, 4.279, 4.499, 4.680, 4.833, 4.965, 5.083.

b. The sum continues to get larger at a slower rate.

Chapter 3

Problem Set 3.1

1. Enter Connie's scores in L1 and Ozzie's scores in L2. Calculate the one-variable statistics for each. The mean is 84 and the median is 84 for both Connie and Ozzie. Neither the mean nor median score indicates the larger test-score variation of Ozzie's scores.

2. The second box plot is longer because it reflects the longer range of Ozzie's scores.

   There is no left whisker for the top box because the lower quarter of the score is made up of a single repeated score; it has no interval length.
   The median isn't in the center of the box because the second quarter of the scores is spread over a longer interval than the third quarter scores.
   Finally, there is a bigger range or longer interval for the lowest quarter of Ozzie's scores than in the upper interval, so the left whisker is longer than the right one.

3. **a.** Enter Homer's scores into a list.

   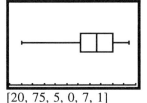

   [20, 75, 5, 0, 7, 1]

   b. Use trace on the box plot to find the five summary points. Xmin = 25; Q1 = 51; Med = 58; Q3 = 65; Xmax = 72.

   c. Find the sum of Homer's home runs and divide by 11 to obtain the mean. $\frac{622}{11} \approx 56.55$

   d. Use guess-and-check to find the 12th term. In the 12th year, he should have 98 home runs.

4. **a.** For Connie: The difference between the upper and lower quartiles is 85 − 82 = 3(1.5) = 4.5. Any value below 82 − 4.5 = 77.5 and any value above 85 + 4.5 = 89.5 would be an outlier. For Ozzie: 94 − 76 = 18. 18(1.5) = 27. Any value below 76 − 27 = 49 and any value above 94 + 27 = 121 would be an outlier.

   b. For Homer: 65 − 51 = 14. 14(1.5) = 21. Any value below 51 − 21 = 30 and any value above 65 + 21 = 86 would be an outlier. Homer has only one outlier (25) that is below 30 or above 86.

5. **a.** Enter the dollars per month into a list and calculate the one-variable statistics to find the mean. Or use the LIST CALC menu.
   The mean cost is $0.70.

   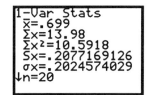

   b.

   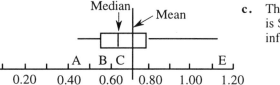

   Cost per month for toothpaste

   c. The median value is $0.64. The mean value is $0.70. The mean is larger because of the influence of several large values in the data.

6. **a.** Enter the attendance numbers into a list. Trace on the box plot or calculate the one-variable statistics to find the five summary values.

   {74,300, 87,050, 105,000, 153,900, 246,900}

   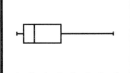

   [50000, 275000, 25000, 0, 10, 1]

   There are no outliers. The difference between Q3 and Q1 is 153,900 − 87,050 = 66,850. (1.5)(66,850) = 100,275. 153,900 + 100,275 = 254,175, so a data value would have to be greater than 254,175 to qualify as an outlier.

b. {74,300, 84,650, 93,600, 105,750, 116,800}

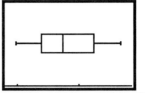

[70000, 120000, 25000, 0, 10, 1]

7. a. The mean is 4601, and the median is 2477. There is one outlier, New York City.
b. The mean is 3062, and the median is 2463. The mean was affected more.
c. Answers will vary.
d. The new mean would be 5601. The new median would be 3477. Each value increased by 1000.
e. The summary values are {57.5, 73.3, 82.1, 92.1, 97.6}. Discussion answers may vary.

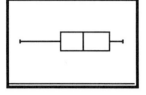

8. a.–c. Answers will vary.

9. a.

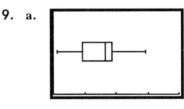

b. Scores less than −2,317 or more than 16,375 would be outliers. If I am an outlier I am more than $7,010 above the upper quartile or more than $7,009 below the lower quartile. There are no outliers.
9366 − 4693 = 4673
4673(1.5) = 7010
4693 − 7010 = −2317
9366 + 7010 = 16,376

c. There is no mode; the median is 8279; the mean is 7683.
d. The United States is in the second quartile.

10. a. The tube price median is $2.01 and the mean is $2.13; the median cleaning rank is 66.5 and the mean rank is 67.25.
b. Price   Rank

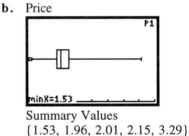   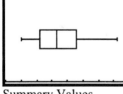

Summary Values   Summary Values
{1.53, 1.96, 2.01, 2.15, 3.29}   {55, 61, 66.5, 73, 86}

c. Answers will vary.

Project: Stem-and-Leaf Plots

	Presidents		Vice Presidents
		3	6
	3 2	4	0 2 3 3 3
	9 9 8 7 6	•	5 6 9 9 9
4 4 4 4 2 2 1 1 1 1 0 0		5	1 1 1 1 2 3 3 3 3 3 4 4 4 4
8 7 7 7 7 6 6 6 5 5 5 5		•	7 7 7 8 8 9
	4 4 4 2 1 1 1 0	6	0 0 1 1
	9 8	•	5 6 6 6 7 9 9
		7	2

Key   3 | 6 = 36 yr old

Problem Set 3.2

1. A MAD of 0.12 implies that no CDs can be shipped that measure more than 12.12 cm or less than 11.88 cm.

2. Answers will vary. One possible answer is {71, 79, 80, 84, 89, 91, 94}.

3. From top to bottom the graphs are for the Northeast, Midwest, South, and West. Summary points for Northeast are {13.2, 13.75, 15.4, 16.35, 17}, for the Midwest are {14.6, 15.5, 16.45, 17.4, 19.9}, for the South are {15.4, 16.25, 17.05, 18.45, 19.9}, and for the West are {14.5, 16.85, 18.95, 19.85, 25}.

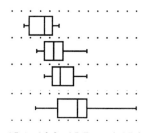

4. a. Add each deviation to 46.3. The actual values were 47.1, 45.9, 47.9, 47.4, 45.1, 46.0, 45.7, and 45.3.

b. Enter the values in L1 and the deviations in L2. Then find the MAD using one of the methods in the Calculator Notes.

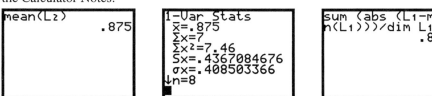

c. To be more than 1 MAD from the mean, the value had to be more than 0.875 away from the mean of 46.3. Those values were 47.9, 47.4, 45.1, and 45.3.

5. a. First period has pulse rates most alike because it has the smallest MAD.

b. You can't really tell which class has the students with the fastest pulse. First period rates are more consistent around the mean of 79.4 because it has the lowest MAD value. Sixth period must have some very high rates and some very low rates to have the highest MAD value.

c. Answers will vary. Data sets with lower MAD values will have shorter box plots.

d. Answers will vary.

6. a. Find the sum of a column and divide by the number of entries in the column.
Column 1: 19.8
Column 2: 23.6
Column 3: 17.3

b. Take the absolute value of the difference between the column entry and the mean. Find the sum of these absolute values and divide by the number of entries.
Column 1: 5.3
Column 2: 6.2
Column 3: 4.9
With your data in L1, place the cursor over the heading of an empty list. Type abs(mean (L1) – L1) and press ENTER . The MAD will be the mean of this list.

c. Calculate the one-variable statistics or trace on a box plot to find these summary values.
Column 1

| | | | | |
| 9.2 | 14.5 | 19.8 | 25.1 | 30.4 |

Column 2

| | | | | |
| 11.2 | 17.4 | 23.6 | 29.8 | 36 |

Column 3

| | | | | |
| 7.5 | 12.5 | 17.3 | 22.2 | 27.1 |

d. Column 1: 1904, 1908, 1911–1918, 1923–1929
   Column 2: 1931, 1934–1942, 1945, 1947, 1948, 1951, 1953, 1955
   Column 3: 1960–1967, 1972–1975, 1977–1981, 1983, 1985
   e. Column 1: 1902, 1906, 1909, 1910, 1920
   Column 2: 1943, 1950, 1958
   Column 3: 1968, 1970, 1986, 1989

7. a.–d. See answers for Problems 6a.–e.
   e. Answers will vary.

8. a. The interquartile range for Juneau, Alaska, is 51 – 30 = 21.
   The interquartile range for New York, New York,
   is 70 – 39.5 = 30.5.

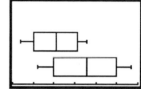

   b. Juneau has more consistent temperatures ranging from 24°F to
   56°F compared to New York temperatures ranging from 32°F to
   77°F. The MAD for Juneau is 9.83°F and for New York 14.0°F.

9. a. The median is the 13th value, 75. To find the interquartile range,
   draw a box plot and trace to find Q1 and Q3. For this box plot,
   Q1 = 67.5 and Q3 = 86.5 so the range is 86.5 – 67.5 = 19.

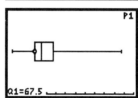

   b. You can find the mean using the LIST MATH menu or by calculating the one-variable
   statistics for the list. To find the MAD, make L2 = ABS(L1 – mean(L1)).

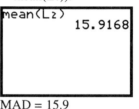

   mean = 80.88   MAD = 15.9

   c. Trace on the box plot to find Q1 and Q3 (Q1 = 67.5; Q3 = 86.5).
   Multiply the interquartile range by 1.5 [(86.5 – 67.5)(1.5) = 28.5].
   An outlier would have to be smaller than 67.5 – 28.5 = 39 or
   larger than 86.5 + 28.5 = 115. The outliers are 147 and 158.

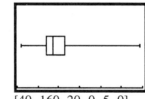

   [40, 160, 20, 0, 5, 0]

   d. Delete 147 and 158 from L1
   and draw another box plot.

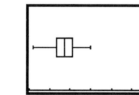

   [40, 160, 20, 0, 5, 0]

   e. i. The mean is 74.65 and the MAD is 9.3.
   ii. The median is 74 and interquartile range is 82 – 67 = 15.
   f. When the outliers are removed, the mean is affected more than the median and the MAD
   is affected more than the interquartile range. This is because MAD is related to the mean
   and interquartile range is related to the median.

10. Answers will vary.

Take Another Look 3.2

a. Refer to the text and the calculator notes. The values for the original data are:
median = 75
interquartile range = 19
five-number summary: {44, 67.5, 75, 86.5, 158}
mean = 80.88
MAD = 15.9

b. Refer to the text.

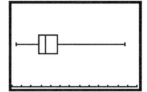

c. Multiply each value in the list of packages of hot chocolate sold by 0.28 and store these values in a new list.
median = $21
interquartile range = 24.22 – 18.9 = 5.32
five-number summary: {12.32, 18.9, 21, 24.22, 44.24}
mean = 22.65
MAD = 4.46

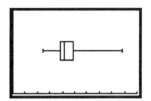

d. Multiply each of the original values by 0.28 to get the new values. In other words, multiply the original mean by 0.28 to get the new mean. The values related to a $0.35 profit are:
median = 75(0.35) = 26.25
interquartile range = 19(0.35) = 6.65
five-number summary: {15.4, 23.63, 26.25, 30.28, 55.3}
mean = 80.88(0.35) = 28.31
MAD = 15.9(0.35) = 5.57

e. Subtract 20 from each original value except those values that measure spread (the interquartile range and the MAD).
median = 75 – 20 = 55
interquartile range = 19 (same as the original)
five-number summary: {24, 47.5, 55, 66.5, 138}
mean = 60.88
MAD = 15.9

The values related to 10 fewer packages are:
median = 75 – 10 = 65
interquartile range = 19
five-number summary: {34, 57.5, 65, 76.5, 148}
mean = 70.88
MAD = 15.9

f. Original data (inches)
median = 68
interquartile range = 70 – 64 = 6
five-number summary: {60, 64, 68, 70, 77}
mean = 67.9
MAD = 3.3

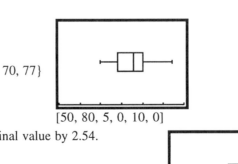

[50, 80, 5, 0, 10, 0]

For centimeters, multiply each original value by 2.54.
median = 172.72
interquartile range = 15.24
five-number summary: {152.4, 162.56, 172.72, 177.8, 195.58}
mean = 172.51
MAD = 8.27

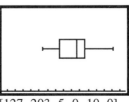

[127, 203, 5, 0, 10, 0]

g. Multiply the Xmin and Xmax values for the "inches" box plot by 2.54. Then the box plots will "look" the same.

Project: Collecting Data

The question most often raised here is the amount of data that should be collected. Is 50 enough? Is 500 enough? There is no simple answer other than that the more data collected, the more useful the conclusions will be. Probably something in the 100 range would be good for this project, but encourage students to collect as much as they can and to make use of their groups to do this.

Problem Set 3.3

1. a.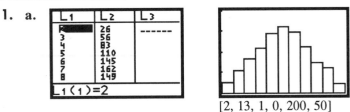
   [2, 13, 1, 0, 200, 50]

   b. It is mound shaped because 7 is the most likely dice total, then 6 and 8, then 5 and 9, and so on.
   c. The mean sum can be computed by evaluating $\frac{2(26) + 3(56) + \cdots + 12(21)}{1000}$ = 6.977. The median sum can be found by counting in from the left or right. The median sum will be the average of the 500th and 501st roll total. 26 + 56 + 83 + 110 + 145 = 420; 420 + 162 = 582. The 500th and 501st roll are both 7.

2. a. This population of 95 farmers tends to plant two to five acres of sweet corn. The frequencies are on the left.
   b.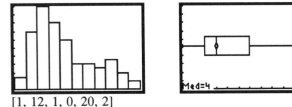
   [1, 12, 1, 0, 20, 2]

   c. There are 95 acres in this distribution. The mean is $\frac{1(3) + 2(14) + 3(20) + \cdots + 2(11)}{95}$ = $\frac{458}{95}$ = 4.8 acres. The MAD is 2.6. The median number of acres planted in corn is 4. (Count the 48th acre.) In a box plot, the center of the box would be 4. The part of the box to the left of the median value of 4 would be smaller than the part to the right of 4 because there are more values close to 4 on the left than on the right. The whiskers would range from 1 to 11.

3. a.–d. Answers will vary.

4. a. About 88% of the students, or 0.88(1500) or 1320 students, did worse; about 12% of the students or 0.12(1500) = 180 students, did better.
   b. Mary scored better than 95% of the students.
   c. The best score of 91 would be at the 99th percentile.
   d. About 10% of the students, or 0.10(1500) or 150 students, earned an A.

5. a. The top box plot is for HW and the bottom is for TV. The five summary points for HW are {4, 27.5, 40.5, 49, 65} and for TV are {5, 26, 36.5, 58, 95}. (Trace on the box plot to find these values.) The spread for HW is 65 – 4 = 61, and the spread for TV is 95 – 5 = 90. The spread for TV is greater. The MAD for HW is 12.78 min and for TV is 20.56 min.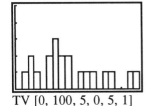
   b. Answers may vary.

   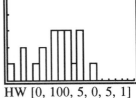

   HW [0, 100, 5, 0, 5, 1]   TV [0, 100, 5, 0, 5, 1]
   c. HW: MAD = 12.78, range = 65 – 4 = 61, IQR = 49 – 27.5 = 21.5
      TV: MAD = 20.56, range = 95 – 5 = 90, IQR = 58 – 26 = 32

6. a. The sum of the deviations is 13. It should be 0.   **b.** 20

   c. Mean of 747

       i.   47.25   ii.   747, 707, 669, 676, 767, 783, 789, 838

       iii. 757   iv.   94.5

      Mean of 850

       i.   47.25   ii.   850, 810, 772, 779, 870, 886, 892, 941

       iii. 860   iv.   94.5

   d. Answers will vary. For example, the MAD and IQR are unaffected by a change in the mean, the median moves the same amount as the mean.

7. a. The MAD of the stadium capacities is 7282. The MAD of the attendance figures is 6254. Attendance MAD is less than stadium capacity MAD. This means the stadium capacity values are more spread out.

   b. A larger MAD should mean the box plot is longer and the histogram distribution is not so mound shaped. A smaller MAD should mean the box plot is shorter and the histogram distribution is more mound shaped.

   c. Capacity

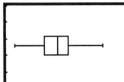 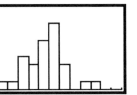

[30000, 90000, 5000, 0, 5, 1]   [30000, 90000, 5000, 0, 10, 1]

Attendance

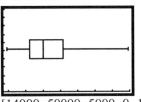 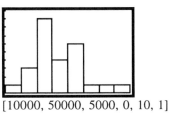

[14000, 50000, 5000, 0, 10, 1]   [10000, 50000, 5000, 0, 10, 1]

   d. Answers will vary.

8. Answers will vary.

Take Another Look 3.3

1. a. The variable, n, represents the number of data values in the set. In this case, $n = 50$.
The variable, i, is the counter and counts from 1 to 50.
The expression, x_i, is used to represent each data value.
The symbol, Σ, means to find the sum.
The entire expression asked you to find the sum of all the data values and divide this sum by the number of values in the set. In other words, find the mean. The mean is 79.1.

   b. The variable, $\bar{x}$, represents the mean. The expression $|x_i - \bar{x}|$ means to find the absolute value of the difference between each data value and the mean of the data set. The entire expression represents the MAD. The MAD is 5.86.

   c. Find the difference between each data value and the mean. Then square this difference. Find the sum of all the squared differences and divide by the number of data values. Finally, take the square root of the result. The standard deviation is 7.49.

2. a.–e. Answers will vary.

Project: Standard Deviation

There are two standard deviations given by the calculator. Students may need to refer to Chapter 11 to learn more about standard deviation and why there are two different values given for this measure of spread.

Chapter Review

Problem Set 3.4

1. Plot B because the data is much more spread out.

2. **a.** Answers will vary here, but the graph for A should be much higher, more mounded and compact. Shapes should take into account the scale on the horizontal axis and the way values are compacted between the quartiles.

   b. Seven data values are in the lower whisker in plot C. Six data values are in each whisker in plot D.

   c. Plot B has the greater MAD because the box plot is longer and the range of data values is much greater.

3. Answers will vary.

4. For the high temperatures, the mean is 118°F with a MAD of 17°F. For the low temperatures, the mean is ⁻60°F with a MAD of 38°F. For outliers for the high temperatures, look for temperatures less than $118 - 2(17) = 84$ or more than $118 + 2(17) = 152$. Antarctica's high temperature is more than two MADs lower than the mean high. For outliers for the low temperatures, look for temperatures less than $-60 - 2(38) = -136$ or more than $-60 + 2(38) = 16$. Antarctica's low temperature is *almost* two MADs from the mean low.

5. **a.** Answers will vary, but the MAD near 0 means a tall, skinny graph.

   b. Answers will vary, but the MAD of about 5 means a shorter but longer graph.

6. **a.** Answers will vary for the prediction. The median value is 95 hr and the mean value is 129 hr.

   b. (The United States flights are Mercury, Gemini, and Apollo.) The window for both graphs is [0, 600, 24, 0, 7, 1].

   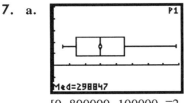   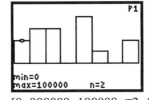

   United States   Soviet Union

   c. Answers for the predictions will vary. The MAD for the Soviet flights is 70 hr and for the United States flights is 96 hr.

7. **a.**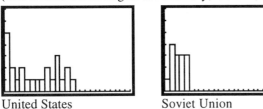

      [0, 800000, 100000, ⁻2, 5, 1]

   b.

      [0, 800000, 100000, ⁻2, 5, 1]

   c.–d. Answers will vary. The shape really depends on how the additional sales are distributed.

8. **a.** Descriptions will vary.

   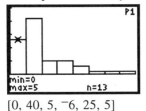

      [0, 40, 5, ⁻6, 25, 5]   [0, 40, 5, ⁻6, 25, 5]

b. Explanations will vary.

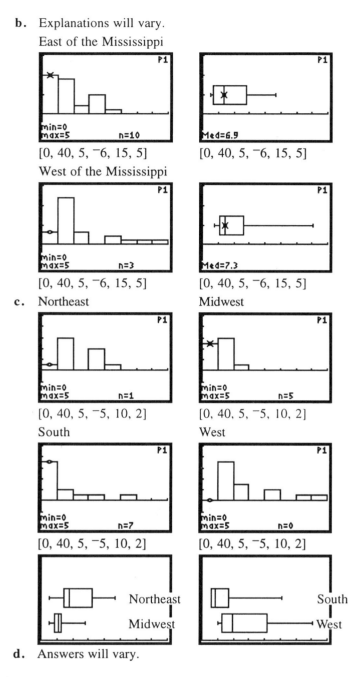

East of the Mississippi

min=0
max=5   n=10

[0, 40, 5, ‾6, 15, 5]

Med=6.9

[0, 40, 5, ‾6, 15, 5]

West of the Mississippi

min=0
max=5   n=3

[0, 40, 5, ‾6, 15, 5]

Med=7.3

[0, 40, 5, ‾6, 15, 5]

c. Northeast

min=0
max=5   n=1

[0, 40, 5, ‾5, 10, 2]

Midwest

min=0
max=5   n=5

[0, 40, 5, ‾5, 10, 2]

South

min=0
max=5   n=7

[0, 40, 5, ‾5, 10, 2]

West

min=0
max=5   n=0

[0, 40, 5, ‾5, 10, 2]

Northeast
Midwest

South
West

d. Answers will vary.

Chapter 4

Problem Set 4.1

1. Answers will vary; here are some examples.
   a. Too many points are above the line. (2nd guideline)
   b. Most of the points at the left are below the line. (4th guideline)
   c. The line doesn't follow the tendency of the data from the first to the last point. (1st guideline)
   d. Points at each end are concentrated on one side of the line. (3rd guideline)
   e. This is the best of the lot. (The line follows the direction of the points, the points are divided evenly and are not concentrated on one end of the line.)
   f. There are no points below the line. (2nd guideline)

2. Answers will vary for parts a.–f.

a.

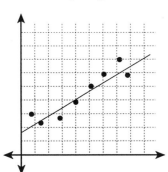

The *y*-intercept is about 1.7.
Two possible points are (4, 4) and (7, 6).

b.

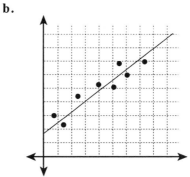

The *y*-intercept is about 1.8.
Two possible points are (3, 4) and (7, 7).

c.

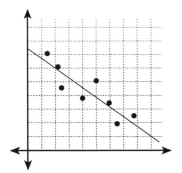

The *y*-intercept is about 7.5.
Two possible points are (2, 6) and (6, 3).

d.

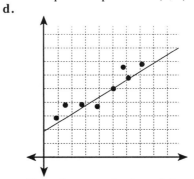

The *y*-intercept is about 2.2.
Two possible points are (4, 5) and (7, 7).

e.

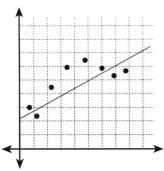

The *y*-intercept is about 2.5.
Two possible points are (3, 4) and (8, 7).

f.

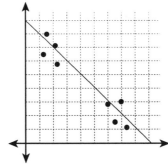

The *y*-intercept is about 8.6.
Two possible points are (2, 6.5) and (7, 2).

3. Answers will vary for the best-fit line.

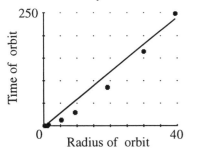

4. Answers will vary for the best-fit line.

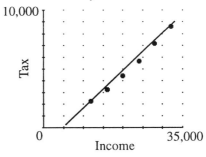

5. Answers will vary.

6. **a.** Six graphs are needed: size versus bust, size versus waist, size versus hips, bust versus waist, bust versus hips, and waist versus hips.

b. [0, 22, 2, 20, 45, 5]

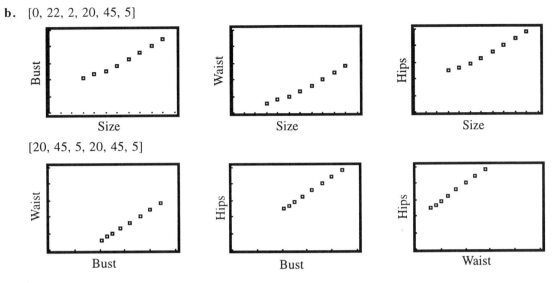

[20, 45, 5, 20, 45, 5]

7. Answers will vary.

Take Another Look 4.1

To find the mean number of acres, first multiply the number of acres (List 1) by the frequency (List 2) and store this new list in List 3. Then divide the sum of List 3 by the sum of List 2. The mean number of acres is 3.82.

To find the MAD, first store (List 1 − mean)List 2 in a separate list. Find the sum of this list and divide it by the sum of List 2. The MAD is 2.116.

Problem Set 4.2

1. a. $\frac{2 - {}^{-}4}{7 - 3} = \frac{6}{4} = \frac{3}{2}$ **b.** $\frac{5 - 3}{2 - 5} = \frac{2}{-3} = \frac{-2}{3}$

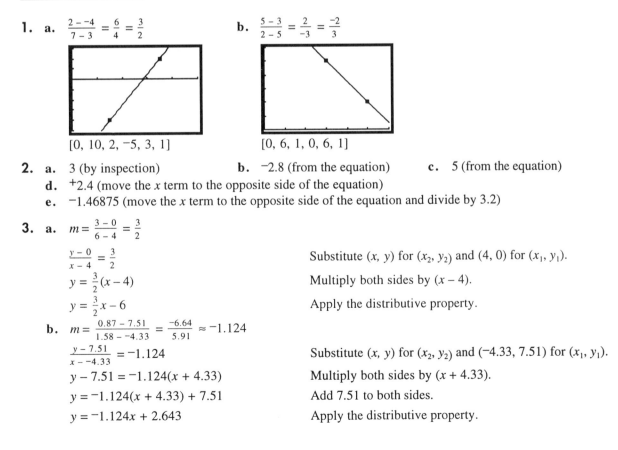

[0, 10, 2, −5, 3, 1] [0, 6, 1, 0, 6, 1]

2. a. 3 (by inspection) **b.** −2.8 (from the equation) **c.** 5 (from the equation)

  d. $^{+}2.4$ (move the x term to the opposite side of the equation)

  e. −1.46875 (move the x term to the opposite side of the equation and divide by 3.2)

3. a. $m = \frac{3 - 0}{6 - 4} = \frac{3}{2}$

$\frac{y - 0}{x - 4} = \frac{3}{2}$ Substitute (x, y) for (x_2, y_2) and $(4, 0)$ for (x_1, y_1).

$y = \frac{3}{2}(x - 4)$ Multiply both sides by $(x - 4)$.

$y = \frac{3}{2}x - 6$ Apply the distributive property.

  b. $m = \frac{0.87 - 7.51}{1.58 - {}^{-}4.33} = \frac{-6.64}{5.91} \approx {}^{-}1.124$

$\frac{y - 7.51}{x - {}^{-}4.33} = {}^{-}1.124$ Substitute (x, y) for (x_2, y_2) and $({}^{-}4.33, 7.51)$ for (x_1, y_1).

$y - 7.51 = {}^{-}1.124(x + 4.33)$ Multiply both sides by $(x + 4.33)$.

$y = {}^{-}1.124(x + 4.33) + 7.51$ Add 7.51 to both sides.

$y = {}^{-}1.124x + 2.643$ Apply the distributive property.

4. a. Select the points $(0, {}^-2)$ and $(4, 1)$. $m = \frac{1 - {}^-2}{4 - 0} = \frac{3}{4}$

$y = \frac{3}{4}(x - 0) + {}^-2$ Point-slope form.

$y = \frac{3}{4}x - 2$ Apply the distributive property.

b. Select the points $(1, 2)$ and $(3, {}^-1)$. $m = \frac{{}^-1 - 2}{3 - 1} = \frac{{}^-3}{2}$

$y = \frac{{}^-3}{2}(x - 1) + 2$ Point-slope form.

$y = \frac{{}^-3}{2}x + \frac{7}{2}$ Apply the distributive property.

5. The answer should be close to the equation of the median-median line, which is $y = 5.59x - 8.03$.

6. The answer should be close to the equation of the median-median line, which is $y = 0.32x - 1820$.

7.

(size, bust)	$y = 0.84x + 24.6$	(size, waist)	$y = 0.79x + 17.5$
(size, hips)	$y = 0.84x + 26.6$	(bust, waist)	$y = 0.94x - 5.7$
(bust, hips)	$y = x + 2$	(waist, hips)	$y = 1.06x + 8.1$

8. 299 payments of \$528.40, 1 payment of \$521.98; $y = {}^-1239.8x + 655{,}104.95$; root is 528.40.

Problem Set 4.3

1. a.

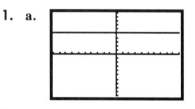

b. Answers will vary, but the y-coordinate should always be 5. For example, $(0, 5), (1, 5), (2, 5), (3, 5)$.

c. $m = \frac{5 - 5}{1 - 0} = \frac{0}{1} = 0$

2. $y = {}^-4$. Horizontal lines have no x-intercepts; they have a slope of 0; all points have the same y-coordinates.

3. $x = 3$. (Note: You can't use the point-slope form because when you find the slope between the two points, there is a division by 0.) To draw a vertical line on a TI calculator, use $\boxed{\text{DRAW}}$ $\boxed{\text{LINE}}$ Line(3, Ymin, 3, Ymax) or use DRAW 4: Vertical 3. (Note: Ymin and Ymax are found in $\boxed{\text{VARS}}$ $\boxed{\text{WINDOW}}$.)

4. a.

b. Answers will vary, but the x-coordinate should always be ${}^-3$. For example, $({}^-3, 0), ({}^-3, 1)$, and $({}^-3, 2)$ are possible answers.

c. $\frac{1 - 0}{{}^-3 - {}^-3} = \frac{1}{0}$ = undefined or no slope.

d. There is no y-intercept.

5. a. For each additional story, the building height increases by about 13 ft.

b. The stories of a building are often not all the same height; the first floor or two are usually taller. The y-intercept of about 20 represents the difference in roof structure height of the initial stories.

c. Domain $0 \le x \le 80$; range $0 \le y \le 1100$.

6. a. $y = 847(4) + 17109 = \$20{,}497$ (Note: In the fifth year, she has four years experience.)

b. $m = 847$

c. Anita gets a \$847 raise each year.

d. y-intercept is 17,109.

e. Her starting salary was \$17,109.

f. Answers may vary. Domain: $0 \le x \le 10$. After a certain number of years, your salary might not increase unless you receive a promotion or increased job responsibilities.

Note: The equations in the answers for Problems 7–10 may vary depending on the chosen point. Any line that fits the data "by eye" should be considered acceptable as long as the student can justify his or her choice of an equation.

7. a. Using the points (44, 19) and (15, 10), the slope is $\frac{19 - 10}{44 - 15} = 0.31$.
$\frac{y - 19}{x - 44} = 0.31$; $y - 19 = 0.31(x - 44)$; $y = 0.31x + 5.36$.

b. There is a cost increase of about 31¢ per picture.

c. Substitute 0 for x and solve for y. $y = 0.31(0) + 5.36 = 5.36$.

d. There is a cost of $5.36 for the sitting fee.

e. $y = 0.31(47) + 5.56 = \$19.93$

f. $14.50 = 0.31x + 5.36$ and solve for x.
$x = \frac{14.5 - 5.36}{0.31} = 29$. They should sell you 29 prints.

8. a. $y = -1.75x + 582.25$ (using the points (87, 430) and (91, 423))

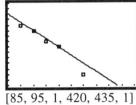

[85, 95, 1, 420, 435, 1]

b. Years after 1900

c. There has been a 1.75 point decrease per year in the average verbal score.

d. 414 points for 1996, 412 for 1997, 411 for 1998, 409 for 1999, 407 for 2000

e. 442 points

f. There is a limit to the extrapolation in this model. Using it to predict very far beyond the given data is very unreliable.

9. The answers given are based on mid-range x-values.

a.

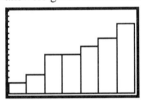

[5000, 40000, 5000, 0, 30, 2]

b. $m = \frac{20 - 7}{32,500 - 12,500} \approx 0.00065$

$\frac{y - 20}{x - 32,500} = 0.00065$

$y - 20 = 0.00065(x - 32,500)$

$y = 0.00065x - 1.125$

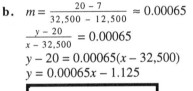

c. As family incomes increase by $1, the percentage of students in grades 9–12 using computers at home increases by 0.00065 or as the incomes increase by $1,000, the student use of computers at home increases by 0.65%.

d. Substitute 62,000 into the equation from part b, and solve for y: $y = 0.00065(62,000) - 1.125 \approx 39.2\%$.

10. a. (If you choose to draw a histogram, you will have to draw it on paper. The calculator requires you to enter whole numbers for the frequencies.)
$m = \frac{19.6 - 96.2}{32 - 17} \approx -5.07$; $\frac{y - 96.2}{x - 17} = -5.07$;
$y = -5.07x + 181.3$. The median-median equation is $y = -5.07x + 172.1$.

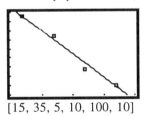

[15, 35, 5, 10, 100, 10]

b. Percent of men not married.

c. About 5.07% of the total male population gets married each year.

d. Substitute 40 for x: $y = -5.07(40) + 172.1 = -31.3\%$.

e. The negative value for percent of married men is not possible. This means that the equation does not extrapolate very well or that the model becomes nonlinear after 30–34 yr of age.

Project: Talkin' Trash

Since the *year vs. waste per year* data is so linear, both least square and median-median produce about the same equation. The relationship is about $y = 3.13x - 100$ million tons per year. From the line you can estimate that the waste is accelerating at 3.13 million tons per year.

The population model is also very linear. Both models give about $y = 2.36x + 37$ million people.

WINDOW FORMAT
Xmin=55
Xmax=105
Xscl=0
Ymin=70
Ymax=280
Yscl=0

X	Y1	Y2
94	194.22	258.84
95	197.35	261.2
96	200.48	263.56
97	203.61	265.92
98	206.74	268.28
99	209.87	270.64
100	213	273
X=94		

Year	Waste (million tons/yr)	Population (millions)	Personal (lb/day)
1960	88	179	2.66
1965	103	190	3.00
1970	122	203	3.27
1975	128	214	3.48
1980	152	227	3.62
1985	164	238	3.82
1990	196	249	4.00

Personal trash can be found by dividing 2000 times the waste by 365 times the population. Though not as linear as the other data, there is a strong linear relationship using years and pounds per person per day of $y = 0.043x + 0.18$, showing that each year personal trash increases by 0.043 lb per day, or 15.7 lb per year.

Problem Set 4.4

1. **a.** 10, 11, 10 **b.** 17, 16, 17

2. **a.** $m = \frac{9.5 - 15.7}{17.3 - 8.1} \approx -0.674; \frac{y - 15.7}{x - 8.1} = -0.674; y = -0.674x + 21.2$

 b. $m = \frac{84 - 47}{18 - 3} \approx 2.47; \frac{y - 47}{x - 3} = 2.47; y = 2.47x + 39.6$

3. Parallel lines have the same slope, so use the slope $m = 0.75$. $\frac{y - 0.9}{x - 14.4} = 0.75; y = 0.75x - 9.9$.

4. $\frac{74.1 + 74.1 + 70.5}{3} = 72.9; y = -1.8x + 72.9$

5. $\frac{19.3 + 19.3 + 26.7}{3} = 21.77; y = 0.65x + 21.8$

6. Substitute the point (12.8, 64) for x and y in the equation $y = 4.7x + b$ to find the y-intercept: $64 = 4.7(12.8) + b; 64 = 60.16 + b; 3.84 = b$. Now find the line one-third of the way between $y = 4.7x + 2.8$ and $y = 4.7x + 3.84$. $\frac{2.8 + 2.8 + 3.84}{3} = 3.15$. The equation is $y = 4.7x + 3.15$.

7. **a.** 5, 5, 5
 b. To find the three representative points, the data needs to be divided into three groups, with each representative point the median x of the group and the median y of the group. The first point would be (30, 58.1), the second (55, 66.2), and the third (80, 70).
 c. $m = \frac{70.0 - 58.1}{80 - 30} = 0.238$; each year the life expectancy of a male child increases by 0.238 yr.
 d. $y - 58.1 = 0.238(x - 30); y = 0.238x + 50.96$
 e. Substitute the point (55, 66.2) for x and y in the equation $y = 0.238x + b$ to find the y-intercept: $66.2 = 0.238(55) + b; b = 53.11$ so the equation is $y = 0.238x + 53.11$.
 f. Find the line one-third of the way from the equation in part d to the equation in part c: $\frac{50.96 + 50.96 + 53.11}{3} = 51.68$. The median-median line is $y = 0.238x + 51.68$.
 g. Substitute 78 for x in the median-median equation: $y = 0.238(78) + 51.68 = 70.24$. The life expectancy of a male child born in 1978 is 70.24 yr.

h. Substitute 91 and then 54 into the equation. $y = 0.238(91) + 51.68 = 73.34$ yr; $y = 0.238(54) + 51.68 = 64.53$ yr.

i. Substitute 80 for y in the median-median equation and solve for x: $80 = 0.238x + 51.68$; $28.32 = 0.238x$; $x = 118.99$. Male children born in the year $1900 + 119$, or 2019, will have a life expectancy of greater than 80 yr.

8. Answers will vary.

9. Answers will vary.

10. a. Using a base year of 1900, the median-median equation is $y = {}^-0.344x + 257.6$.
  b. The world record for the one-mile run drops 0.344 sec each year.
  c. Substitute 92 for x in the equation: $y = {}^-0.344(92) + 257.6 = 225.95$ so the record would be 225.95 seconds, or 3:45.95.
  d. Eventually, with a negative slope, the record would drop to one mile in zero seconds or even negative seconds, both of which are impossible.
  e. Answers may vary. For example, a new world record of 3:44.39 for the mile was set in Italy on September 5, 1993 by Noureddine Morceli. The model would predict the record in 1993 to be $y = {}^-0.344(93) + 257.6 = 225.6$ or 3:45.6.

11. Answers may vary. (Note: This answer uses a base year of 1900, so the year 1875 is entered as $^-25$.) Group the data into three groups with 11 data points in each group. Find the three representative points by finding the mean x-values and mean y-values in each group. The three points would be $(^-5.27, 258.21)$, $(37.82, 245.73)$, and $(63.36, 234)$. Find the equation of the line between the first and third representative point, and then find the equation one-third of the way from that line to the parallel line containing the second point. $m = \frac{234 - 258.21}{63.36 - {}^-5.27} = {}^-0.353$; $y - 258.21 = {}^-0.353(x - {}^-5.27)$; $y = {}^-0.353x + 260.1$.

A parallel line through $(37.82, 245.73)$, would be $y = {}^-0.344x + b$. Now substitute the values for x and y into the equation to find b. $245.73 = {}^-0.353(37.82) + b$; $b = 259.1$. Then find the average for the y-intercept. $\frac{260.1 + 260.1 + 259.1}{3} = 259.8$. The mean-mean line is $y = {}^-0.353x + 259.8$.

12. Answers will vary.

Take Another Look 4.4

The coordinates of the centroid are $x = \frac{5 + 2 + 8}{3} = 5$ and $y = \frac{11 + 32 + 41}{3} = 28$. The three representative points will always form a triangle unless all of the data points are collinear.

a. The centroid point is (5, 28). The equation of the line that passes through the centroid and has a slope of 5 is $y - 28 = 5(x - 5)$ or $y = 5x + 3$. The equation of the median-median line given by the calculator is the same.

b. Once you have identified three representative points for a data set, find the slope between the first and third points. Find the centroid of the three points. Then find the equation of the line that passes through the centroid that is parallel to the line through the first and third points.

c. Answers will vary.

Project: Counting Forever

Range	Avg. time	Number	Time (sec)
1–10	0.15	10	1.5
11–99	0.45	90	40.5
$1 \cdot 10^2 - 1 \cdot 10^3$	0.95	1,000	950
$1.1 \cdot 10^3 - 1 \cdot 10^4$	1.35	9,900	13,365
$1.1 \cdot 10^4 - 1 \cdot 10^5$	1.85	99,000	183,150
$1.1 \cdot 10^5 - 1 \cdot 10^6$	2.35	890,000	2,091,500

Now the author is not generally know as a "fast talker," but he can hold his own when words are flying. Using the "full word" method I found the following average times. Reading the first line of the table: for the numbers 1 to 10, I took an average of 0.15 sec per number; multiplied by 10 numbers it makes 1.5 seconds. The total time for 1 million numbers is 2,289,007 seconds, or 26.5 days. But since I can't go 24 hours a day, I figure I could maintain 12 hours a day for the 53-day duration. Using similar values I determined that going 24 hours a day with help, some future descendant of mine would reach 1 billion in 105 years and finally reach 1 trillion in about 139 millennia.

Then I tried the "syllable count" method. This is more complicated to explain. First I separated words into classes by the number of times they were repeated. Then I looked at the words in each class by the number of syllables it had and collected data about how long it took to say one-, two-, and three-syllable words. The total time using this method came to only 18.9 full days, or 37.8 twelve-hour days, to get to 1 million. This means it would take only 81 years to reach a billion and only 107 millennia to reach a trillion.

Class	Words	Said
I	one	380,000
II	ten	20,000
III	twenty	200,000
IV	hundred	990,000
V	thousand	900,000

Syllables	Class					Time each	Time total
	I	II	III	IV	V		
1	8	2	0	0	0	0.20	616,000
2	1	7	7	1	1	0.25	952,500
3	0	1	1	0	0	0.30	66,000

Problem Set 4.5

1. a. Substitute 2 for x in the equation $y = 2.4x + 3.6$ and subtract the resulting y-value from 8.2:
$y = 2.4(2) + 3.6 = 8.4$; $8.2 - 8.4 = ^-0.2$.

b. Substitute 4 for x in the equation $y = 2.4x + 3.6$ and subtract the resulting y-value from 12.8:
$y = 2.4(4) + 3.6 = 13.2$; $12.8 - 13.2 = ^-0.4$.

c. Substitute 10 for x in the equation $y = 2.4x + 3.6$ and subtract the resulting y-value from 28.2:
$y = 2.4(10) + 3.6 = 27.6$; $28.2 - 27.6 = 0.6$.

2. a. The residuals are below the x-axis on either end and above the x-axis in the middle.

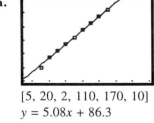

[10, 100, 10, ⁻4, 3, 1]

b. By drawing a line that is parallel to the median-median line but with a smaller y-intercept, more points will lie closer to the line.

c. $y = 0.238x + 50.95$

d. 0.7 yr

3. a.

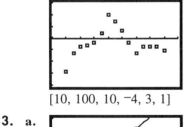

[5, 20, 2, 110, 170, 10]
$y = 5.08x + 86.3$

b.

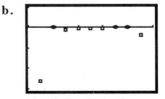

[6, 16, 2, ⁻3, 1, 1]
The range of the residuals is from ⁻2.6 to 0.017.

c. The points (7, 119.3) and (15, 162.2), or the ages of 7 and 15, stand out in the residual plot.

d. Answers may vary. At age 7 you are at the end of the initial growth of a child, and at age 15 you are at the end of the secondary growth of a child.

4. a.

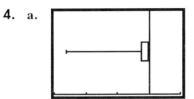

[⁻3, 1, 1, 0, 1, 0]

b. The residuals are not evenly divided. There are more negative values than positive ones, and the most negative value is an outlier indicating that this point does not fit the model well at all.

5. a. The median-median equation is $y = 0.48x − 14.2$.

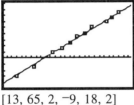

[13, 65, 2, ⁻9, 18, 2]

b.

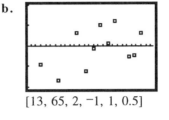

[13, 65, 2, ⁻1, 1, 0.5]

c. Answers will vary. Vary the slope (slightly steeper) and the y-intercept (slightly lower) to get a better set of residuals. An improvement would be $y = 0.50x − 15$.

d. Substitute 85° into the equation from part c. Answers will vary but should be close to 27°C.

e. 30°F

6. a.

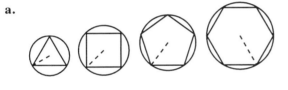

b. The median-median line is $y = 0.153x + 0.093$.

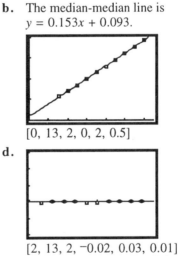

[0, 13, 2, 0, 2, 0.5]

c.

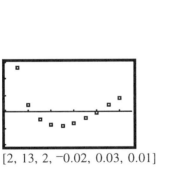

[2, 13, 2, ⁻0.02, 0.03, 0.01]

d.

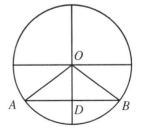

[2, 13, 2, ⁻0.02, 0.03, 0.01]
The range of the residuals is from ⁻0.00056 to 0.00035.

e. The measure of each side is 1, so $\overline{AB} = 1$, and the measure of $\angle AOB = \frac{360}{n}$. Construct OD perpendicular to $\overline{AB}$. The measure of $\angle AOD = \frac{1}{2}$ the measure of $\angle AOB = \frac{180}{n}$. The measure of side $\overline{AD} = \frac{1}{2}$. Sin $(\angle AOD) = \frac{AD}{AO}$; $\overline{AO} = \frac{AD}{\sin(\angle AOD)} = \frac{0.5}{\sin\left(\frac{180}{x}\right)}$

7. a. This graph shows that the equation is not a good model because the residuals form a pattern, which suggests that there is a better model to fit the data.

b. This graph shows that the equation is a good model because the residuals are close to 0, centered around the x-axis, and do not form a pattern.

c. This graph shows that the equation is a good model, but because there is a definite slope to the residuals, you should adjust the slope of the line.

Problem Set 4.6

1. To find the three groups, circle the first three dots on the left, then the next two dots, and finally the right three dots. To find the summary points, find the median *x*-value and median *y*-value for each of the three groups. For both graphs, the three summary points remain the same, so the median-median line will be the same. This will not always be the case. The outliers could change the summary points if they affect the medians of the groups.

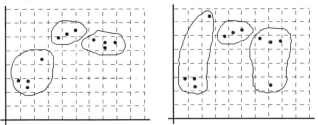

2. The least-squares equation for the line uses all of the data; the median-median equation for the line uses only three points. The least-squares line minimizes the residuals, while the median-median line ignores outliers. The least-squares equation gives you other values useful for fitting a line; the median-median equation can be found easily even without a calculator.

3. The original least-squares equation is $y = 0.471x - 0.0023$. With the outlier removed, the equation is $y = 0.4699x - 0.0013$. The original equation for the median-median line is $y = 0.4699x - 0.0017$. With the outlier removed, the equation is $y = 0.4699x - 0.00195$. The outlier has less effect on the median-median line, which you can see by looking at the slopes and the *y*-intercepts. The median-median line is said to be resistant because an outlier will not have as great an effect on this equation as it does on the least-squares equation. With the outlier removed, the equations for the median-median line and the least-squares line are almost the same.

4. Squaring the residuals makes them all positive, so the minimum sum is an indicator of a better fit. However, if one line has two residuals such as 1 and 5 and another line has residuals of 3 and 3, the sum of the residuals would be the same in both cases (6). But the sum of the squares of the residuals would be 26 and 18. This is why squaring the residuals is preferable to finding the absolute value.

5. **a.** The equation of the least-squares line is $y = 5.235x + 84.3$.
   b. The mean age is 11. The mean height is 141.89. Substitute the *x*-value (11) into the least-squares equation to verify that the point (11, 141.89) satisfies the equation.
   c. The median-median line is a better fit than the least-squares line in this problem because the median-median line ignores the outliers.

   Residuals for median-median line   Residuals for least-squares line

   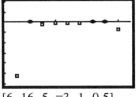   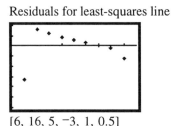

   [6, 16, 5, −3, 1, 0.5]   [6, 16, 5, −3, 1, 0.5]

6. **a.** The equation of the least-squares line is $y = 0.498x - 14.96$.
   b. The mean Fahrenheit temperature is 42.09. The mean Celsius temperature is 6. Substitute the *x*-value (42.09) into the least-squares equation to verify that the point (42.09, 6) satisfies the equation: $0.498(42.09) - 14.96 = 6$.
   c. The least-squares line gives a somewhat more even spread to the residuals.

   Residuals for median-median line   Residuals for least-squares line

   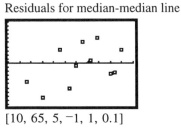   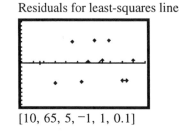

   [10, 65, 5, −1, 1, 0.1]   [10, 65, 5, −1, 1, 0.1]

7. a. To find the ending balance, choose sequence mode. Enter the equation $u_n = u_{(n-1)}(1 + 0.095/12) - payment$ into y=, and find the ending balance for 20(12), or 240, for several payment amounts. Set uStart = 60,000 and nStart = 0. Four possible payments and balances are (400, 113,394.27), (500, 42,201.91), (600, −28,990.44), and (700, −100,182.80). At least two points are needed.

b. The equation of the least-squares line is $y = 398,163.69 - 711.92x$.

c. To find a payment that would give a balance near zero, substitute $y = 0$ into the equation and solve for x: $0 = {}^-711.92x + 398,163.69$; $711.92x = 398,163.69$; $x = 398,163.69/711.92$; $x \approx \$559.28$.

8. The deviations are the differences between the mean and the data values. (See Section 3.2.) The residuals are the differences between the data values and the predicted values from the equation. The equation is giving a sort of average by summarizing the data. This is similar to the mean, so values for deviation and residual should be similar.

9. Answers will vary.

10. a. Remember to change the latitude to decimal degrees. (The latitude 16°51′ can be entered as 16 + 51/60.) The equation of the least-squares line is $y = {}^-1.212x + 110.2$.

b. Answers may vary, but an appropriate domain is 10°N – 60°N.

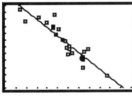

c. To find the cities that appear not to follow the pattern, plot the data points on the same graph as the least-squares line. Or you can plot the residuals.

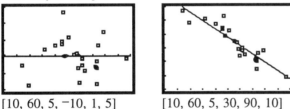

[10, 60, 5, −10, 1, 5]   [10, 60, 5, 30, 90, 10]

The cities that appear not to follow the pattern are Bakersfield, which is in desert terrain; Denver, which is a high, mountainous city; Mexico City, which is also a high, mountainous city; Phoenix, which is in desert terrain; and Vancouver, which is subject to the Pacific currents. (Note: Using trace allows you to move through the data points and select the points that do not follow the pattern.)

d. Answers will vary.

11. a. The equation of least squares is $y = 0.405x + 9.43$.

b. Each year, 0.405% more of the United States labor force was women. The y-intercept of 9.43 means that in 1900, 9.43% of the labor force was women.

c. Answers will vary. For 1994, $x = 94$ and the model predicts 47.5% of the labor force is women. According to the 1994 *World Almanac*, in the year 1992, women represented 45% of the labor force and this percentage will rise to 47% by the year 2005.

12. Answers will vary.

Project: Linear Extrapolation

In addition to least-squares and median-median lines, the most common type of forecasting bases a model on the last two data points. You could also use the last three or five data points for finding a model. Any of these methods could work to find a recommended model. It will depend on the data and patterns that you see.

Problem Set 4.7

1. Parallel lines have the same slope, so the slope $m = 12$.

2. Using the point-slope form of the equation of a line, $y - 0 = \frac{-3 - 0}{6 - 4}(x - 4)$; $y = {}^-1.5(x - 4)$, or $y = {}^-1.5x + 6$.

3. Substitute $x = {}^-19.5$ into the equation: $y = 16.8({}^-19.5) + 405 = 77.4$, so the point is $({}^-19.5, 77.4)$.

4. a. The equation of the least-squares line is $y = 59.2 - 0.536x$.
  b. $r = {}^-0.9966$
  c. The data has a negative correlation (as the years increase, the percentage of dropouts decreases), and about $({}^-0.09966)^2$ or 99.3% of the points lie between narrow bands on either side of the least-squares line.
  d. Substitute 72 for x and solve for y: $y = {}^-0.536(72) + 59.2 = 20.6\%$.
  e. Because of the high correlation number, the prediction is very accurate and would probably rate a number of 9 or 10 out of 10.

5. a. Volumes versus cost: Circulation versus cost:
  $r = 0.60458$, $r^2 = 37\%$ $r = 0.5826$, $r^2 = 34\%$

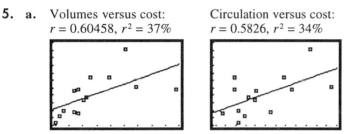

  b. Volumes and cost seem to have a better connection than circulation and cost since the r^2-value for the former is slightly greater. However, there are two outliers on the first plot (Boston and Buffalo) with very high volumes numbers. If these two cities are disregarded, then the r^2-value rises to 0.9111 with r^2 jumping from 37% to 83%. By the same token, an attempt to remove outliers from the circulation versus cost data (Denver) only raises the r^2-value to 0.6994 with r^2 changing from 39% to 47%. Volumes seems to contribute more to the cost than does the number of people who use the library.

6. a. Seats versus cost: $r = 0.9735$, $r^2 = 95\%$; speed versus cost: $r = 0.8940$, $r^2 = 80\%$
  b. The number of seats is more closely related to cost than speed.
  c. One possible explanation might be that the increase in number of seats will cause an increase in weight (both passengers and luggage) and thus cause an increase in the amount of fuel needed. Another possibility is that an increase in seats means an increase in overall plane size, which would mean more cost.

7. Answers will vary.

8. a. Student to faculty: $f = 0.066s + 55.08$; faculty to student: $s = 5.12f + 631.5$
  b. The correlation coefficient, r, is 0.85 for both equations, so the r^2-value is about 72.2%. This does not indicate a real strong correlation.

9. a. Student to faculty: $f = 55.32 + 0.07s$; faculty to student: $s = 629.58 + 5.13f$
  b. The correlation coefficient, r, is 0.58 for both equations, so $r^2 = 34\%$.

10. Answers will vary.

Take Another Look 4.7

The point furthest to the left will have the greatest residual. This point represents Jordan. The median-median line should be a better fit because it will not be affected as much by the outlier. The equation of the least-squares line is $y = {}^-655.01 + 0.78x$. The equation of the median-median line is $y = 0.43x - 175.45$.

Project: Least-Squares Formulas

Using 1900 as the reference year means that you subtract 1900 from each x-value. If there is no rounding off, then the answers will match the calculator exactly.

n	x	y	x^2	y^2	xy
1	65	1,181	4,225	1,394,761	76,765
2	70	1,239	4,900	1,535,121	86,730
3	75	1,499	5,625	2,247,001	112,425
4	79	1,655	6,241	2,739,025	130,745
5	80	1,733	6,400	3,003,289	138,640
6	81	1,933	6,561	3,736,489	156,573
7	82	1,986	6,724	3,944,196	162,852
Sum	532	11,226	40,676	18,599,882	864,730

$$a = \frac{40{,}676(11{,}226) - 532(864{,}730)}{7(40{,}676) - 532^2} = \frac{456{,}628{,}776 - 460{,}036{,}360}{284{,}732 - 283{,}024}$$

$$a = \frac{-3{,}407{,}584}{1{,}708} = {}^-1995.0726$$

$$b = \frac{7(864{,}730) - 532(11{,}226)}{7(40{,}676) - 532^2} = \frac{6{,}053{,}110 - 5{,}972{,}232}{284{,}732 - 283{,}024}$$

$$b = \frac{80{,}878}{1{,}708} = 47.35245902$$

$$r = \frac{7(864{,}730) - 532(11{,}226)}{\sqrt{7(40{,}676) - 532^2}\,\sqrt{7(18{,}599{,}882) - 11{,}226^2}} = \frac{6{,}053{,}110 - 5{,}972{,}232}{\sqrt{1708}\,\sqrt{4176098}}$$

$$r = \frac{80{,}878}{84{,}455.75992} = 0.9576374669$$

Problem Set 4.8

1. **a.** The first plot shows the least linear correlation because the points appear to follow a curve instead of a line.
   b. The second plot has the most linear correlation because the points most closely fall in a line.
   c. The second plot shows a negative correlation (which means as x increases, y decreases) because the slope is negative.

2. **a.** $y = {}^-5.693 + 7.250x$

x	4	7	11	12.9	16	18.5
y	22	47	74	87	111	128
$y_1(x)$	23.3	45.1	74.1	87.8	110.3	128.4
Residual	-1.31	1.94	-0.06	-0.83	0.69	-0.43
Residual^2	1.710	3.772	0.003	0.695	0.478	0.188

   b. The range of the residuals is -1.3 to 1.9.　　**c.** $\sum |r| = 5.27$
   d. The mean absolute residual is 0.88.　　**e.** The sum of the squares of the residuals is 6.85.
   f. The residuals are all close to the line, with the mean absolute residual only 0.88 from the line. If you find the mean of the squares of the residuals, you get 1.14, which again is rather close to the line. The line is a good fit.

3. Answers will vary.

4. The residuals have a definite pattern, which would indicate that the least-squares model may not be appropriate.

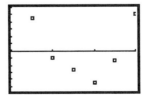

5. **a.** $y = 0.497 + 0.312x$　　**b.** $0.497 + 0.312(13) = 4.55$
   c. The average (mean) distance of a point from the line is 0.33. This is a fairly accurate model.

6. **a.** $12.5 + 4.17(19) = 91.73$ **b.** Answers will vary.

7. **a.** To find the MAD, find the sum of the absolute values of the deviations and divide by the number of schools. The MAD is 303.

b. Schools more than one MAD from the mean:

Boston University	University of Central Florida
Bowling Green State University	University of Cincinnati
DePauw University	University of Iowa
Florida State University	University of Massachusetts
Howard University	University of Miami
Miami University of Ohio	University of Michigan
Michigan State University	University of Nevada
New Mexico State University	University of South Florida
New York University	University of Utah
Penn State	University of Virginia
Princeton University	Webster University
Stanford University	Western Michigan University

All but two of the schools have enrollments greater than 10,000.

c. Schools more than two MADs from the mean:

Michigan State University	University of Michigan
New York University	University of South Florida
Penn State	University of Utah
University of Miami	Western Michigan University

All but three schools have enrollments greater than 30,000.

d. As the enrollment gets larger, there is more variation in the student-faculty ratios.

8. **a.** The equation of least-squares line is $y = 46.3 + 0.00323x$.

b. Substitute $\frac{10{,}000 + 25{,}000}{2}$ or 17,500 for x: $y = 46.3 + 0.00323(17{,}500) = 103$ g. (If you store 17,500 into x and evaluate the entire function without rounding, $y = 103$ g.)

c. For the equation, $r = 0.985$ and $r^2 = 0.969$, so 96.9% of the data would fall within a narrow linear band. The mean absolute value of the residuals is 33 grams (obtained by creating a list of residuals in L_3 and finding the mean absolute value of L_3). The largest residual is 68.18 g.

d. Answers will vary. One possible answer might be to discard the data for the small animals and the very large animal.

Chapter Review

Problem Set 4.9

1. The slope is $\frac{3250 - 1300}{-22 - 16} = -51.316$.

2. By inspection, the slope is 23.45.

3. Substitute 740 for y and solve for x: $740 = 16.8x + 405$; $335 = 16.8x$; $x = 19.94$.

4. Answers may vary, but the windows listed below will work.
a. [1500, 3500, 250, 40, 80, 10] **b.** [0, 110, 10, 0, 200, 20] **c.** [0, 110, 10, 0, 110, 10]

5. $m \approx 0.024$

6. $y = 0.024x - 0.699$

7. Answers will vary.

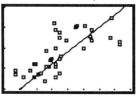

8. The domain is nonnegative numbers that make sense in this situation. ($1667 \leq$ daily calorie supply ≤ 3336.) The units of the domain are calories.

9. The units of slope are years of life expectancy per number of calories.

10. For each calorie you would expect your life expectancy to increase by 0.024 yr.

11. Answers will vary between 2300 and 2400.

12. Answers will vary between 46 and 52.

13. 55.5 yr

14. (34, 51), (57, 53), (88, 69)

15. $m \approx 0.33$

16. $y = 0.33x + 37.7$

17.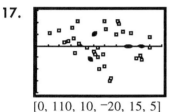

[0, 110, 10, −20, 15, 5]

The residuals seem to be evenly distributed above and below the line. There is no pattern in the residuals, which indicates a line is a good model.

18. The residual for Ethiopia is 1.89.

19. Guinea

20. $y = 166.8 - 1.26x$

21. For every 1% increase in the availability of health services, the number of infant deaths decreases by 1.26.

22. $y = -1.31x + 176.23$

Least-squares   Median-median

[20, 110, 10, −65, 70, 20]   [20, 110, 10, −65, 70, 20]
MAD = 21.03   MAD = 21.36

The least-squares line is slightly better than the median-median line if you compare the MADs.

23. Least-squares model: 97.33; median-median model: 104.45

24. $r \approx -0.77$, $r^2 \approx 0.6$; 60% of the points lie in a narrow band on either side of the least-squares line.

25. $y = 165.41 - 1.25x$; $r \approx -0.86$, $r^2 \approx 0.74$

26. 74% of the points will lie in a narrow band on either side of the least-squares line.

27. Answers will vary.

Chapter 5

Problem Set 5.1

1. **a.** Answers will vary. The curve, which appears to be a parabola, might describe the relationship between the amount of time the ball is in the air and how far away from the ground it is.
   b. Answers will vary. The units might be seconds and feet.
   c. Answers will vary. A realistic domain might be $0 \le t \le 60$ seconds; a range might be $0 \le h \le 200$ feet.
   d. No, the graph is measuring time versus height. The distance traveled is not measured directly.

2. Answers will vary. Zeke the fish was swimming around his bowl one day when his owner came into the room. When the owner turned on the light, Zeke slowly swam toward the surface. When the owner put the food in the tank, Zeke swam quickly to the surface and stayed there to eat. When he finished eating, he swam down to the bottom of the tank to eat the food that had fallen. Then he floated to the surface for a nap.

3. a.

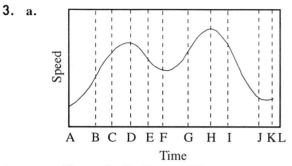

Time

b. It is moving fastest at point H.

c. It is moving slowest at point A.

d. The speed of the roller coaster would be about the same at points C and G.

Answers will vary for Problems 4–21.

4. The amount of money in your account continues to grow. Money is added each year, causing a jump in the total amount of the account, and as the money is compounded, the jumps will get increasingly bigger over time.

5. The amount of money will remain constant over time since no interest is added to it.

6. As speed increases, it takes a greater distance to stop.

7. At the time the ball is hit, the ball is about chest height. It goes up in the air and eventually hits the ground.

8. When a hot drink is first poured, its temperature starts off high and then decreases. It decreases more slowly as time goes on until it levels out at room temperature.

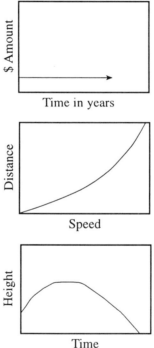

9. The temperature of an iced drink starts off low and gradually increases as the ice melts, and it levels out at room temperature.

10. You get on a Ferris wheel a short distance above the ground. As the Ferris wheel revolves, you go up and then down and up, and so on.

11. The more hours you work, the more money you make. The money you make is directly proportional to the hours you work.

12. After the squirrel drops the acorn, the acorn's speed accelerates with time due to the force of gravity.

13. When you are born, you have an initial height. You grow rapidly during your youth, slow down but continue growing until puberty, and maintain your height until later in life when you begin to lose some of your height.

14. As you pedal up the hill, your speed continues to drop until you reach the top of the hill at which point your speed accelerates until you reach the bottom of the hill.

15. As you fly from Detroit to Newark, the distance from Detroit increases. When you fly in the holding pattern, your distance from Detroit varies quickly and minutely as you circle.

16. In the winter the daily maximum temperature is low; as the season changes to spring, the temperature increases until in summer the temperature reaches its highest values, then decreases again in the fall and reaches the low in the winter.

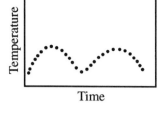

Temperature / Time

17. As the weight of the letter increases, you must put more and more stamps on it (each 0.5 ounce of weight requires another first-class stamp).

Postage / Weight

18. You need a larger shoe size as your foot length increases. After a certain increase, you must go up a size in shoes.

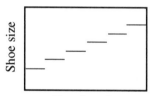

Shoe size / Foot length

19. If you are close to the lamp, the light is intense. The further away you are from the lamp, the less intense is the light.

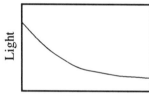

Light / Distance

20. The wrapper is high when it is dropped from the top row of the stadium. It starts to drop and then catches the wind, drops some more until it catches more wind and floats for a while, then continues the drop-and-float pattern until it hits the ground.

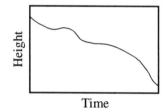

Height / Time

21. Answers will vary.

Take Another Look 5.1

Answers will vary.

Problem Set 5.2

1. For graph A, the unlabeled points are (4, 17) and (5, 21). The sequence is arithmetic and the common difference is $d = 9 - 5 = 4$; for graph B, the unlabeled points are (3, 14.0625), (4, 10.547), (5, 7.910), (6, 5.933), and (7, 4.449). The sequence is geometric with a common ratio of $r = \frac{18.75}{25} = .75$; for graph C, the unlabeled points are (2, 10), (3, 20), (4, 40), (5. 80), and (6, 160). The sequence is geometric and is increasing so $r > 1$. Use guess-and-check to find $r = 2$.

For problems 2–4, enter several discrete points for n in one list and the values for $u(n)$ in another list. Then plot the points.

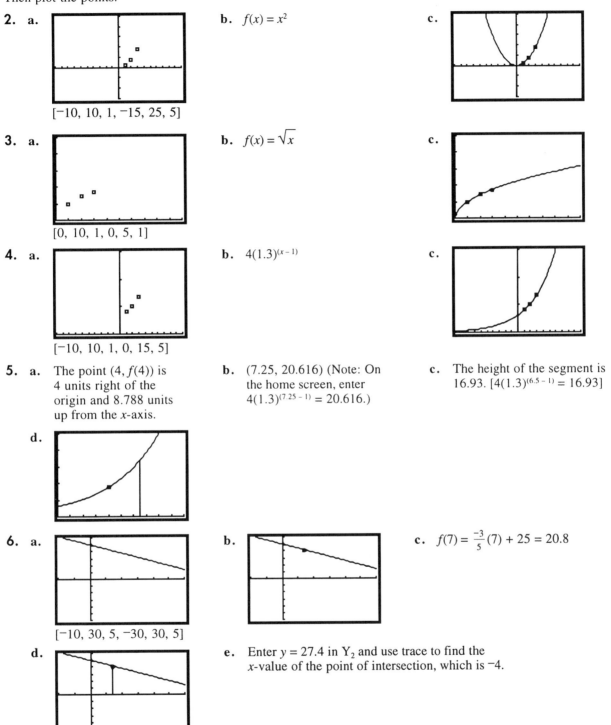

2. a.

[−10, 10, 1, −15, 25, 5]

b. $f(x) = x^2$

c.

3. a.

[0, 10, 1, 0, 5, 1]

b. $f(x) = \sqrt{x}$

c.

4. a.

[−10, 10, 1, 0, 15, 5]

b. $4(1.3)^{(x-1)}$

c.

5. a. The point $(4, f(4))$ is 4 units right of the origin and 8.788 units up from the x-axis.

b. (7.25, 20.616) (Note: On the home screen, enter $4(1.3)^{(7.25-1)} = 20.616$.)

c. The height of the segment is 16.93. $[4(1.3)^{(6.5-1)} = 16.93]$

d.

6. a.

[−10, 30, 5, −30, 30, 5]

b.

c. $f(7) = \frac{-3}{5}(7) + 25 = 20.8$

d.

e. Enter $y = 27.4$ in Y_2 and use trace to find the x-value of the point of intersection, which is −4.

7. a. $y = 100(1 + 0.03)^x$
where x represents the
number of weeks.

b. $y = 100(1 + 0.03)^{10.5} = \$136.39$
c. $y = 100(1 + 0.03)^{52} = \$465.09$
d. Something that starts the year costing \$100 will cost \$465.09 at
the end of the year.
e. Enter $y = 295$ in Y_2 and use trace to find
the x-value of the point of intersection.
By 36.6 weeks, the inflationary value
will reach \$295.

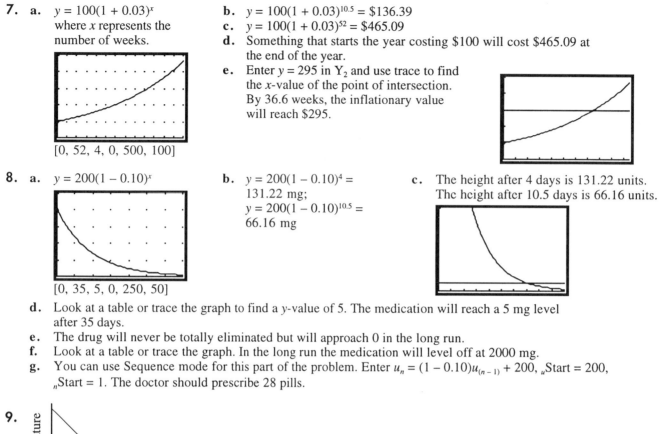

[0, 52, 4, 0, 500, 100]

8. a. $y = 200(1 - 0.10)^x$

b. $y = 200(1 - 0.10)^4 =$
131.22 mg;
$y = 200(1 - 0.10)^{10.5} =$
66.16 mg

c. The height after 4 days is 131.22 units.
The height after 10.5 days is 66.16 units.

[0, 35, 5, 0, 250, 50]

d. Look at a table or trace the graph to find a y-value of 5. The medication will reach a 5 mg level
after 35 days.
e. The drug will never be totally eliminated but will approach 0 in the long run.
f. Look at a table or trace the graph. In the long run the medication will level off at 2000 mg.
g. You can use Sequence mode for this part of the problem. Enter $u_n = (1 - 0.10)u_{(n-1)} + 200$, $_u$Start = 200,
$_n$Start = 1. The doctor should prescribe 28 pills.

9.

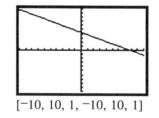

Take Another Look 5.2

On a TI-82 or TI-83, the "friendly" window in the first quadrant that would give integer trace values
is [0, 94, 0, 0, 62, 0]. For a "friendly" window with a center at the origin, use [−47, 47, 0, −31, 31, 0].

Problem Set 5.3

1. a. There are many correct answers including (4, 0), (2, −4), (1, −6), and (0, −8).
b. Each of the points listed works in both forms of the equation.
c. Select another point and demonstrate that it works for both equations.
d. Answers will vary. Two equations are equivalent if they have identical solution sets.

2. First solve the equation for y: $y = \dfrac{-2.8}{5.1}x + \dfrac{22}{5.1}$
or $y = -0.549x + 4.314$. The slope is -0.549,
and the y-intercept is approximately 4.314.
Trace the graph or solve the equation for
$y = 0$ to find the x-intercept, which is
approximately 7.857.

[−10, 10, 1, −10, 10, 1]

3. a. To find the slope, you can use the slope formula
        $\frac{y_2 - y_1}{x_2 - x_1} = \frac{-4.4 - 3.18}{1.4 - -5.2} = \frac{-7.58}{6.6} = -1.1485$. Next use
        the point-slope form of the equation of a line,
        $y = m(x - x_1) + y_1$; $y = -1.1485(x - 1.4) - 4.4$
        or $y = -1.1485x - 2.7921$.

        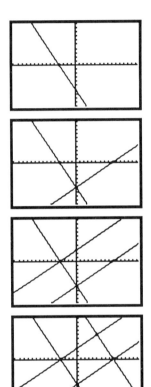

        $[-10, 10, 1, -10, 10, 1]$

    b. $y = -1.1485x - 2.7921 + 2 = -1.1485x - 0.7921$.

        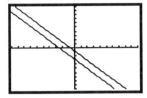

4. In order for your calculator to accurately picture
    perpendicular lines, you must use a "friendly"
    window.

    a. $3x + 2y + 12 = 0$; $2y = -3x - 12$;
        $y = \frac{-3}{2}x - 6$

    b. Since perpendicular lines have slopes that
        multiply to -1, a perpendicular line to the line
        in part a will have a slope of $\frac{2}{3}$. This new line
        will have the same y-intercept as the original
        line. The equation of the new line is $y = \frac{2}{3}x - 6$.

    c. To be perpendicular at the x-intercept, the line
        would have to go through the point $(-4, 0)$.
        $y = \frac{2}{3}(x - -4) + 0 = \frac{2}{3}x + \frac{8}{3}$

    d. A line perpendicular to g would have a slope
        of $\frac{-3}{2}$. The x-intercept of g is $(9, 0)$ so
        the line would have to go through that point.
        $y = \frac{-3}{2}(x - 9) + 0 = \frac{-3}{2}x + \frac{27}{2}$.

    e. The figure formed is a rectangle.

5. a. Answers will vary with the calculators. For a TI-82, a window would be $[-4.7, 4.7, 1, -3.1, 3.1, 1]$.
    b. Answers will vary with the calculators. For a TI-82, a window would be $[0, 9.4, 1, 0, 6.2, 1]$.

6. For the first graph the y-intercept is 2 and the slope is $\frac{-3}{4}$ so the equation is $y = \frac{-3}{4}x + 2$. For the
    second graph the y-intercept is -1 and the slope is $\frac{2}{3}$ so the equation is $y = \frac{2}{3}x - 1$.

7. a. Answers will vary. Some possible points
        are $(1, 1.414)$, $(2, 2.828)$, $(3, 4.243)$, and
        $(4, 5.657)$. The equation of a best-fit line
        is $y = 1.414x$.

        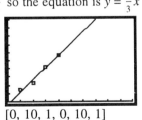

        $[0, 10, 1, 0, 10, 1]$

    b. The constant of variation is the slope, which is approximately 1.414.
    c. $d = 1.414s = 1.414(6.4) \approx 9.05$ cm.   d. $d = 1.414s$; $14\sqrt{6} = 1.414$; $x \approx 24.25$.

8. a. The y-intercept is 12,500. The original value of the equipment is \$12,500.
    b. The x-intercept is $(0, 10)$. After 10 yr the equipment has no value.

c. The slope is $\frac{12500 - 0}{0 - 10}$ = $^{-}$1250. Every year the value of the equipment decreases by $1,250.

d. $y = ^{-}1{,}250x + 12{,}500$.

e. After 4.8 yr the equipment will be worth $6,500. You could get this answer by substituting 6500 for y and solving for x or by graphing the equation as well as the line $y = 6500$ and tracing to find the intersection point.

9. a. $(86 + 73 + 76 + 90 + 79)/5 = 80.8$ average

b. To find the average of five scores, you would add all five scores and divide by 5. If you know the sum of the first 4 scores $(86 + 73 + 76 + 90 = 325)$, then their contribution to the average would be $\frac{325}{5} = 65$ and the fifth score would contribute $\frac{1}{5}x$ to the average. The function would be $y = \frac{1}{5}x + 65$.

c. A fifth game score of 95 would give an average of 84. You could get this answer by substituting 84 for y and solving for x or by graphing the equation as well as the line $y = 84$ and tracing to find the intersection point.

10. a. Answers will vary. Some possible answers are $(500, 35{,}203.96)$, $(600, ^{-}88{,}776.24)$, $(550, ^{-}26{,}786.14)$, $(520, 10{,}407.92)$, $(540, ^{-}14{,}388.12)$.

b. Enter the points into calculator lists and plot them.

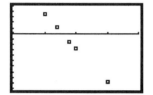

c. The least-squares equation of the line of best fit is $y = ^{-}1{,}239.80x + 655{,}104.96$.
(Note: The answer will vary depending on the accuracy of your ending balances.)

d. The y-intercept is 655,104.96. If no payments were made, $655,104.96 would be owed to the bank.

e. The x-intercept is 528.40. This is the payment that would pay off the loan in 25 yr.

f. The slope is $^{-}$1239.80. Each dollar increase in payment will reduce the final balance by $1,239.80.

11. The equation in Problem 8 was $y = ^{-}1{,}250x + 12{,}500$. Substitute values of 0–10 for x and solve for y.

Year	0	1	2	3	4	5	6	7	8	9	10
Value	12,500	11,250	10,000	8,750	7,500	6,250	5,000	3,750	2,500	1,250	0

For the first 10 yr (0 to 9 in the chart), the average value of the equipment is $6,875.

Problem Set 5.4

1. The following answers should be found by guess-and-check, based on what the students learned in Investigation 5.4.1.

   a. $y = x^2 - 6$ b. $y = x^2 - 3$ c. $y = x^2 + 2$ d. $y = x^2 + 4$

2. a. i. $f(x) = x^2 - 6$ ii. $f(x) = x^2 + 2$

   b. i. $y = x^2 - 5$; the graph is down 5 units from $y = x^2$.
      ii. $y = x^2 + 4$; the graph is up 4 units from $y = x^2$.

   c. $f(x) + c$ is c units up or down from $f(x)$. It goes up if c is positive and down if c is negative.

3. a. $y = (x - 4)^2$ b. $y = (x - 7)^2$ c. $y = (x + 5)^2$

4. a. The graph moves 3 units to the right.   b. The graph moves 3 units to the left.
   c. The graph moves 2 units up.   d. The graph moves 2 units down.

5. a. $y = (x - 2)^2$ b. $y = (x - 2)^2 - 5$ c. $y = (x + 6)^2$ d. $y = (x + 6)^2 + 2$

6. a. First move the graph 5 units to the right, and then move it 3 units down.
   b. $y = (x - 5)^2 - 3$ c. The vertex is $(5, ^{-}3)$.
   d. $(6, ^{-}2)$, $(4, ^{-}2)$, $(7, 1)$, $(3, 1)$
   e. Segment b has a length of 1 and segment c has a length of 4.

7. **a.** $y = {}^-x^2$
   b. $y = {}^-x^2 + 2$

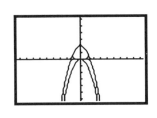

   c. $y = {}^-(x - 6)^2$
   d. $y = {}^-(x - 6)^2 - 3$

8. $y = {}^-(x - 2)^2 + 2$

9. For $^+1$, the graph opens upward. For $^-1$, it opens downward. The graph is shifted horizontally by h units, to the right if h is positive, and left if h is negative. The graph is shifted vertically by k units, up if k is positive, and down if k is negative.

10. Since the vertex of the broken stick area problem was (25, 625) and the parabola opens down, the equation would be $y = {}^-(x - 25)^2 + 625$.

11. For each additional team, you need to add double the previous number of teams to represent playing each of those teams twice.

Number of teams	1	2	3	4	5	6	7	8	9	10
Number of games	0	2	6	12	20	30	42	56	72	90

To plot these data points, enter the values in two lists, set an appropriate window such as [0, 12, 2, 0, 100, 10], and plot the points.

The points appear to be part of a parabola with an equation of $y = (x - 0.5)^2 - 0.25$. Students will need to do some guess-and-check to find the vertex.

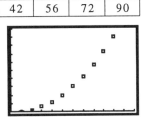

12. **a.** To find the values for the chart, substitute times of 0, 0.5, 1, and so on, seconds into the equation $h = {}^-16t^2 + 64$.

Time	0	0.5	1	1.5	2
Height	64	60	48	28	0

The average height is 40 ft. ((64 + 60 + 48 + 28 + 0)/5 = 40)

b. To find the values for the chart, substitute times of 0, 0.25, 0.5, and so on, seconds into the equation $h = {}^-16t^2 + 64$ or put the equation into $\boxed{\text{Y=}}$ and go to $\boxed{\text{TblSet}}$ to set TblMin to 0 and ΔTbl to 0.25 and then go to $\boxed{\text{TABLE}}$.

Time	0	0.25	0.5	0.75	1	1.25	1.5	1.75	2
Height	64	63	60	55	48	39	28	15	0

The calculator table will look like this:

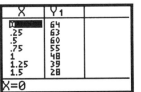 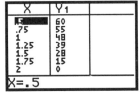

The average height is 41.3 feet.

c. Now change the ΔTbl to 0.1 and go to $\boxed{\text{TABLE}}$.

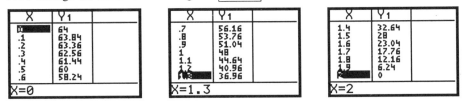

The average height is 42.13 ft.

d. The ball starts out moving slowly and speeds up as it falls. As you increase the frequency of the measurements, you are adding more large numbers to the list. This makes the average increase.

Take Another Look 5.4

Element	Atomic number	Atomic mass	Residual
Hydrogen	1	1.008	−1.051
Helium	2	4.003	−0.1104
Lithium	3	6.939	0.77167
Beryllium	4	9.012	0.79074
Boron	5	10.811	0.5358
Carbon	6	12.01115	−0.318
Nitrogen	7	14.007	−0.3761
Oxygen	8	15.999	−0.438
Flourine	9	18.998	−0.50707
Neon	10	20.183	−0.3619
Sodium	11	22.990	0.39121
Magnesium	12	24.312	−0.3407

A least-squares model is $y = 2.0539x + 0.00553$ with the residuals given in the chart above.

The sum of the first twelve residuals is $7 \cdot 10^{-12}$, but with the other five elements the sum becomes 125.035. So over the long run, the model gets worse.

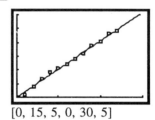

[0, 15, 5, 0, 30, 5]

Element	Prediction	Actual value	Residual
Mercury	163.32017	200.59	36.27
Copper	59.569589	63.54	3.9704
Lead	168.42804	207.19	38.762
Silver	96.540384	107.87	11.33
Gold	162.26624	196.97	34.707

Project: Even and Odd Functions

Even functions: Opposite x-values produce the same y-values thus giving the symmetry about the y-axis.

Odd functions: Since opposite x-values produce opposite y-values, the points are located on the opposite sides of the x-axis as well as opposite sides of the y-axis.

	$f(g(x))$	$g(f(x))$	$f(x) + g(x)$	$f(x)g(x)$	$\frac{f(x)}{g(x)}$
$f(x)$ even, $g(x)$ even	even	even	even	even	even
$f(x)$ even, $g(x)$ odd	even	even	neither	odd	odd
$f(x)$ odd, $g(x)$ odd	odd	odd	odd	even	even

Proofs:

$f(x)$ even, $g(x)$ even

If $f(x)$ is even, then $f(-x) = f(x)$. If $g(x)$ is even, then $g(-x) = g(x)$.

The properties follow from the above definitions.

$f(g(-x)) = f(g(x))$, so $f(g(x))$ is even.
$g(f(-x)) = g(f(x))$, so $g(f(x))$ is even.
$f(-x) + g(-x) = f(x) + g(x)$, so $f(x) + g(x)$ is even.
$f(-x)g(-x) = f(x)g(x)$, so $f(x)g(x)$ is even.
$\frac{f(-x)}{g(-x)} = \frac{f(x)}{g(x)}$, so $\frac{f(x)}{g(x)}$ is even.

$f(x)$ even, $g(x)$ odd

If $f(x)$ is even, then $f(^-x) = f(x)$. If $g(x)$ is odd, then $g(^-x) = ^-g(x)$.

The properties follow from the above definitions.

$f(g(^-x)) = f(^-g(x)) = f(g(x))$, so $f(g(x))$ is even.

$g(f(^-x)) = g(f(x))$, so $g(f(x))$ is even.

$f(^-x) + g(^-x) = f(x) - g(x)$, so $f(x) + g(x)$ is neither even nor odd.

$f(^-x)g(^-x) = f(x)(-g(x)) = ^-f(x)g(x)$, so $f(x)g(x)$ is odd.

$\frac{f(-x)}{g(-x)} = \frac{f(x)}{-g(x)} = \frac{-f(x)}{g(x)}$, so $\frac{f(x)}{g(x)}$ is odd.

$f(x)$ odd, $g(x)$ odd

If $f(x)$ is odd, then $f(^-x) = ^-f(x)$. If $g(x)$ is odd, then $g(^-x) = ^-g(x)$.

The properties follow from the above definitions.

$f(g(^-x)) = f(^-g(x)) = ^-f(g(x))$, so $f(g(x))$ is odd.

$g(f(^-x)) = g(^-f(x)) = ^-g(f(x))$, so $g(f(x))$ is odd.

$f(^-x) + g(^-x) = ^-f(x) - g(x) = ^-(f(x) + g(x))$, so $f(x) + g(x)$ is odd.

$f(^-x)g(^-x) = [^-f(x)][^-g(x)] = f(x)g(x)$, so $f(x)g(x)$ is even.

$\frac{f(-x)}{g(-x)} = \frac{-f(x)}{-g(x)} = \frac{f(x)}{g(x)}$, so $\frac{f(x)}{g(x)}$ is even.

Problem Set 5.5

1. **a.** $y = \sqrt{x} + 3$ **b.** $y = \sqrt{x} - 4$ **c.** $y = \sqrt{x} + 1$

    d. $y = \sqrt{x} - 3$ **e.** $y = \sqrt{x + 5}$ **f.** $y = \sqrt{x - 2}$

    g. $y = \sqrt{x + 5} + 2$ **h.** $y = \sqrt{x - 3} + 1$ **i.** $y = \sqrt{x - 1} - 4$

2. **a.** If x is replaced with $(x - 3)$, the graph moves 3 units to the right; if it is replaced with $(x + 3)$, the graph moves 3 units to the left.

    b. If y is replaced with $(y - 2)$, the graph moves 2 units up; if it is replaced with $(y + 2)$, the graph moves 2 units down.

3. **a.** $y = ^-\sqrt{x}$ **b.** $y = ^-\sqrt{x} - 3$ **c.** $y = ^-\sqrt{x + 6} + 5$

4. **a.** Answers will vary. Some possible points are $(^-4, ^-2)$, $(^-3, ^-1)$, and $(0, 0)$.

    b. $y = \sqrt{x + 4} - 2$ **c.** $y = ^-\sqrt{x - 2} + 3$

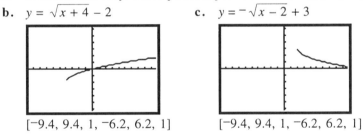

    $[^-9.4, 9.4, 1, ^-6.2, 6.2, 1]$ $[^-9.4, 9.4, 1, ^-6.2, 6.2, 1]$

5. **a.** In order to graph the parabola that is shown, which is not a function because it doesn't pass the vertical line test, you need to enter two functions, one as a positive square root and one as a negative square root. The functions should be $y_1 = \sqrt{x}$ and $y_2 = ^-\sqrt{x}$.

    b. $y = ^\pm\sqrt{x}$; the resulting equation is $y^2 = x$.

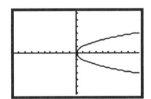

6. **a.** There are x-values on each parabola that have more than one y-value so the parabola does not pass the vertical line test of a function.

    b. $y = ^\pm\sqrt{x + 4}$; $y = ^\pm\sqrt{x} + 2$ **c.** $y^2 = x + 4$; $(y - 2)^2 = x$

7. First, rewrite the parabola into the form $y = \pm\sqrt{x+3} + 2$.

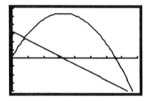

$[{-}9.4, 9.4, 1, {-}6.2, 6.2, 1]$

8. a. $y = \sqrt{-x}$ **b.** $y = -\sqrt{-x}$

9. a.–d. Answers will vary.

10. Answers will vary; $v = 8\sqrt{d}$ works.

11. Change the second line of the program to AJ(X−H)+K→ Y₄.

Take Another Look 5.5

a.

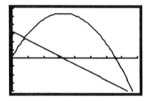

i.

Time (sec)	Height (m)	Velocity (m/sec)
0	2.1	32
1	29.2	22.2
2	46.5	12.4
3	54	2.6
4	51.7	−7.2
5	39.6	−17
6	17.7	−26.8
7	−14	−36.6

ii. In the table, the maximum height of 54 ft occurs at 3 sec. The velocity at that height is 2.6 m/sec. However, if you trace or look at the table, the maximum height is closer to 54.345 ft and it occurs at 3.265 sec, and the velocity at this height is 0 m/sec. The velocity before the maximum height is decreasing. After the maximum height, the velocity is increasing. (The negative sign indicates the ball is falling.)

iii. Before the ball reaches its maximum height, the rate of increase of the height is decreasing. After the ball reaches its maximum height, the rate of decrease in height increases. The velocity graph shows where the rate is positive or negative.

iv. A realistic domain for the height function is $0 \le t \le 6.6$. A realistic range is $0 \le h \le 55$. A realistic domain for the velocity function is $0 \le t \le 6.6$. A realistic range is $-32 \le v \le 32$.

v. h: height
t: time
v: velocity
−4.9: half the acceleration due to gravity
32: initial vertical velocity at time zero
−9.8: the acceleration due to gravity
2.1: the initial height

b. Look at table values or trace the graph. At a height of 0, the velocity is −32.6 m/sec.

c. If you change the window to [0, 6.6, 1, ⁻40, 60, 10] and take the absolute value of the velocity function, then you can see the symmetry of the graph better.

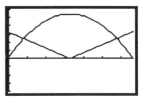

The graphs show that whenever the heights are the same, the velocities are the same.

Problem Set 5.6

1. **a.** $y = |x| + 2$ **b.** $y = |x| - 5$

2. **a.** $y = |x + 4|$ **b.** $y = |x - 3|$

3. **a.** $y = |x| - 1$ **b.** $y = |x - 4| + 1$

4. **a.** $y = |x + 5| - 3$ **b.** $y = |x - 6|$ **c.** $y = -|x|$

5. **a.** $y = (x - 5)^2$ **b.** $y = -|x + 4|$ **c.** $y = -|x + 4| + 3$

6. **a.** $y = -(x + 3)^2 + 4$ **b.** $y = \pm\sqrt{x - 4} + 3$ **c.** $y = -|x - 3| - 1$

7. **a.** $y = -|x - 2| + 3$
   b. The negative sign in front flips the graph over the x-axis. The $(x - 2)$ in the radical moves the graph 2 units to the right and the ⁺3 moves the graph up 3 units.

8. **a.** The graph will move 5 units to the right.
   b. The graph will flip over the y-axis.
   c. The graph will move up 3 units.
   d. The graph will flip over the x-axis.

9. The points of intersection are (1, 3) and (7, 3). The x-coordinates, 1 and 7, are the two values of x that satisfy the equation $y = |x - 4| = 3$.

10. Graph $y_1 = |x + 3|$ and $y_2 = 5$. The two intersection points are (⁻8, 5) and (2, 5). The solutions are ⁻8 and 2, the x-coordinates of these intersection points.

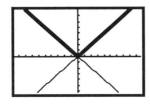

11. Graph $y_1 = -(x + 3)^2 + 5$ and $y_2 = |x - 1| - 4$. The solutions are the x-coordinates of the intersection points (⁻0.2, ⁻2.8) and (⁻4.8, 1.8).

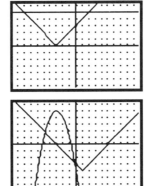

12. $|x| = \begin{cases} -x & \text{if } x < 0 \\ x & \text{if } x \geq 0 \end{cases}$

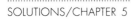

13. a. The original mean was 83.75, and the original MAD was 5.975. The new mean is 89.75, and the new MAD is 5.975. By adding 6 points to each score, the mean increases by 6, but the MAD remains the same.

b.

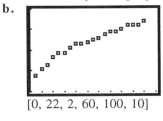

[0, 22, 2, 60, 100, 10]

c.

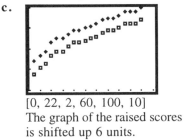

[0, 22, 2, 60, 100, 10]
The graph of the raised scores
is shifted up 6 units.

14. From the given data, several observations can be made. The values are decreasing in a linear fashion from 0 to 16 and then appear to increase in the same linear fashion, so a mathematical model could be an absolute value function. Use guess-and-check to find the vertex, which would be between 16 and 20. The equation is $y = |x - 18.4|$. The homing transmitter is located at 18.4 mi along the road.

Problem Set 5.7

1. $y = 2\sqrt{1 - x^2}$

2. a. $y = 3\sqrt{1 - x^2}$ **b.** $y = 0.5\sqrt{1 - x^2}$

3. a.

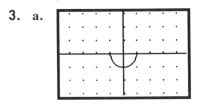

b.

c.

4. a. $y = 2\sqrt{1 - x^2} + 1$ **b.** $y = -4\sqrt{1 - x^2} + 2$

5. Graph 1   Graph 2

   a. $f(x + 3) + 1$ **a.** $2f(x - 3) + 1$

   b. $y = \sqrt{1 - (x + 3)^2} + 1$ **b.** $y = 2\sqrt{1 - (x - 3)^2} + 1$

6. Graph 1: $y = -5\sqrt{1 - (x + 2)^2} + 3$

   Graph 2: $y = 4\sqrt{1 - (x - 3)^2} - 2$

7. a. $y = \sqrt{1 - x^2} + 2$ **b.** $y = \sqrt{1 - (x + 3)^2}$

    Vertical shift of 2 units   Horizontal shift of −3 units

[−4.7, 4.7, 1, −3.1, 3.1, 1]   [−4.7, 4.7, 1, −3.1, 3.1, 1]

   c. $y = 2\sqrt{1 - x^2}$ **d.** $y = \sqrt{1 - \left(\frac{x}{2}\right)^2}$

    Vertical stretch of 2 units   Horizontal stretch of 2 units

[−4.7, 4.7, 1, −3.1, 3.1, 1]   [−4.7, 4.7, 1, −3.1, 3.1, 1]

8. a. $y = \sqrt{1 - \left(\frac{x}{3}\right)^2}$ **b.** $\frac{x}{3}$ **c.** $f\left(\frac{x}{3}\right)$

9. a. $y = 2\sqrt{1 - \left(\frac{x}{3}\right)^2}$ **b.** $-2\sqrt{1 - \left(\frac{x}{3}\right)^2}$

10. a. $y = \frac{1}{2}\sqrt{1 - x^2}$ **b.** $y = \sqrt{1 - (2x)^2}$ **c.** $y = \frac{1}{2}\sqrt{1 - \left(\frac{x}{2}\right)^2}$

11. a. $y = +3\sqrt{1 - (2x)^2}$; $y = -3\sqrt{1 - (2x)^2}$

   b. $y = \pm 3\sqrt{1 - (2x)^2}$

   c. $y^2 = 9(1 - (2x)^2)$

12. a. $\sqrt{1 - \left(\frac{x-1}{2}\right)^2}$ **b.** $f\left(\frac{x-1}{2}\right)$

13. a. They should multiply each rating by $\frac{100}{94}$ to make the highest score 100.

   b.

Exhibit	1	2	3	4	5	6	7	8	9	10
Rating	72.34	75.53	77.66	81.91	84.04	84.04	86.17	88.30	88.30	89.36

Exhibit	11	12	13	14	15	16	17	18	19	20
Rating	90.43	91.49	93.62	94.68	94.68	95.74	97.87	97.87	97.87	100

   c. The mean of the original scores (from Problem Set 5.6, Problem 13) was 83.75, and the MAD of the original scores was 5.975. For the new scores the mean is 89.10 and the MAD is 6.36.

   d. Plot both sets of test scores. The scores have been stretched by a factor of $\frac{100}{94}$. All scores increased so the mean increased. The high scores differ from the original by more than the lower ones, so they are more spread and the MAD is increased.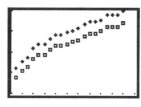

   e. Answers will vary.

14. a. Average value = 0.546

x	−1	−0.5	0	0.5	1
$f(x)$	0	0.87	1	0.87	0

   b. Average value = 0.690

x	−1	−0.8	−0.6	−0.4	−0.2	0	0.2	0.4	0.6	0.8	1
$f(x)$	0	0.6	0.8	0.92	0.98	1	0.98	0.92	0.8	0.6	0

   c. For x-values spaced 0.1 units apart, the average value is 0.739. For x-values spaced 0.01 units apart, the average value is 0.781.

   d. Input and run the average-value program in Calculator Note 5D using increasingly smaller values of x. The average value will approach 0.785.

   e. Answers will vary depending on the calculator.

15. Answers will vary.

Project: The Greatest Integer Function

The function has no effect on integer values, but it rounds down to the preceding integer any decimal. Thus it gives the largest integer that is smaller than the argument. The greatest integer that is less than 2.5 is 2, and the greatest integer that is less than −3.1 is −4.

The graph creates a sequence of steps going up to the right. A vertical shift, like $y = \text{int}(x) + 1$, moves all the steps up (or down). A horizontal shift, like $y = \text{int}(x + 1)$, looks just like a vertical shift. A vertical stretch, like $y = 2\text{int}(x)$, increases (or decreases) the distance between steps. A horizontal stretch, like $y = \text{int}(x/2)$, increases the length of each step.

Any horizontal shift can also be written as a vertical shift and vice versa. There is no way to achieve horizontal stretching using the vertical stretch parameter. Note that this is just the opposite of the parabola family.

The vertical flip, $y = {}^-\text{int}(x)$, and the horizontal flip, $y = \text{int}(-x)$, both cause the steps to go down to the right, but they are not identical. One is a shift of the other.

Problem Set 5.8

1. **a.** $f(3) = 4$ **b.** $f(-2) = 2$ **c.** At $x = -4$ and 4
   d. At -2, 0, and 3.5 **e.** $0 \le y \le 4$ **f.** $-4 \le x \le 4$

2. **a.** Shift down 3 units.   **b.** Shift down 3 units.   **c.** Reflect across x-axis.

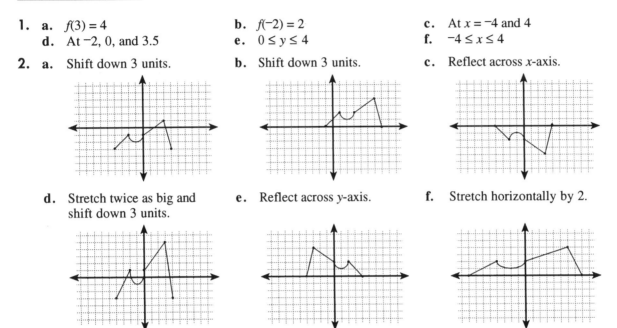

d. Stretch twice as big and shift down 3 units.   **e.** Reflect across y-axis.   **f.** Stretch horizontally by 2.

3. **a.** $y = 2|x| + 1$; stretch y-values by 2 and slide up 1 unit.

   b. $y = -0.5|x - 3|$; flip vertically across x-axis, compress y-values by 0.5, and slide to the right 3 units.

   c. $y = 2x^2 - 1$; stretch y-values by 2 and slide down 1 unit.

   d. $y = -3(x + 4)^2 + 2$; flip across the x-axis, stretch y-values by 3, slide left 4 units and up 2 units.

   e. $y = -2\sqrt{-(x + 4)}$; flip across the x-axis and across the y-axis, stretch y-values by 2, and slide left 4 units.

   f. $y = \frac{5}{2}|x - 2| - 1$; stretch y-values by $\frac{5}{2}$, slide right 2 units and down 1 unit.

   g. $y = \frac{1}{2}(x + 3)^2 - 2$; compress y-values by $\frac{1}{2}$, slide left 3 units and down 2 units.

   h. $y = 4\sqrt{x - 1} - 4$; stretch y-values by 4, slide right 1 unit and down 4 units.

4. **a.** None   **b.** Some   **c.** Some

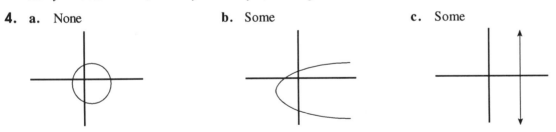

5. **a.** Stretch y-values by 2 and slide down 3 units.
   b. Slide right 4 units and down 2 units.
   c. Flip vertical, slide 3 units left and 1 unit up.
   d. Compress y-values by $\frac{1}{2}$, slide 2 units right and 3 units down.

6. **a.** $y = 2(x - 4)^2 + 1$
$= 2(x^2 - 8x + 16) + 1$
$= 2x^2 - 16x + 33$

b. $y = ^-(x + 3)^2 + 2$
$= ^-(x^2 + 6x + 9) + 2$
$= ^-x^2 - 6x - 7$

c. $y = 0.5(x - 2)^2 - 3$
$= 0.5(x^2 - 4x + 4) - 3$
$= 0.5x^2 - 2x - 1$

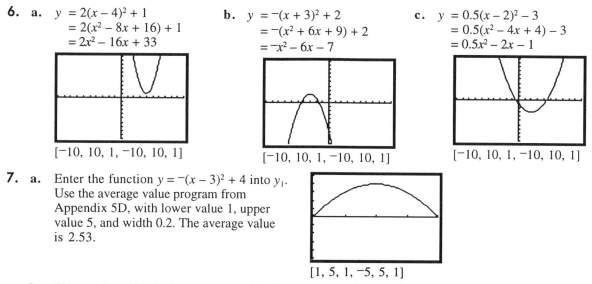

[−10, 10, 1, −10, 10, 1]

[−10, 10, 1, −10, 10, 1]

[−10, 10, 1, −10, 10, 1]

7. **a.** Enter the function $y = ^-(x - 3)^2 + 4$ into y_1. Use the average value program from Appendix 5D, with lower value 1, upper value 5, and width 0.2. The average value is 2.53.

[1, 5, 1, −5, 5, 1]

b. Change the width in the program to 0.1. The average value is 2.6.

c. Try increasingly smaller widths in the program. The average value appears to approach $\frac{8}{3}$. With a width of 0.01 the average value is 2.66; with a width of 0.001, the average value is 2.666.

d. Interval on the x-axis is $(5 - 1) = 4$. The average height is $\frac{8}{3}$. The area of the rectangle, length times width, is $4\left(\frac{8}{3}\right) = 10.667$.

e. This answer is the same as the area enclosed by the curve. By taking increasingly smaller widths to find the average value, you are getting an answer closer and closer to the area enclosed by the curve.

8. Evaluate the function at many points, and then average these values to find the average value. The function is $y = (x - 4)^2 + 1$. Or you could use the average value program to find the average value using increasingly smaller widths. The average value is 2. Then multiply this average value (2) by the width of the interval, $(5 - 2 = 3)$, to get an area of 6 square units.

9. Evaluate the function at many points and then average these values to find the average value. The function is $y = 450 - \frac{d^2}{2}$. Or you could use the average value program and use increasingly smaller widths. The average value is 300 cans. Multiply by the cost of 0.02 cents to find the average daily holding cost; $300(0.02) = \$6$.

10. **a.** $2x - 3y = ^-12$; $^-3y = ^-2x - 12$; $y = \frac{2}{3}x + 4$

b. $^-2(x + 1.5) + 3(y - 2) - 3 = 0$; $^-2x - 3 + 3y - 6 - 3 = 0$; $^-2x + 3y - 12 = 0$; $3y = 2x + 12$; $y = \frac{2}{3}x + 4$. (The graph is the same as the one in part a.)

c. $\frac{y}{2} = (x - 3)^2 - 2$; $y = 2(x - 3)^2 - 4$

d. $^-y + \frac{(x - 3)^2}{2} = 1$; $^-y = \frac{^-(x - 3)^2}{2} + 1$; $y = \frac{(x - 3)^2}{2} - 1$.

11. If f is a linear function, then the slope is $\frac{6 - ^-4}{2 - ^-3} = \frac{10}{5} = 2$. Using the point-slope form for the equation of a line, the equation is $y = 2(x - 2) + 6$ or $y = 2x + 2$.

12. **a.**

[0, 80, 10, 0, 350, 50]

b. Answers will vary, but should be close to $y = 0.07(x - 3)^2 + 21$.

c. To find the residual sum, find the difference between the y-value of each point and the function value at that point. Answers will depend on your choice of equation in part b. For the equation in part b, the sum is 0.19.

d. Replace x with 56.5 in the function in part b.
$y = 0.07(56.5 - 3)^2 + 21 \approx 221$ ft.

e. Replace y with 385 and solve for x. $385 = 0.07(x - 3)^2 + 21$. Enter each side of the equation into y_1 and y_2 respectively. Graph and trace or use the table function to find the point of intersection. The car is going ≈ 75 mi/hr.

13. Answers will vary.

Project: Boolean Graphs

Many creative and interesting results are possible. Students may wish to begin by making a sketch on graph paper to determine the window size and some of the parameters needed for the equations. Next create a program that contains only ClrDraw to begin with. It may be easiest for students to find each new equation using the DrawF on the home screen until they are satisfied with the placement and size of the curve. Then go to the program and press 2nd Enter to move that command to the program. Now back to the home screen to work on the next feature.

Problem Set 5.9

1. **a.** Draw a vertical line at $x = 20$, intersecting the graph at $y = 1.5$. Draw a horizontal line at $y = 1.5$, intersecting the graph of the line $y = x$ at the point (1.5, 1.5). Draw a vertical line down to the graph of speed vs. oxygen at $x = 1.5$, intersecting at the point (1.5, 12). The oxygen consumption is 12 L/min.

b.

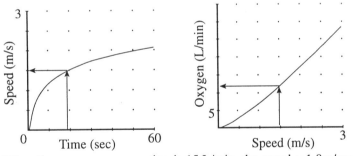

c. When the oxygen consumption is 15 L/min, the speed ≈ 1.8 m/sec. From the first graph, when the speed is ≈ 1.8 the time is between 40 and 45 sec.

2. **a.** $y = |(x - 3)^2 - 1|$

b. First you would graph a parabola and then take the absolute value of the equation of the parabola: $f(x) = |x|; g(x) = (x - 3)^2 - 1$.

3. **a.** For thermometers A and B, plot the points (12, 13) and (36, 29), and draw the line that contains these two points. For thermometers B and C, plot the points (20, 57) and (32, 84), and draw the line that contains these two points.

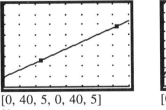

[0, 40, 5, 0, 40, 5]

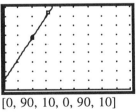

[0, 90, 10, 0, 90, 10]

b. If A reads 12, $B \approx 13$ and from the second graph, $C \approx 41$.

c. First find the slope between the two points (12, 13) and (36, 29). The slope is $\frac{2}{3}$. The function is $B = \frac{2}{3}(A - 12) + 13$ or $B = \frac{2}{3}A + 5$.

d. First find the slope between the two points (20, 57) and (32, 84). The slope is $\frac{9}{4}$. The function is $C = \frac{9}{4}(B - 20) + 57$ or $C = \frac{9}{4}B + 12$.

e. $C = \frac{9}{4}\left(\frac{2}{3}A + 5\right) + 12 = \frac{3}{2}A + 23.25$

4. **a.**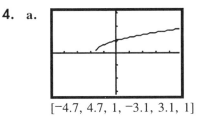

[−4.7, 4.7, 1, −3.1, 3.1, 1]

b.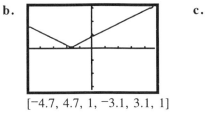

[−4.7, 4.7, 1, −3.1, 3.1, 1]

c.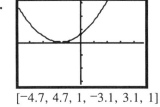

[−4.7, 4.7, 1, −3.1, 3.1, 1]

5. **a.** $g(f(4)) = g(1) = 2$ **b.** $f(g(-2)) = f(4) = 1$

6. **a.** $g(f(2)) = g(1) = 2$ **b.** $f(g(6)) = f(-2) = 6$

   c. Answers will vary. Select 1 from g: $f(g(1)) = f(2) = 1$. The composition of f and g will always give back the original number because they "undo" the effects of each other.

7. **a.** $f(2) = 2(2) - 1 = 4 - 1 = 3$

$g(3) = \frac{1}{2}(3) + \frac{1}{2} = \frac{3}{2} + \frac{1}{2} = \frac{4}{2} = 2$

$g(f(2)) = g(3) = 2$

   b. $g(-1) = \frac{1}{2}(-1) + \frac{1}{2} = \frac{-1}{2} + \frac{1}{2} = 0$

$f(g(-1)) = f(0) = -1$

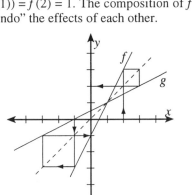

   c. Answers will vary. In general, $g(f(x)) = g(2x - 1) = x$ for all x.

   d. Answers will vary. In general, $f(g(x)) = f\left(\frac{1}{2}x + \frac{1}{2}\right) = x$.

   e. The two functions "undo" the effects of each other and thus give back the original starting value.

8. **a.** $f(g(3)) = f(1) = 4$ **b.** $f(g(2)) = f(0) = 3$

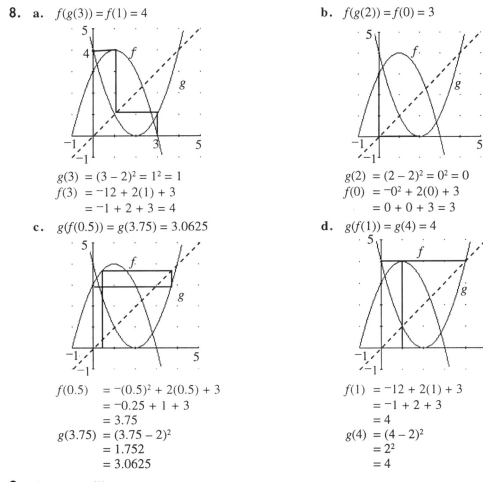

$g(3) = (3 - 2)^2 = 1^2 = 1$
$f(3) = -12 + 2(1) + 3$
   $= -1 + 2 + 3 = 4$

$g(2) = (2 - 2)^2 = 0^2 = 0$
$f(0) = -0^2 + 2(0) + 3$
   $= 0 + 0 + 3 = 3$

   c. $g(f(0.5)) = g(3.75) = 3.0625$ **d.** $g(f(1)) = g(4) = 4$

$f(0.5) = -(0.5)^2 + 2(0.5) + 3$
   $= -0.25 + 1 + 3$
   $= 3.75$
$g(3.75) = (3.75 - 2)^2$
   $= 1.75^2$
   $= 3.0625$

$f(1) = -12 + 2(1) + 3$
   $= -1 + 2 + 3$
   $= 4$
$g(4) = (4 - 2)^2$
   $= 2^2$
   $= 4$

9. Answers will vary.

10. If the parent function is $y = x^2$, then the equation would be $y = -3x^2 + 3$. If the parent function is
$y = \sqrt{1 - x^2}$, then the equation would be $y = 3\sqrt{1 - x^2}$. It appears that the point (0.5, 2.5) lies on
the graph. Substituting 0.5 for x in each equation gives the following results.
$3(-(0.5)^2 + 1) = 2.25$
$3\sqrt{1 - 0.5^2} = 2.598$
So the stretched semicircle seems to be the better fit.

Chapter Review
Problem Set 5.10

1. For a time there are no pops. Then the popping rate begins to slowly
increase. When it reaches a furious intensity, it seems to nearly level
out. Shortly after it peaks intensity, the number of pops per second
drops radically to a minimal value. This then tapers off quickly until
the last pop is heard.

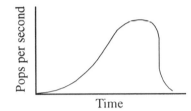

2. **a.** $g(3) = 3^2 - 2$
$= 9 - 2$
$= 7$
$f(7) = -2(7) + 7$
$= -7$

b. $h(-2) = (-2 + 1)^2$
$= (-1)^2$
$= 1$
$g(1) = 1^2 - 2$
$= 1 - 2$
$\neq -1$

c. $f(-1) = -2(-1) + 7$
$= 2 + 7$
$= 9$
$h(9) = (9 + 1)^2$
$= 10^2$
$= 100$

d. $g(x) = x^2 - 2$
$f(x^2 - 2) = -2(x^2 - 2) + 7$
$= -2x^2 + 4 + 7$
$= -2x^2 + 11$

e. $f(x) = -2x + 7$
$h(-2x + 7) = ((-2x + 7) + 1)^2$
$= (-2x + 8)^2$
$= 4x^2 - 32x + 64$

f. $f(x) = -2x + 7$
$g(-2x + 7) = (-2x + 7)^2 - 2$
$= 4x^2 - 28x + 49 - 2$
$= 4x^2 - 28x + 47$

3. **a.** The graph is translated 3 units down.

b. The graph is translated 3 units right.

4. **a.** Slide the graph 2 units left and then 3 units down.
b. First double all x-values of the graph. Next reflect or flip the graph over the x-axis. Then slide
the graph up 1.
c. Shrink the x-values of the graph by dividing them by 2, double the y-values, and finally slide the
graph 1 unit to the right and 3 units up.

5. **a.** $2x - 3y = 6$; $-3y = -2x + 6$; $y = \frac{2}{3}x - 2$

b. $(y + 1)^2 - 3 = x$; $(y + 1)^2 = x + 3$; $y + 1 = \pm\sqrt{x + 3}$; $y = \pm\sqrt{x + 3} - 1$

c. $\sqrt{1 - y^2} + 2 = x$; $\sqrt{1 - y^2} = x - 2$; $1 - y^2 = (x - 2)^2$; $-y^2 = (x - 2)^2 - 1$
$y^2 = -(x - 2)^2 + 1$; $y = \pm\sqrt{-(x - 2)^2 + 1}$ or $y = \pm\sqrt{1 - (x - 2)^2}$

6. **a.** Slide the graph down 2 units.

b. Slide the graph 2 units to the right and then 1 unit up.

c. Reflect the graph over the *x*-axis.

d. Double all the *y*-values. Then slide the graph 1 unit to the left and 3 units down.

e. Reflect the graph over the *y*-axis, and then slide the graph up 1 unit.

f. Double all the *x*-values, and then slide the graph 2 units down.

g. Reflect the graph over the *x*-axis, slide the graph 3 units to the right, and then slide the graph 1 unit up.

h. Multiply all the *x*-values by 1.5. Then multiply all the *y*-values by ⁻2, and slide the graph 1 unit right and 2 units down. (Instead of multiplying the *y*-values by ⁻2, you could have multiplied by 2 and reflected or flipped the graph over the *x*-axis.)

7. **a.** Parent function: $y = \sqrt{1 - x^2}$; equation is $y = 3\sqrt{(1 - x^2)} - 1$.

b. Parent function: $y = \sqrt{1 - x^2}$; equation is $y = 2\sqrt{1 - \left(\frac{x}{5}\right)^2} + 3$.

c. Parent function: $y = \sqrt{1 - x^2}$; equation is $y = 4\sqrt{1 - \left(\frac{x-3}{4}\right)^2} - 1$.

d. Parent function: $y = x$; equation is $y = (x - 2)^2 - 4$

e. Parent function: $y = x^2$; equation is $y = {}^{-}2(x + 1)^2$

f. Parent function: $y = \sqrt{x}$; equation is $y = {}^{-}\sqrt{{}^{-}(x - 2)} - 3$

g. Parent function: $y = |x|$; equation is $y = 0.5|x + 2| - 2$

h. Parent function: $y = |x|$; equation is $y = {}^{-}2|x - 3| + 2$

Project: Melting Ice

With a little equipment you could duplicate Mel's experiment and collect your own data. He used an electronic balance from the chemistry room and hung the ice cube to the side so that the water dripped into a small bowl beside the balance.

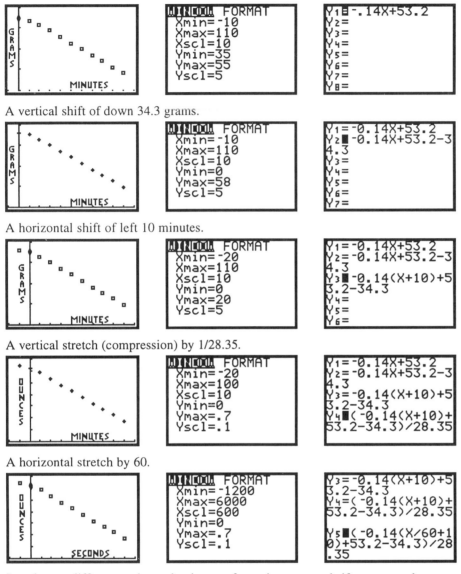

A vertical shift of down 34.3 grams.

A horizontal shift of left 10 minutes.

A vertical stretch (compression) by 1/28.35.

A horizontal stretch by 60.

It makes no difference what order the transformations are made if you remember to convert the mass of the hanger to ounces before you subtract in the second conversion. The last graph is a reflection over the x-axis and a vertical shift of 0.638 up.

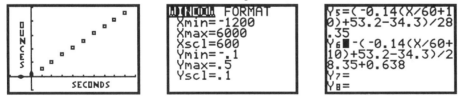

Whether you are using a function or a set of data, none of the transformations that we have looked at (shift, stretch, or flip) will change the type of function. A line to start with will still be a line even after many transformations.

Chapter 6

Problem Set 6.1

1. a.
    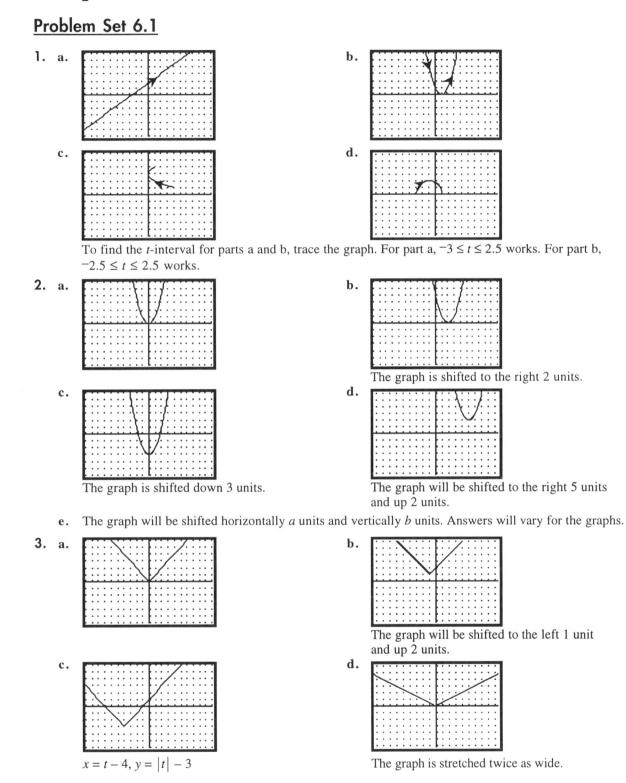
    b.

    c.
    d.

    To find the *t*-interval for parts a and b, trace the graph. For part a, $-3 \leq t \leq 2.5$ works. For part b, $-2.5 \leq t \leq 2.5$ works.

2. a.
    b.

    The graph is shifted to the right 2 units.

    c.
    d.

    The graph is shifted down 3 units.   The graph will be shifted to the right 5 units and up 2 units.

    e. The graph will be shifted horizontally *a* units and vertically *b* units. Answers will vary for the graphs.

3. a.
    b.

    The graph will be shifted to the left 1 unit and up 2 units.

    c.
    d.

    $x = t - 4, y = |t| - 3$ The graph is stretched twice as wide.

e.

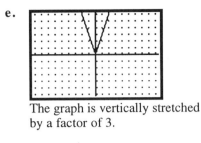

The graph is vertically stretched
by a factor of 3.

f.

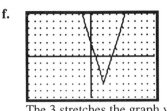

The 3 stretches the graph vertically,
the 2 slides it 2 units to the right,
and the ⁻4 slides it down 4 units.

4. a. This looks like the family of half-circles from Chapter 5. The parametric equations would be $x = t$ and
$y = 2\sqrt{1 - \left(\frac{t}{2}\right)^2}$.

b. Slide the graph 2 units to the right. The parametric equations would be $x = t + 2$ and $y = 2\sqrt{1 - \left(\frac{t}{2}\right)^2}$.

c. Flip the graph over the x-axis and slide up 1 unit. The parametric equations would be $x = t$ and
$y = -2\sqrt{1 - \left(\frac{t}{2}\right)^2} + 1$.

d. Stretch the graph horizontally by a factor of 2 and slide up 1 unit. The parametric equations would be
$x = 2t$ and $y = 2\sqrt{1 - \left(\frac{t}{2}\right)^2} + 1$.

5. a.

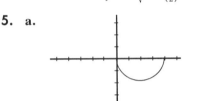

The graph is reflected over the x-axis.

b.

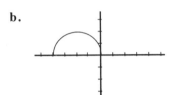

The graph is reflected over the y-axis.

6. a. The graph is translated 2 units left and 2 units up, so $x = f(t) - 2$ and $y = g(t) + 2$.

b. The graph is stretched vertically by a factor of 2 so $x = f(t)$ and $y = 2g(t)$.

c. The graph is stretched horizontally by a factor of 2 so $x = 2f(t)$ and $y = g(t)$.

d. The graph is reflected over the x-axis and is translated 1 unit left so $x = f(t) - 1$ and $y = -g(t)$.

Problem Set 6.2

1. a. $x = t + 1$, $t = x - 1$; now substitute this value into the second
equation: $y = (x - 1)^2$.

b. Solve one of the equations for t, and substitute that value
into the second equation: $x = 3t - 1$, $3t = x + 1$, $t = \frac{x + 1}{3}$.
Now substitute this value into the second equation:
$y = 2\left(\frac{x + 1}{3}\right) + 1 = \frac{2}{3}x + \frac{5}{3}$. Check that the graphs are the same
by first graphing the given parametric equations and then
changing the mode on the calculator to Function mode and
graphing the above function answer.

c. $x = t^2$, $t = \pm\sqrt{x}$; now substitute into the second equation:
$y = \pm\sqrt{x} + 3$. (Except for the restrictions on t, the graphs
are the same.)

d. $x = t - 1$, $t = x + 1$; now substitute into the second equation: $y = \sqrt{4 - (x + 1)^2}$. (Except for the restrictions on t, the graphs are the same.)

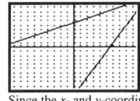

2. a. Solve one of the equations for t and substitute this value into the second equation: $x = 2t - 3$, $2t = x + 3$, $t = \frac{x + 3}{2}$. Now substitute into the second equation: $y = \frac{x + 3}{2} + 2 = \frac{x + 3}{2} + \frac{4}{2} = \frac{x + 7}{2}$.

b. $x = t^2$, $t = \pm \sqrt{x}$; now substitute into the second equation: $y = t + 1 = \pm \sqrt{x} + 1$.

c. $x = \frac{1}{2}t + 1$, $\frac{1}{2}t = x - 1$, $t = 2x - 2$; now substitute into the second equation: $y = \frac{2x - 2 - 2}{3} = \frac{2x - 4}{3}$.

d. $x = t - 3$, $t = x + 3$; now substitute into the second equation: $y = 2((x + 3) - 1)^2 = 2(x + 2)^2$.

3. a. 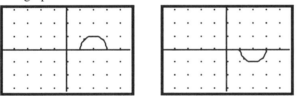 **b.**

Since the x- and y-coordinates are to be interchanged, interchange the original equations: $x = 2t - 1$ and $y = t + 5$.

c. All pairs of coordinates of the original graph are switched in the new graph. The original graph is reflected across the line $y = x$.

4. The "friendly" window in which the distance between pixels is 0.2 on the TI-82 and TI-83 is [-9.4, 9.4, 1, -3.1, 3.1, 1]. First solve each inequation for the minimum and maximum x- and y-values of the window. Then compare the results to find the smallest interval for t.
$-9.4 \leq t + 2 \leq 9.4$, $-11.4 \leq t \leq 7.4$ and $-6.2 \leq t^2 \leq 6.2$, $-\sqrt{6.2} \leq t \leq \sqrt{6.2}$
The smallest interval would be $-\sqrt{6.2} \leq t \leq \sqrt{6.2}$.

5. a. The graph is reflected over the x-axis.

b. The graph is reflected over the y-axis.

c. The graph is reflected over the x-axis and then the y-axis (or over the y-axis and then the x-axis).

6. To have a slope of $^-0.5$, the change in y over the change in x should be $\frac{-1}{2}$. A perpendicular line would have a slope of 2. To go through the point (3, 2), the x-equation should have $^+3$ and the y-equation should have $^+2$. (When $t = 0$, x will equal 3 and y will equal 2.) One example of a pair of equations is $x_1 = 3 + t$ and $y_1 = 2 + 2t$; $x_2 = 3 + 2t$ and $y_2 = 2 - t$.

7. a. Tanker A: $x = 18t$ and $y = 1$; Tanker B: $x = 22(t - 5)$ and $y = 2$

  b. First set an appropriate window. Since the tankers are traveling 900 mi, $0 \le x \le 900$.
  The tankers are moving horizontally, so the domain merely represents the lanes.
  One possible window is [0, 50, .5, 0, 900, 100, −1, 3, 1]. (To get the following graphs,
  set the Tmax to the hours above each graph.)

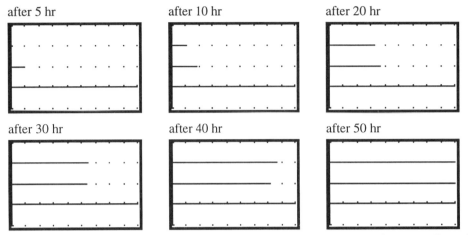

after 5 hr   after 10 hr   after 20 hr

after 30 hr   after 40 hr   after 50 hr

  c. To find when and where Tanker A is overtaken, you must realize that the x-coordinate is the
  distance from Corpus Christi, so set both x-equations equal to each other and solve for t.
  $18t = 22(t - 5)$; $18t = 22t - 110$; $4t = 110$; $t = 27.5$ hr after leaving.
  To find the distance, substitute 27.5 hr for t and solve for x in each equation.
  $x = 18t = 18(27.5) = 495$ mi from Corpus Christi.

  d. Tanker A: $x = 18t$ and $y = 1$; Tanker B: $x = 900 - 22t$ and $y = 2$ (since Tanker B leaves from
  St. Petersburg 900 mi away and is traveling toward Corpus Christi).

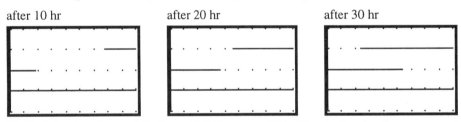

after 10 hr   after 20 hr   after 30 hr

  To find the time interval during which they are within 50 mi of each other, you must realize
  that the x-coordinate is the distance from Corpus Christi, so find when the difference of the
  x-coordinates is 50.
  $18t - (900 - 22t) = 50$; $40t - 900 = 50$; $40t = 950$; $t = 23.75$
  $900 - 22t - 18t = 50$; $900 - 40t = 50$; $-40t = -850$; $t = 21.25$
  The time interval is $21.25 \le t \le 23.75$.

Take Another Look 6.2

Students should show that the results are the same using either method.

Problem Set 6.3

1. a. $\cos 32° = \frac{14.7}{a}$, $a = \frac{14.7}{\cos 32°} \approx 17.334$

  b. $\cos 23° = \frac{53}{b}$, $b \cos 23° = 53$, $b = \frac{53}{\cos 23°} \approx 57.577$

  c. $\tan 47.2° = \frac{24.6}{c}$, $c \tan 47.2° = 24.6$, $c = \frac{24.6}{\tan 47.2°} \approx 22.780$

  d. $\sin 58.7° = \frac{d}{9.62}$, $d = 9.62 \sin 58.7° \approx 8.220$

  e. $\sin 68.2° = \frac{14.7}{e}$, $e \sin 68.2° = 14.7$, $e = \frac{14.7}{\sin 68.2°} \approx 15.832$

  f. $\tan 47.2° = \frac{18.1}{f}$, $f \tan 47.2° = 18.1$, $f = \frac{18.1}{\tan 47.2°} \approx 16.761$

2. a. $\tan a = \frac{8.9}{14.7}$, $a = \tan^{-1}\left(\frac{8.9}{14.7}\right) \approx 31.19°$
    b. $\tan b = \frac{4.2}{7.3}$, $b = \tan^{-1}\left(\frac{4.2}{7.3}\right) \approx 29.91°$

    c. $\sin c = \frac{21.2}{27.8}$, $c = \sin^{-1}\left(\frac{21.2}{27.8}\right) \approx 49.69°$
    d. $\sin d = \frac{6.8}{11.5}$, $d = \sin^{-1}\left(\frac{6.8}{11.5}\right) \approx 36.25°$

    e. $\cos e = \frac{14.7}{20.4}$, $e = \cos^{-1}\left(\frac{14.7}{20.4}\right) \approx 43.90°$
    f. $\cos f = \frac{47.2}{67.8}$, $f = \cos^{-1}\left(\frac{47.2}{67.8}\right) \approx 45.88°$

3. a. $\tan a = \frac{28.5}{60.3}$, $a = \tan^{-1}\left(\frac{28.5}{60.3}\right) \approx 25.30°$

    b. To find the distance between the ants, solve for the hypotenuse. You could use
$\sin 25.30° = \frac{28.5}{x}$ or $\cos 25.30° = \frac{60.3}{x}$. The answers will vary slightly because the
angle measure has been rounded, but $x \approx 66.7$ cm. Or use the Pythagorean theorem:
distance $= \sqrt{28.5^2 + 60.3^2} \approx 66.7$ cm.

4. a. The graph is a line segment at a 39° angle with the horizontal axis.
The initial point and end point depend on the interval used for t.

    b. Trace and select a point. For example, at $T = 1$, $x = 0.7771$ and
$y = 0.6293$. These two values become the lengths of the legs.

$\tan a = \frac{0.6293}{0.7771}$, $a = \tan^{-1}\left(\frac{0.6293}{0.7771}\right) = 39°$

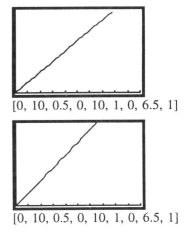

[0, 10, 0.5, 0, 10, 1, 0, 6.5, 1]

5. The graph is a line segment at a 45° angle with the horizontal axis.
The initial and end points depend on the interval used for t. The angle
with a tangent ratio $\frac{y}{x}$ or $\frac{t \sin 45°}{t \cos 45°} = 45°$.

[0, 10, 0.5, 0, 10, 1, 0, 6.5, 1]

6. The parametric equations would be $x = t \cos 57°$ and $y = t \sin 57°$. To find the smallest interval
for t to show the complete graph in the window, solve the inequalities $-4.7 \le t \cos 57° \le 4.7$
and $-3.1 \le t \sin 57° \le 3.1$ and select the smallest interval, which is $\frac{-3.1}{\sin 57°} \le t \le \frac{3.1}{\sin 57°}$.
(The t-interval assumes you are using a "friendly" window on a TI-82 or TI-83 in which the
distance between the pixels is 0.1.)

7. The parametric equations would be $x = t \cos 29°$ and $y = t \sin 29°$.

8. Since tan involves the ratio $\frac{\sin}{\cos}$, use the equations $x = t$ and $y = t \tan 29°$.

9. a. $x = t \cos 47°$ and $y = t \sin 47°$. To find the smallest interval for t to show the complete graph
in the window, solve the inequalities $-4.7 \le t \cos 47° \le 4.7$ and $-3.1 \le t \sin 47° \le 3.1$ and select
the smallest interval, which is $\frac{-3.1}{\sin 47°} \le t \le \frac{3.1}{\sin 47°}$. (The t-interval assumes you are using a "friendly"
window on a TI-82 or TI-83 in which the distance between the pixels is 0.1.)

    b. $x = t \cos 115°$ and $y = t \sin 115°$. To find the smallest interval for t to show the complete graph
in the window, solve the inequalities $-4.7 \le t \cos 115° \le 4.7$ and $-3.1 \le t \sin 115° \le 3.1$ and
select the smallest interval, which is $\frac{-3.1}{\sin 115°} \le t \le \frac{3.1}{\sin 115°}$.

10. a. $x = 10t \cos 30°$ and $y = 10t \sin 30°$.

    b. Since the tanker is moving at 10 mi/hr, you would need $0 \le t \le 10$ to show 100 mi of motion. ($10t = 100$)

    c. The 10 represents the rate of the tanker, 10 mi/hr, t represents time in hours, 30° is the angle that the
tanker is making with the x-axis, x is the horizontal position at any time, and y is the vertical position
at any time.

    d. The points on the graph are drawn as a simulation of the actual position of the tanker at any time t.
The line shown on the graph is the motion of the tanker.

11. a. The equations used to describe the movement of Tanker A would be $x = 18t \cos 17°$ and $y = 18t \sin 17°$.
(Remember that a heading is given as an angle from due north moving clockwise, so 73° from due north is 17°
from the horizontal axis.) To find the time needed to travel the 750 mi, remember that distance = rate • time
or time $= \frac{\text{distance}}{\text{rate}} = \frac{750}{18} \approx 41.7$ hr.

b. To find the east and north distance, substitute 41.7 for t:
$x = 18(41.7)\cos 17° \approx 717$ mi east;
$y = 18(41.7)\sin 17° \approx 219$ mi north.

[0, 42, 0.5, 0, 750, 100, 0, 350, 100]

12. a. From due north, a heading of 285° is an angle in the second quadrant, 15° above the horizontal axis.

b. To find the time needed to travel the 510 mi (Tmax), remember that distance equals rate • time or time = $\frac{distance}{rate} = \frac{510}{22} \approx 23.2$ hr.

c. The distance west is $\cos 15° = \frac{x}{510}$; $x = 510 \cos 15°$; $x \approx 493$ mi. The distance north is $\sin 15° = \frac{y}{510}$; $y = 510 \sin 15° \approx 132$ mi.

d. Since St. Petersburg is 900 mi east of Corpus Christi, the equations are $x = 900 - 22t \cos 15°$ and $y = 22t \sin 15°$. Place the equations for Tanker B in x_2 and y_2, leaving the equations for Tanker A in x_1 and y_1. Adjust the Tmax until you find a point about where the paths of the tankers cross (about 23 hr). Tanker B crosses just in front of Tanker A.

[0, 23, 1, 0, 900, 100, 0, 300, 100]

Problem Set 6.4

1. There are many other possibilities for these equations. Use a "friendly" window in which the distance between pixels is 0.1.

a. $x = 3 \cos t$, $y = 3 \sin t$; $0° \leq t \leq 360°$ with steps of 72. (To get the steps of 72, divide 360 by 5 sides.)

b. $x = 3 \cos t$, $y = 3 \sin t$; $18° \leq t \leq 738°$ with steps of 144. (To get the steps, you need to connect every other corner of the pentagon in part a, so double the steps from part a. To have the star pointing straight up, the Tmin has to be increased by 18 to have a point lie on the vertical axis. The Tmax has to be increased to go around the circle twice to get all 5 points, so Tmax = 2(360) + 18 = 738.)

c. $x = 3 \cos t$, $y = 3 \sin t$; $30° \leq t \leq 390°$ with steps of 120. (To get the steps, divide 360 by 3 sides. In order to have the top side of the triangle parallel to the horizontal axis, the first point has to be rotated by 30° so that 30° and 30° + 120°, or 150°, are equidistant from the horizontal axis.)

d. $x = 3 \cos t$, $y = 3 \sin t$; $0° \leq t \leq 1080°$ with steps of 135. (Tmax has to be increased to go around the circle three times, so Tmax = 3(360) = 1080 and to make eight points, the step should be $\frac{1080}{8} = 135$.)

2. a. $x = 1 \cos t$, $y = 1 \sin t$

b.

Angle A	0°	30°	45°	60°	90°	120°	135°
$\cos A$	1	0.866	0.707	0.5	0	−0.5	−0.707
$\sin A$	0	0.5	0.707	0.866	1	0.866	0.707

c. Cosine A is the x-coordinate of the point where the line extending the central angle A crosses the perimeter of the unit circle.

d. Sine A is the y-coordinate of the point where the line extending the central angle A crosses the perimeter of the unit circle.

3. a. The circle has been slid 2 units to the right. The equations are $x = 2 \cos t + 2$ and $y = 2 \sin t$.

b. The circle has been slid 3 units to the left. The equations are $x = 2 \cos t - 3$ and $y = 2 \sin t$.

c. The circle has been slid 4 units up. The equations are $x = 2 \cos t$ and $y = 2 \sin t + 4$.

d. The circle has been slid 2 units down. The equations are $x = 2 \cos t$ and $y = 2 \sin t - 2$.

e. The circle has been slid 3 units right and 2 units up. The equations are $x = 2 \cos t + 3$ and $y = 2 \sin t + 2$.

4. a. $x = 3 \cos t$, $\cos t = \frac{x}{3}$ and $y = 3 \sin t$, $\sin t = \frac{y}{3}$ **b.** $(\cos t)^2 = \frac{x^2}{9}$ and $(\sin t)^2 = \frac{y^2}{9}$

  c. $(\cos t)^2 + (\sin t)^2 = \frac{x^2}{9} + \frac{y^2}{9}$ **d.** $1 = \frac{x^2}{9} + \frac{y^2}{9}$

  e. $9 = x^2 + y^2$ or $x^2 + y^2 = 9$ **f.** The value of r is 3, which is the radius of the circle.

5. a. $x = 2 \cos t + 3$ and $y = 2 \sin t + 2$; $\cos t = \frac{x-3}{2}$, and $\sin t = \frac{y-2}{2}$

  b. $(\cos t)^2 = \frac{(x-3)^2}{4}$, $(\sin t)^2 = \frac{(y-2)^2}{4}$; $(\cos t)^2 + (\sin t)^2 = \frac{(x-3)^2}{4} + \frac{(y-2)^2}{4}$

  c. $1 = \frac{(x-3)^2}{4} + \frac{(y-2)^2}{4}$ **d.** $4 = (x-3)^2 + (y-2)^2$ or $(x-3)^2 + (y-2)^2 = 4$

  e. $(x-3)^2 + (y-2)^2 = 4$, $h = 3$, $k = 2$, $r = 2$ **f.**

6. a. $x = 2 \cos t$ **b.** $x = 4 \cos t$ **c.** $x = 2 \cos t$
     $y = 3 \sin t$ $y = \sin t$ $y = 4 \sin t$

7. a. $x = 4 \cos t$ **b.** $x = 3 \cos t + 4$ **c.** $x = 2.5 \cos t$ **d.** $x = 2 \cos t + 1$
     $y = 3 \sin t$ $y = 2 \sin t$ $y = 1.5 \sin t + 2$ $y = 3.5 \sin t + 3$

8. a. For Problem 7a   **b.** For Problem 7c

    a. $\cos t = \frac{x}{2}$, $\sin t = \frac{y}{3}$ **a.** $\cos t = \frac{x}{2.5}$, $\sin t = \frac{y-2}{1.5}$

    b. $(\cos t)^2 + (\sin t)^2 = \frac{x^2}{4} + \frac{y^2}{9}$ **b.** $(\cos t)^2 + (\sin t)^2 = \frac{x^2}{6.25} + \frac{(y-2)^2}{2.25}$

    c. $1 = \frac{x^2}{4} + \frac{y^2}{9}$ **c.** $1 = \frac{x^2}{6.25} + \frac{(y-2)^2}{2.25}$

  c. For the ellipse in 8a, the center is at $(0, 0)$. The lengths of the axes are 4 units and 3 units. For the ellipse in 8b, the center is at $(0, 2)$. The lengths of the axes are 2.5 units and 1.5 units.

9. Many answers are possible. Those listed below are only one way of generating each figure. Tsteps only affect the smoothness of the curve.

  a. This is a line through the origin, with a slope of $\frac{2}{5}$. $x = 5t$, $y = 2t$; Tmin = ⁻9.4, Tmax = 9.4, Tstep = 0.5.

  b. This is an ellipse with horizontal radius 5 and vertical radius 3: $x = 5 \cos t$ and $y = 3 \sin t$; Tmin = 0, Tmax = 360, Tstep = 10.

  c. This is a five-pointed star with a radius of 6. $x = 6 \cos t$, $y = 6 \sin t$; Tmin = 0, Tmax = 720, Tstep = 144. Note: You need to go twice around the circle to complete the star and connect every other point of a pentagon so the Tstep = $2\left(\frac{360}{5}\right)$.

  d. This is a circle of radius 2 shifted right 4 units and up 3 units: $x = 2 \cos t + 4$ and $y = 2 \sin t + 3$; Tmin = 0, Tmax = 360, Tstep = 10.

10. a. This is a five-pointed star with a radius of 2 that has been shifted 4 units right and 3 units up from the origin: $x = 2 \cos t + 4$, $y = 2 \sin t + 3$; Tmin = 0, Tmax = 720, Tstep = 144.

  b. To reflect over the x-axis, the y-coordinates need to be negative: $x = 2 \cos t + 4$, $y = ⁻(2 \sin t + 3)$.

  c. To reflect over the y-axis, the x-coordinates need to be negative: $x = ⁻(2 \cos t + 4)$, $y = 2 \sin t + 3$.

  d. To rotate 180°, both coordinates need to be negative: $x = ⁻(2 \cos t + 4)$, $y = ⁻(2 \sin t + 3)$.

  e. Tmin = 0, Tmax = 720, Tstep = 144

  f. Answers will vary. One possibility is $x = ⁻(2 \cos t + 4)$ and $y = 2 \sin t - 3$.

Project: Viewing Angle

There is room for some variation in the answers for the students' viewing angles. Assuming that the students sit at the back edge of the desks with their heads leaning up against the wall, the angles of view can be calculated with the following expressions:

First student: $\tan^{-1}\left(\frac{25}{4}\right) - \tan^{-1}\left(\frac{5}{4}\right) = 29.6°$

Second student: $\tan^{-1}\left(\frac{25}{7}\right) - \tan^{-1}\left(\frac{5}{7}\right) = 38.8°$

Third student: $\tan^{-1}\left(\frac{25}{10}\right) - \tan^{-1}\left(\frac{5}{10}\right) = 41.6°$

Fourth student: $\tan^{-1}\left(\frac{25}{13}\right) - \tan^{-1}\left(\frac{5}{13}\right) = 41.5°$

Fifth student: $\tan^{-1}\left(\frac{25}{16}\right) - \tan^{-1}\left(\frac{5}{16}\right) = 40.0°$

The third and fourth students have almost equally good views of the board. If you change the assumptions and place the students' heads at the middle of the desks, the answers will change slightly.

Depending on the arrangement of boards and available floor space, your students may come up with some rather unusual desk arrangements. Perhaps trying them out in the classroom could serve as a partial presentation of their project results.

Problem Set 6.5

1. A compass heading is always given as a clockwise direction from due north. If the direction Pat was moving was 36.9° from the positive horizontal axis, then the compass heading was (90 – 36.9) = 53.1°. The pilot is on the compass heading of (270 – 4.6) = 265.4°.

2. You need to establish a coordinate system. Assume the river flows toward the top of the page and the boat is heading from left to right.
   a. Effect of the river: $y = 2t$ b. Pa's contribution: $x = 6t$
   d. Trace on the graph or look at the table to find the point where $x = 1.5$. The corresponding y-coordinate will be how far Pa landed downstream. (You might have to change your Tstep in order to trace in to the exact point.) He landed 0.5 mi downstream.
   e. Use the Pythagorean theorem to find the total distance traveled:
      distance = $\sqrt{1.5^2 + 0.5^2} \approx 1.58$ mi.

   c.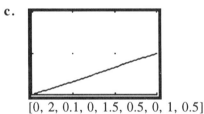
   [0, 2, 0.1, 0, 1.5, 0.5, 0, 1, 0.5]

3. You need to establish a coordinate system. Assume Toledo is the origin so that the plane's path is in a negative x-direction and the wind's path is in a positive y-direction.
   a. Effect of the wind: $y = 25t$ b. Plane's contribution: $x = -120t$
   c.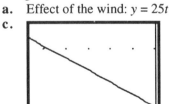
   [0, 3, 0.1, −280, 0, 50, 0, 70, 50]
   d. Trace on the graph or look at the table to find the point where $x = -280$. The corresponding y-coordinate will be how far north the plane is when it has traveled 280 mi west. (You might have to change your Tstep in order to trace in to the exact point.) The plane is approximately 58.3 mi to the north.
   e. Use the Pythagorean theorem to find the total distance traveled:
      distance = $\sqrt{280^2 + 58.3^2} \approx 286$ mi.
   f. Since distance = rate • time, you know it took $\frac{280}{120} = 2.33$ hr. If the plane actually traveled 286 mi, then the plane's rate was $\frac{286}{2.33} \approx 122.6$ mi/hr.

4. Assume Fred starts at (0, 0) and heads in the positive x-direction. Assume the river's current flow is in the positive y-direction.
   a. Effect of the current: $y = 5t$ b. Fred's contribution: $x = 3t$

c. [0, 2, 0.1, 0, 4, 1, 0, 3]

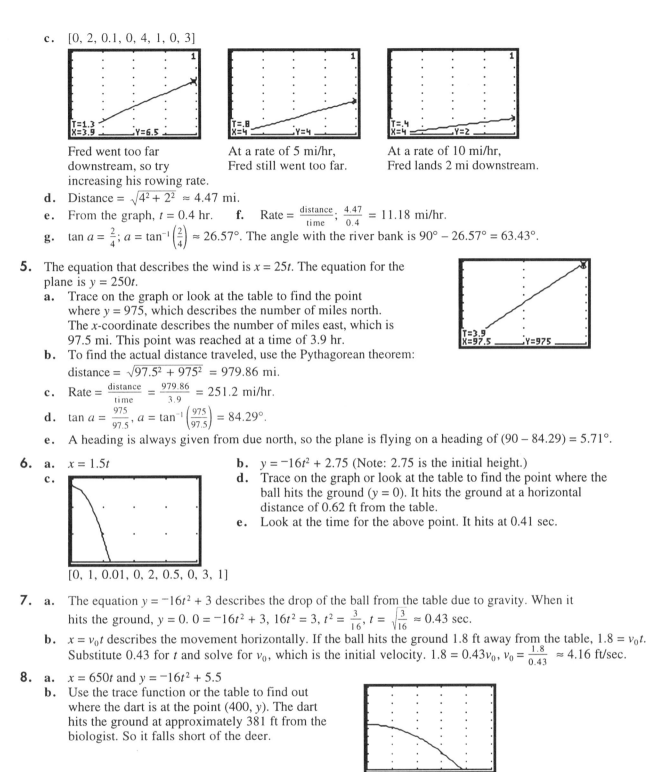

Fred went too far
downstream, so try
increasing his rowing rate.

At a rate of 5 mi/hr,
Fred still went too far.

At a rate of 10 mi/hr,
Fred lands 2 mi downstream.

d. Distance = $\sqrt{4^2 + 2^2} \approx 4.47$ mi.

e. From the graph, $t = 0.4$ hr.　**f.**　Rate = $\dfrac{\text{distance}}{\text{time}}$; $\dfrac{4.47}{0.4} = 11.18$ mi/hr.

g. $\tan a = \dfrac{2}{4}$; $a = \tan^{-1}\left(\dfrac{2}{4}\right) \approx 26.57°$. The angle with the river bank is $90° - 26.57° = 63.43°$.

5. The equation that describes the wind is $x = 25t$. The equation for the
plane is $y = 250t$.

  a. Trace on the graph or look at the table to find the point
where $y = 975$, which describes the number of miles north.
The x-coordinate describes the number of miles east, which is
97.5 mi. This point was reached at a time of 3.9 hr.

  b. To find the actual distance traveled, use the Pythagorean theorem:
distance = $\sqrt{97.5^2 + 975^2} = 979.86$ mi.

  c. Rate = $\dfrac{\text{distance}}{\text{time}} = \dfrac{979.86}{3.9} = 251.2$ mi/hr.

  d. $\tan a = \dfrac{975}{97.5}$, $a = \tan^{-1}\left(\dfrac{975}{97.5}\right) = 84.29°$.

  e. A heading is always given from due north, so the plane is flying on a heading of $(90 - 84.29) = 5.71°$.

6. a. $x = 1.5t$

  b. $y = -16t^2 + 2.75$ (Note: 2.75 is the initial height.)

  c.

  d. Trace on the graph or look at the table to find the point where the
ball hits the ground ($y = 0$). It hits the ground at a horizontal
distance of 0.62 ft from the table.

  e. Look at the time for the above point. It hits at 0.41 sec.

[0, 1, 0.01, 0, 2, 0.5, 0, 3, 1]

7. a. The equation $y = -16t^2 + 3$ describes the drop of the ball from the table due to gravity. When it
hits the ground, $y = 0$. $0 = -16t^2 + 3$, $16t^2 = 3$, $t^2 = \dfrac{3}{16}$, $t = \sqrt{\dfrac{3}{16}} \approx 0.43$ sec.

  b. $x = v_0 t$ describes the movement horizontally. If the ball hits the ground 1.8 ft away from the table, $1.8 = v_0 t$.
Substitute 0.43 for t and solve for v_0, which is the initial velocity. $1.8 = 0.43v_0$, $v_0 = \dfrac{1.8}{0.43} \approx 4.16$ ft/sec.

8. a. $x = 650t$ and $y = -16t^2 + 5.5$

  b. Use the trace function or the table to find out
where the dart is at the point $(400, y)$. The dart
hits the ground at approximately 381 ft from the
biologist. So it falls short of the deer.

[0, 2, 0.1, 0, 500, 100, 0, 10, 1]

  c. She should hold her gun between 9.1 and 10.6 ft high.

  d. The y-equation describes the drop in height. To find the time to drop 1 foot, solve: $4.5 = -16t^2 + 5.5$;
$16t^2 = 1$; $t^2 = 0.0625$; $t = 0.25$ sec. In that time the ball will travel $650(0.25) = 162.5$ ft. The original
height makes no difference because it takes 0.25 sec to drop one foot. Using $x = v_0 t$ or $x = 0.25v_0$ to
describe the horizontal distance shows that the initial velocity will affect the distance traveled.

9. The horizontal movement is described by $x = 5t$, and the vertical movement is described by $y = -16t^2 + s_0$. Changing from feet to inches makes the equations $x = 60t$ and $y = -192t^2 + 112$. Graph the equations and use the table or trace to find the y-coordinate when x is 8, 16, 24, and so on. (Note: The level of each step from the top would be 112≤, 104″, 96″, 88″, 80″, and so on.) When $x = 8$, the height ≈ 109″, which is above 104″; when $x = 16$, the height ≈ 98″, which is above 96″; when $x = 24″$, the height ≈ 81″, which is below the stair of 88″, so the ball will bounce on the third step.

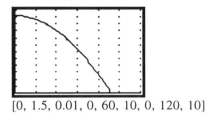

[0, 1.5, 0.01, 0, 60, 10, 0, 120, 10]

10. Answers will vary.

11. Answers will vary.

Take Another Look 6.5

a. The equations for the original graph are $x_{1t} = 2 \cos t + 4$ and $y_{1t} = 2 \sin t + 3$. To reflect the shape across the line $x = -2$, use the equations $x_{2t} = 4 - (2 \cos t + 4)$ and $y_{2t} = 2 \sin t + 3$. To check that the average of the x-coordinates of corresponding points on the two graphs is -2, choose a value for t, and substitute this value into the two x-equations and find the average. At $t = 30$,
$x = \frac{-4 - (2 \cos 30 + 4) + 2 \cos 30 + 4}{2} = -2$.

b. Solve for y_{2t} in the equation $\frac{y_{1t} + y_{2t}}{2} = -1$. $y_{2t} = -2 - y_{1t}$. To reflect the shape across the line $y = -1$, use the equations $x_{2t} = -4 - (2 \cos t + 4)$, $y_{2t} = -2 - (2 \sin t + 3)$. To check that the average of the y-coordinates of corresponding points on the two graphs is -1, choose a value for t and substitute this value into the the two y-equations and find the average. At $t = 30$,
$y = \frac{-2 - (2 \sin 30 + 3) + 2 \sin 30 + 3}{2} = -1$.

c. The original equations are $x_{1t} = t + 2$ and $y_{1t} = t^2$. Solve the equations $\frac{x_{1t} + x_{2t}}{2} = 5$ to get $x_{2t} = 10 - x_{1t}$. The new equations that will reflect the original shape over the line $x = 5$ are $x_{2t} = 10 - (t + 2)$ or $8 - t$ and $y_{2t} = t^2$. You can check these equations by graphing or by finding the average value of the two x-coordinates for some value of t.

d. Answers will vary.

Project: Projectile Motion

Use a window of [0, 50, 10, 0, 25, 10] and the equations $x = 40t \cos 60°$ and $y = 40t \sin 60° - 16t^2$. Yes! the Great Gonzo makes a perfect landing.

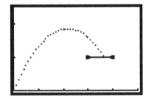

Problem Set 6.6

1. a. $\sin A = \frac{-y}{4t}$, $y = -4t \sin A$ b. $y = 3t$
   c. $-4t \sin A = 3t$, $\sin A = \frac{3t}{-4t} = \frac{3}{-4}$, $A = \sin^{-1}\left(\frac{3t}{-4t}\right) ≈ -48.59°$ or 48.59° below the horizontal axis.
   d. $\cos 48.59 = \frac{x}{4t}$, $x = 4t \cos 48.59°$ for the boat, and $x = 0$ for the river.

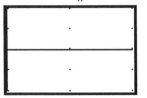

   e. $x = 4t \cos 48.59°$ and $y = -4t \sin 48.59° + 3t$
      Graph on your calculator using an appropriate window (suggestion: [0, 1, 0.1, 0, 2, 1, -2, 2, 1]).
      Trace to follow the path directing west across the river.

2. a.

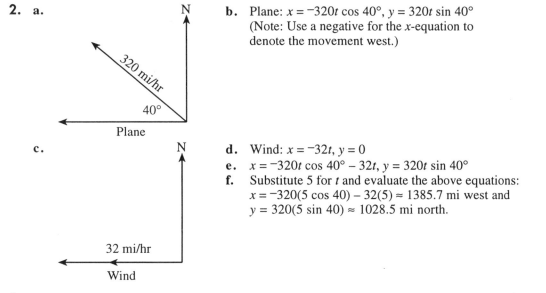

b. Plane: $x = -320t \cos 40°$, $y = 320t \sin 40°$
(Note: Use a negative for the x-equation to denote the movement west.)

c.

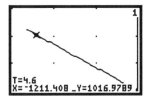

d. Wind: $x = -32t$, $y = 0$

e. $x = -320t \cos 40° - 32t$, $y = 320t \sin 40°$

f. Substitute 5 for t and evaluate the above equations:
$x = -320(5 \cos 40) - 32(5) \approx 1385.7$ mi west and
$y = 320(5 \sin 40) \approx 1028.5$ mi north.

3. a. If there was no wind, the equations would be $x = -320t \cos 40$ and $y = 320t \sin 40$. After 5 hr, the plane's location would be $x = -320(5 \cos 40)$ and $y = 320(5 \sin 40)$ or $(-1225.67, 1028.46)$. This is the point at which to aim. Make better and better guesses for angle A. You could change the Tstep in order to zoom in or look at the table to check the plane's location. The plane should fly on an angle of 43.7° or a heading of 313.7°.

b. $x = -320t \cos 43.7° - 32t$ and $y = 320t \sin 43.7°$.

c.

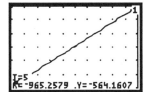

$[0, 5, 0.1, -1500, 0, 500, 0, 1500, 500]$

4. a. The angle for the plane is $270° - 250° = 20°$.
The angle for the wind is $160° - 90° = 70°$.

b. Plane: $x = -220t \cos 20°$ and $y = -220t \sin 20°$
Wind: $x = 40t \cos 70°$ and $y = -40t \sin 70°$.
(Negative values for the plane and wind denote directions toward the west and south.)

c. $x = -220t \cos 20° + 40t \cos 70°$ and
$y = -220t \sin 20° + -40t \sin 70°$

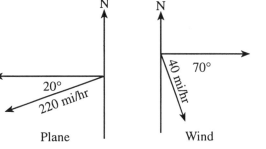

$[0, 8, 0.1, -1000, 0, 100, -600, 0, 100]$

d. Substitute 5 for t: $x = -220(5 \cos 20) + 40(5 \cos 70)$ and $y = -220(5 \sin 20) + -40(5 \sin 70)$; $x = -965.26$ and $y = -564.16$. After 5 hr, the plane is 965.26 mi west and 564.16 mi south of its starting point.

e. Use the Pythagorean theorem: distance $= \sqrt{965.26^2 + 564.16^2} \approx 1118.04$ mi from the starting point.

f. To find the heading, first find the angle made with the horizontal axis:
$\tan A = \frac{-564.16}{-965.26}$, $A = \tan^{-1}\left(\frac{-564.16}{-965.26}\right) \approx 30.30°$. The heading from due north is $(270 - 30.30) = 239.70°$.

5. a. If there was no wind, the equations would be $x = -220t \cos 20$ and $y = -220t \sin 20$. After 5 hours the plane would land at $(-1033.66, -376.22)$. Because the wind is blowing the plane east and south, the pilot should fly slightly to the north of the airport and travel slightly longer to compensate for the east movement of the wind.

b.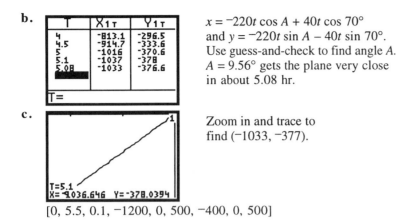

$x = {}^-220t \cos A + 40t \cos 70°$
and $y = {}^-220t \sin A - 40t \sin 70°$.
Use guess-and-check to find angle A.
$A = 9.56°$ gets the plane very close
in about 5.08 hr.

c.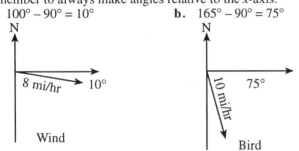

Zoom in and trace to
find $({}^-1033, {}^-377)$.

$[0, 5.5, 0.1, {}^-1200, 0, 500, {}^-400, 0, 500]$

6. a. You need the vertical component of Superman to balance the vertical component of the wind:
$y = 75t \sin A = 32t \sin 30°$. (Note: A wind blowing toward a heading of 300° is making an
angle of $(300° - 270°) = 30°$ with the x-axis.) To solve for A: $\sin A = \frac{32t \sin 30}{75t} \approx 0.2133$;
$A = \sin^{-1}(2133) \approx 12.32°$. Since the wind is blowing Superman slightly north, he would
compensate by flying on a heading of $(270° - 12.32°) = 257.68°$.

b. For Superman, the horizontal component is $x = {}^-75t \cos 12.32°$, and for the wind the horizontal
component is $x = {}^-32t \cos 30°$. So the combined equation is $x = {}^-75t \cos 12.32° + {}^-32t \cos 30° = {}^-800$.

c. Solve the above equation for t: $73.27t + 27.71t = 800$, $100.98t = 800$, $t = 7.92$ hr.

7. Remember to always make angles relative to the x-axis.

a. $100° - 90° = 10°$

b. $165° - 90° = 75°$

c. $x = 8t \cos 10° + 10t \cos 75°$, $y = {}^-8t \sin 10° - 10t \sin 75°$. To find the location after 8 hr of
travel, substitute 8 for t: $x = 8(8 \cos 10°) + 10(8 \cos 75°)$ and $y = {}^-8(8 \sin 10°) - 10(8 \sin 75°)$,
which gives the point $(83.73, {}^-88.39)$. The bird ends up 83.73 mi east and 88.39 mi south of
its starting point.

d. $\tan A = \frac{88.39}{83.73}$, $A = \tan^{-1}\left(\frac{88.39}{83.73}\right) \approx 46.6°$ or a heading of $(90° + 46.6°) = 136.6°$.

e. Answers will vary.

8. a. Distance = rate • time, so rate $= \frac{\text{distance}}{\text{time}} = \frac{12,000}{3} = 4000$ mi/hr.

b. $x = {}^-4000t$, $y = {}^-30t$; after the plane has traveled 12,000 mi (taking 3 hr), the wind will have
blown the plane off course $30(3) = 90$ mi.

c. Use guess-and-check to find the best angle. Since the wind is blowing the plane south, the pilot
should correct by an angle of 0.43°. It is not practical to try to adjust to such a small angle.
The relatively small 90 mi error can be corrected at the end of the trip.

9. Answers will vary.

Take Another Look 6.6

a. Solving the equation $^-250t = {}^-1000$ gives a t-value of 4 hr. $x = {}^-250t$ and $y = {}^-80t$. Substituting
$t = 4$ into each equation gives you the final location of 1000 mi west and 80 mi south.

b. The equation $y = -16t^2 + 3$ describes the drop of the ball from the table due to gravity. When it hits the ground $y = 0$, so $0 = -16t^2 + 3$, $16t^2 = 3$, $t^2 = \frac{3}{16}$, $t = \sqrt{\frac{3}{16}} \approx 0.43$ sec.

The equation $x = v_0 t$ describes the movement horizontally. If the ball hits the ground 1.8 ft away from the table, $1.8 = v_0 t$. Substitute 0.43 for t and solve for v_0, which is the initial velocity. $1.8 = 0.43 v_0$, $v_0 = \frac{1.8}{0.43} \approx 4.16$ ft/sec.

Project: Boolean Expressions

$x(t) = -3t \cos 60 \cdot (t \le 2.5) + (-7.5 \cos 60 + 3(t - 2.5) \cos 0) \cdot (t > 2.5)(t \le 4.25)$
$y(t) = -3t \sin 60 \cdot (t \le 2.5) + (-7.5 \sin 60 + 3(t - 2.5) \sin 0) \cdot (t > 2.5)(t \le 4.25)$

During the first two and a half hours ($t \le 2.5$), the first part of the expressions will be used since they will be multiplied by 1 and the second terms will be multiplied by 0. During the next hour and three-quarters ($2.5 \le t \le 4.25$), the first Boolean expressions will be false so the first terms will be multiplied by 0. The second terms will be multiplied by 1 so they will be used to graph Trodd's position. The expressions $-7.5 \cos 60$ and $-7.5 \sin 60$ give the location of Trodd after 2.5 hr have passed. The second parts of the terms give his motion relative to that point.

To complete the trip, add third terms to each equation. First you must determine the starting point for the third leg, the value of the equations at $t = 4.25$. Then determine the angle to travel to reach the original starting point, the origin. Next, create the expressions for this third leg in the form (starting x-coordinate + (rate($t - 4.25$) cos angle) ($t > 4.25$) and (starting y-coordinate + (rate($t - 4.25$) sin angle)($t > 4.25$). The final equations should look like this:

$x(t) = -3t \cos 60 \cdot (t \le 2.5) + (-7.5 \cos 60 + 3(t - 2.5) \cos 0) \cdot (t > 2.5)(t \le 4.25)$
$+ (-7.5 \cos 60 + 5.25 + 3(t - 4.25)\cos 77)(t > 4.25)$
$y(t) = -3t \sin 60 \cdot (t \le 2.5) + (-7.5 \sin 60 + 3(t - 2.5) \sin 0) \cdot (t > 2.5)(t \le 4.25)$
$+ (-7.5 \sin 60 + 3(t - 4.25)\sin 77)(t > 4.25)$

To see the complete trip, adjust the Tmax to be 6.47 or more.

Chapter Review

Problem Set 6.7

1. a.

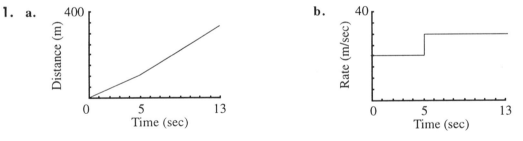

2. a. $x = -3t + 1$, $y = \frac{2}{t+1}$. Substitute for t: If $t = 3$, $x = -3(3) + 1$, $y = \frac{2}{3+1}$, $x = -8$, $y = 0.5$; if $t = 0$, $x = -3(0) + 1$, $y = \frac{2}{0+1}$, $x = 1$, $y = 2$; if $t = -3$, $x = -3(-3) + 1$, $y = \frac{2}{-3+1}$, $x = 10$, $y = -1$.

b. If $x = -7$, then $-7 = -3t + 1$, $-8 = -3t$, $t = \frac{8}{3}$. Substitute that value for t into the y-equation and solve for y: $y = \frac{2}{\frac{8}{3} + 1} = \frac{2}{\frac{11}{3}} = \frac{6}{11}$.

c. If $y = 4$, then $4 = \frac{2}{t+1}$, $t + 1 = \frac{2}{4}$, $t = \frac{-1}{2}$. Substitute that value for t into the x-equation and solve for x: $x = -3\left(\frac{-1}{2}\right) + 1 = \frac{5}{2}$.

d.

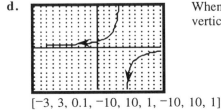

When $t = -1$, the y-value is undefined as there is a vertical asymptote.

$[-3, 3, 0.1, -10, 10, 1, -10, 10, 1]$

3. a. i.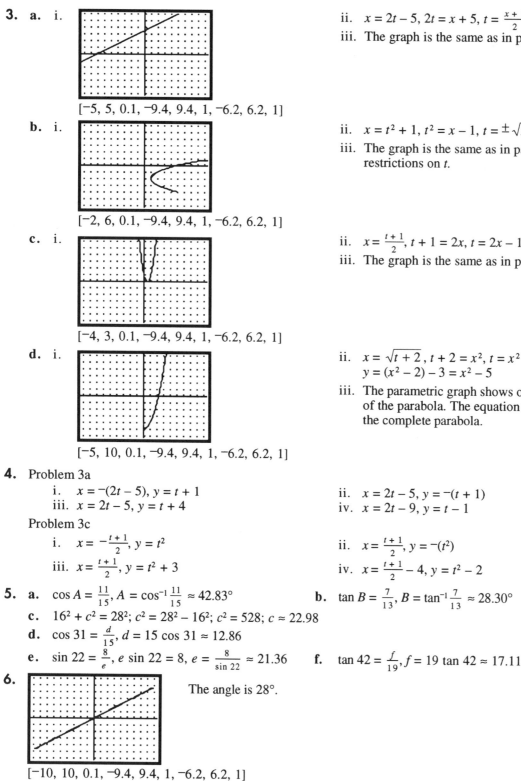

[−5, 5, 0.1, −9.4, 9.4, 1, −6.2, 6.2, 1]

ii. $x = 2t - 5$, $2t = x + 5$, $t = \frac{x+5}{2}$; $y = \frac{x+5}{2} + 1 = \frac{x+7}{2}$

iii. The graph is the same as in part i.

b. i.

[−2, 6, 0.1, −9.4, 9.4, 1, −6.2, 6.2, 1]

ii. $x = t^2 + 1$, $t^2 = x - 1$, $t = \pm\sqrt{x-1}$; $y = \pm\sqrt{x-1} - 2$

iii. The graph is the same as in part i except for the restrictions on t.

c. i.

[−4, 3, 0.1, −9.4, 9.4, 1, −6.2, 6.2, 1]

ii. $x = \frac{t+1}{2}$, $t + 1 = 2x$, $t = 2x - 1$; $y = t^2 = (2x - 1)^2$

iii. The graph is the same as in part i.

d. i.

[−5, 10, 0.1, −9.4, 9.4, 1, −6.2, 6.2, 1]

ii. $x = \sqrt{t+2}$, $t + 2 = x^2$, $t = x^2 - 2$; $y = (x^2 - 2) - 3 = x^2 - 5$

iii. The parametric graph shows only one side of the parabola. The equation in part ii gives the complete parabola.

4. Problem 3a

i. $x = -(2t - 5)$, $y = t + 1$

ii. $x = 2t - 5$, $y = -(t + 1)$

iii. $x = 2t - 5$, $y = t + 4$

iv. $x = 2t - 9$, $y = t - 1$

Problem 3c

i. $x = -\frac{t+1}{2}$, $y = t^2$

ii. $x = \frac{t+1}{2}$, $y = -(t^2)$

iii. $x = \frac{t+1}{2}$, $y = t^2 + 3$

iv. $x = \frac{t+1}{2} - 4$, $y = t^2 - 2$

5. a. $\cos A = \frac{11}{15}$, $A = \cos^{-1}\frac{11}{15} \approx 42.83°$

b. $\tan B = \frac{7}{13}$, $B = \tan^{-1}\frac{7}{13} \approx 28.30°$

c. $16^2 + c^2 = 28^2$; $c^2 = 28^2 - 16^2$; $c^2 = 528$; $c \approx 22.98$

d. $\cos 31 = \frac{d}{15}$, $d = 15 \cos 31 \approx 12.86$

e. $\sin 22 = \frac{8}{e}$, $e \sin 22 = 8$, $e = \frac{8}{\sin 22} \approx 21.36$

f. $\tan 42 = \frac{f}{19}$, $f = 19 \tan 42 \approx 17.11$

6.

The angle is 28°.

[−10, 10, 0.1, −9.4, 9.4, 1, −6.2, 6.2, 1]

7. Using the edge of the pool as the point (0, 0), the x-equation would be $x = 4t + 1.5$ and the y-equation would be $y = -4.9t^2 + 10$. Trace or use the table to find the point where $y = 0$ (where she hits the water). Zoom in and trace to find the x-coordinate at this point. She hits at a point 7.2 m from the edge.

8. First set up the coordinate system. Assume she starts at (0, 0) and paddles directly west across the river. The x-equation would be $x = 2.4t$ and the y-equation would be $y = ct$, where c represents the rate of the current. When she has traveled 47 ft across the river, $47 = 2.4t$ so $t = \frac{47}{2.4} \approx 19.58$ sec. In that time the current pushed her 28 ft down river so $28 = ct = 19.58c$, so the current $c = \frac{28}{19.58} \approx 1.43$ ft/sec.

9. First set up the coordinate system. Assume R. E. Searcher is at (0, 0) and the monkey is directly west of him. The x-equation would be $x = -150t$ and the y-equation would be $y = -16t^2$. Put these equations into your calculator and graph. Trace to find the point 94 ft away. At that point, the tranquilizer dart is 6.35 ft below the monkey, so it misses him. The window used is [0, 1, 0.01, −100, 0, 25, −15, 5, 5].

10. He will hit the monkey. Both the monkey and the dart are falling at the same rate.

11. Her destination should be the point (700 cos 15, −700 sin 15) or (676.15, −181.17). The equations for the plane are $x = 500t \cos A$ and $y = -500t \sin A$. The equations for the wind are $x = 25t \cos 70$ and $y = 25t \sin 70$. (Remember to change all headings to angles made with the x-axis.) The combined equations are $x = 500t \cos A + 25t \cos 70$ and $y = -500t \sin A + 25t \sin 70$. Use guess-and-check to find the correct heading for the pilot to end up at her destination. Trace the graph or look at the table to check your guesses. She should fly at a heading of 107.77° if the wind averages 25 mi/hr.

    If the wind were 30 mi/hr continuously, she could miss her destination by as much as 8 mi.

12. Answers will vary.

Project: Baseball Pitcher

The pitch may be released as high as 8 ft by a tall pitcher throwing from the top of his arc, and as low as 5.5 ft by a short pitcher throwing side-arm. The strike zone may extend from 2 ft to 5 ft for a tall batter standing erect, or it may reach only from 1.5 ft to 4 ft for a short batter in a crouch.

Because $y = -16t^2 + h$, then solving for time you get $t = \frac{\sqrt{h - y}}{4}$. Using this in the equation $x = vt$, you get $x = v \frac{\sqrt{h - y}}{4}$. The distance from mound to plate is 60.5 ft so the velocity is $v = \frac{242.4}{\sqrt{h - y}}$. In the extreme cases, v could be as high as 342 ft per sec, or 233 mi/hr, for a short pitcher and a tall batter, and as slow as 64.9 ft per sec, or 64 mi/hr, for a tall pitcher and a short batter. You will have to check all values students used and the assumptions they made.

Chapter 7

Problem Set 7.1

1. a. $y = 1.151(1 + 0.015)^x$
    b. Enter the equation into $y =$ and look at the table.

Year	Population (in billions)	Year	Population (in billions)
1991	1.151	1996	1.240
1992	1.168	1997	1.259
1993	1.186	1998	1.277
1994	1.204	1999	1.297
1995	1.222	2000	1.316

c. Use the above equation for China and the equation $y = 867 \cdot (1.019)^x$ for India. (Use 867 as the starting population for the year 1991.) You could either extend the table or the two graphs of the functions to see when the y-values are the same. The populations will both be about 3.364 billion in 2063 (1991 + 72).

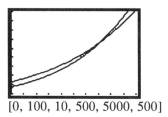

[0, 100, 10, 500, 5000, 500]

d. Answers will vary. You must assume that the populations will continue to grow at this rate for a long time and that there will be no natural disasters such as drought or plague or human disasters such as war. The dangers involved in this long-range prediction are great, so you should not place much confidence in the answer.

2. a. $\frac{6.4}{2.56} = \frac{16.0}{6.4} = \frac{40.0}{16.0} = 2.5$. The equation is $y = 2.56(2.5)^x$. For the fifth day, $y = 2.56(2.5)^5 = 250$ cm and for the sixth day, $y = 2.56(2.5)^6 = 625$ cm.

b. At 8:00 p.m. on the third day, the time is 3.5 days. $y = 2.56(2.5)^{3.5} \approx 63.25$ cm.

c. At noon on the sixth day, the time is 6.1667 days. $y = 2.56(2.5)^{6.1667} \approx 728$ cm.

d. To find the day and time when the stalk reached its final height of 100,000 cm, you could use guess-and-check, you could graph the equation and zoom in to find the time, or you could graph a second function, $y = 100,000$, and find the intersection point of the two graphs.

The time is 11 days 13 hr or 9 p.m. on day 11 $(0.538825(24) \approx 13$ hr).

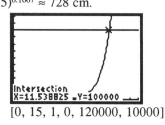

Intersection
X=11.538825 _Y=100000
[0, 15, 1, 0, 120000, 10000]

3. a. 49   **b.** 79.7023   **c.** 129.6418   **d.** 210.8723   **e.** 343

f. 79.7023 − 49 = 30.7023
129.6418 − 79.7023 = 49.9395
210.8723 − 129.6418 = 81.2305
343 − 210.8723 = 132.1277
The sequence is not arithmetic because there is not a common difference.

g. $\frac{79.7023}{49} = 1.627; \frac{129.6418}{79.7023} = 1.627; \frac{210.8723}{129.6418} = 1.627; \frac{343}{210.8723} = 1.627$
The ratio is always the same.

h. Answers will vary. The values are not linear (differences are not constant). The values are geometric (ratios are constant). Noninteger powers produce noninteger values. Decimal powers form a geometric sequence.

4. Answers will vary between 2000 and 2300. To compute the actual value, find the ratio $\frac{3442}{1229} \approx 2.801$ and then multiply; $1229\sqrt{2.801} \approx 2056$.

5. a. $f(3) = 480(0.5)^3 = 60$ rads. After 3(25) = 75 days, the radiation is 60 rads.

b. $f(3.2) = 480(0.5)^{3.2} = 52.23$ rads. After 3.2(25) = 80 days, the radiation is 52.23 rads.

c. $f(0) = 480(0.5)^0 = 480$ rads. The initial radiation was 480 rads.

d. $f(-1) = 480(0.5)^{-1} = 960$ rads. The radiation was 960 rads for one time period, 25 days, before we started keeping track.

e. $f(1) = 480(0.5)^1 = 240$ rads. After one time period, 25 days, the radiation was 240 rads.

f. 110 days is $\frac{110}{25} = 4.4$ time periods. $f(4.4) = 480(0.5)^{4.4} = 22.74$ rads.

6. a. $f(x) = 5000(1 + 0.065)^x$ **b.** $y = 5000(1.065)^5 = \$6,850.43.$

c. After 5 yr, there will be \$6,850.43 in the account.

d. $y = 5000(1.065)^{4.333} = \$6,568.78.$

e. After 4 yr 4 mo, there will be \$6,568.78 in the account.

f. $y = 5000(1.065)^0 = 5000$. Initially there was \$5,000 invested in the account.

g. $y = 5000(1.065)^{7.75} = \$8,145.72$. Answers will vary. Probably the bank would not pay this amount because you did not leave the money in for a full year. Therefore, you would lose interest on the last 9 mo.

7. a. The water temperature drops 6% each minute.

b. The initial temperature of the water is 23°C.

c. $g(7.4) = 23(0.94)^{7.4} = 14.55$. After 7.4 min, the temperature of the water at the bottom is 14.55°C.

d. $g(5.75) = 23(0.94)^{5.75} = 16.11$.

e. You could use guess-and-check, graph the *g* function and the function *y* = 10, or use the table to find the point of intersection of the two functions.

After 13 min 28 sec, the water at the bottom of the glass has cooled to 10°C.

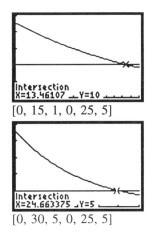

Intersection
X=13.46107 ___Y=10

[0, 15, 1, 0, 25, 5]

f. Graph the *g* function and the function *y* = 5, and look for the intersection of the two.

After 24.66 min, the water at the bottom of the glass has cooled to 5°C.

Intersection
X=24.663375 ___Y=5

[0, 30, 5, 0, 25, 5]

Project: Baseball for Bucks

Exponential curves will best fit these data. The minimum salary has a growth rate of 11.4% and the average salary has a growth rate of 17.9%.

$min = 4.8931 \, (1.11469233)^x$

$avg = 0.276524 \, (1.17815723)^x$

Unless there is a change in the wind, we can expect minimum salaries of $250,000 by the year 2000 and $400,000 by 2005. The average salary is growing even faster and will reach $3,600,000 by 2000 and $8,300,000 by 2005.

Problem Set 7.2

1. a. $49^{5/2}$ is the square root of 49 raised to the fifth power = 16,807.
   b. $16^{3/4}$ is the fourth root of 16 raised to the third power = 8.
   c. $64^{5/3}$ is the cube root of 64 raised to the fifth power = 1024.
   d. $32^{2/5}$ is the fifth root of 32 squared = 4.

2. a. $w(h) = h^{2/3}$; $w(64) = 64^{2/3} = 16$ kg   **b.** $w(125)^{2/3} = 25$ kg
   c. $w(h) = h^{2/3} = 20.25$; $h^2 = 20.25^3 = 8303.77$; $h = \sqrt{8303.77} \approx 91$ cm

3. a. $x^{1/4}$ **b.** $x^{3/5}$ **c.** $x^{7/3}$ **d.** $x^{4/5}$

4. a. $(8^{(1/3)})^7 = 128$ **b.** $(243^4)^{0.2} = 81$ **c.** $(25^6)^{(1/3)} = 625$ **d.** $(9^5)^{0.3} = 27$

5. a. $^{1/2}\sqrt{cin} \; nati = (cin)^2 nati = $ Cincinnati   **b.** Answers will vary.

6. a. $\sqrt[3]{x^2}$ **b.** $2.75 = 2\frac{3}{4} = \frac{11}{4}$ so $\sqrt[4]{x^{11}}$ or $x^2\sqrt[4]{x^3}$.

7. a. Enter 9^x into y_1 and 27 into y_2. Trace the graph or look at the table to find the point of intersection. $x = \frac{3}{2}$ or 1.5.

Intersection
X=1.5 _____Y=27

[0, 3, 1, 0, 30, 5]

b. Enter 32^x into y_1 and 128 into y_2. Trace the graph or look at the table to find the point of intersection. $x = \frac{7}{5}$ or 1.4.

Intersection
X=1.4 _____Y=128

[0, 3, 1, 0, 150, 25]

8. a. $u_n = \begin{cases} 1 & \text{if } n = 0 \\ u_{(n-1)}(1.04) & \text{if } n > 0 \end{cases}$ **b.** $b(x) = 1^{1.04x}$

c. Enter 1.04^x into y_1 and 50 into y_2. Trace the graph or look at the table to find the point of intersection. $x = 100$, or in about 100 yr.

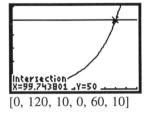

[0, 120, 10, 0, 60, 10]

9. Answers will vary. One possibility is to enter $y = x \,\wedge\, (1/5)$.

10. a. 4000 is the initial investment.
 b. You are earning 7.2% interest on your investment.
 c. The interest is compounded monthly.
 d. This is one month after the investment was made.
 e. This is at the time the investment was made.
 f. This is one month before the investment was made.
 g. Enter the equation into y_1 and 8000 into y_2. Trace the graph or look at the table to find the point of intersection. $(x = 115.87)$ In approximately 116 mo, or 9 yr 8 mo, the investment will double to 8000.

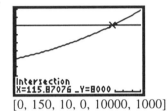

[0, 150, 10, 0, 10000, 1000]

11.

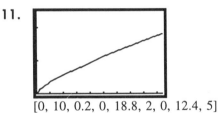

[0, 10, 0.2, 0, 18.8, 2, 0, 12.4, 5]

Because $x(t) = t^4$, $t = \sqrt[4]{x}$. Now substitute that value of t into the equation for y: $y(t) = \left(\sqrt[4]{x}\right)^3 = x^{3/4}$.

Take Another Look 7.2

The set of data shows a geometric sequence.

Time period	Students standing
0	38
1	32
2	27
3	23
4	19
5	16
6	14
7	12
8	10

Recursive: $u_0 = 38$
$\qquad\qquad u_n = (0.85)u_{n-1}$
Explicit: $\quad u_n = 38\,(0.85)^n$

Half life = 4 trials

To make a decay of 20%, all students with a display less than 0.20 should sit down.

Problem Set 7.3

1. a. $3^{-3} = \frac{1}{3^3} = \frac{1}{27} = 0.037037\ldots$

 b. $25^{-1/2} = \frac{1}{\sqrt{25}} = \frac{1}{5} = 0.2$

 c. $-36^{3/2} = -\sqrt{36^3} = -6^3 = -216$

 d. $(-12)^{-2} = \frac{1}{(-12)^2} = \frac{1}{144} = 0.0069444\ldots$

 e. $\left(\frac{3}{4}\right)^{-2} = \left(\frac{4}{3}\right)^2 = \frac{16}{9} = 1.777\ldots$

 f. $\left(\frac{2}{7}\right)^{-1} = \left(\frac{7}{2}\right)^1 = 3.5$

 g. $-\left(\frac{8}{27}\right)^{-1/3} = -\left(\frac{27}{8}\right)^{1/3} = -\sqrt[3]{\frac{27}{8}} = \frac{-3}{2} = -1.5$

 h. $\left(\frac{4}{9}\right)^{-5/2}\left(\frac{2}{3}\right)^5 = \left(\sqrt{\frac{4}{9}}\right)^{-5}\left(\frac{2}{3}\right)^5 = \left(\frac{2}{3}\right)^{-5}\left(\frac{2}{3}\right)^5 = \left(\frac{2}{3}\right)^{(-5+5)} = \left(\frac{2}{3}\right)^0 = 1$

2. a. $(2x)^{-3} = \dfrac{1}{(2x)^3} = \dfrac{1}{8x^3}$ 　　**b.** $2x^{-3} = 2\left(\dfrac{1}{x^3}\right) = \dfrac{2}{x^3}$ 　　**c.** $x^{(1/2)}x^{(2/3)} = x^{(1/2\,+\,2/3)} = x^{7/6}$

　　d. $(4x)^{(-1/2)}(8x^3)^{2/3} = \dfrac{1}{\sqrt{4x}} \cdot \sqrt[3]{(8x^3)}\,^2 = \dfrac{1}{2\sqrt{x}} \cdot (2x)^2 = \dfrac{1}{2\sqrt{x}} \cdot (4x^2) = 2x^{(2\,-\,1/2)} = 2x^{3/2}$

3. $\dfrac{(\text{Eas})^{-1}(\text{ter})^0 \text{Egg}}{y} = \dfrac{1\ \text{Egg}}{\text{Easy}} = $ one egg over easy

4. a. False; you must have the same base for the multiplication property.
　　b. False; you must raise to the power before multiplying by 100 (order of operations).
　　c. False; the power of a product property is not true for a binomial.
　　d. False; the division property is not true for part of a binomial.
　　e. True; $\sqrt[4]{16x^{20}} = 2x^{(20/4)} = 2x^5$
　　f. True; $\dfrac{6.6 \cdot 10^{12}}{8.8 \cdot 10^{-4}} = 0.75 \cdot 10^{(12\,-\,-4)} = 0.75 \cdot 10^{16} = 7.5 \cdot 10^{15}$

5. a. $3^x = \dfrac{1}{9};\ 3^x = \dfrac{1}{3^2};\ 3^x = 3^{-2};\ x = -2$ 　　**b.** $\left(\dfrac{5}{3}\right)^x = \dfrac{27}{125};\ \left(\dfrac{5}{3}\right)^x = \left(\dfrac{3}{5}\right)^3;\ \left(\dfrac{5}{3}\right)^x = \left(\dfrac{5}{3}\right)^{-3};\ x = -3$

　　c. $\left(\dfrac{1}{3}\right)^x = 243;\ \left(\dfrac{1}{3}\right)^x = 3^5;\ 3^{-x} = 3^5;\ x = -5$ 　　**d.** $5(3^x) = 5;\ 3^x = 1;\ x = 0$

6. As the base increases, the graph becomes steeper. They all intersect the y-axis at $(0, 1)$.

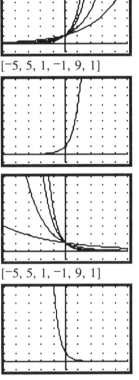

[−5, 5, 1, −1, 9, 1]

　　The graph of $y = 6^x$ should be steeper than any of these. It will contain the points $(0, 1)$ and $(1, 6)$.

7. As the base increases, the graph flattens out. They all intersect the y-axis at $(0, 1)$. All of these equations involve raising a number between 0 and 1 to a power.

[−5, 5, 1, −1, 9, 1]

　　The graph of $y = 0.1^x$ should be steeper than any of these given. It will contain the points $(0, 1)$ and $(−1, 10)$.

8. The equations in Problem 6 all involve a base larger than 1. In Problem 7 the bases are all less than 1.
　　a. $y = 2.5^x$ 　　　　**b.** $y = 0.35^x$

9. a. All of the functions in Problem 6 are increasing. None of the functions in Problem 7 are increasing.
　　b. A function is a decreasing function if and only if for each $x_1 > x_2, f(x_1) \le f(x_2)$.

10. a. The graph will be reflected across the y-axis. It is the same as $y = a\left(\dfrac{1}{b}\right)^x$.
　　b. The graph will be reflected across the x-axis.
　　c. The graph will be translated 2 units to the right.

11. a. False; $b^{-a} = \left(\dfrac{1}{b}\right)^a$. The negative exponent makes the expression a fraction but does not make the answer necessarily positive.
　　b. False; $b^a = \sqrt[a]{b}$ if $0 \le a \le 1$, so b does not become larger.
　　c. False; $b^0 = 1$ for $b > 0$.
　　d. False; if $a < b$, then $a^n < b^n$ if $n > 0$, but $a^n > b^n$ if $n < 0$ and $a^n = b^n$ if $n = 0$.

Problem Set 7.4

1. **a.** The inverse equations are $x = t + 2$, $y = 2t - 3$. To graph both sets of equations, enter the original equations in x_{1T} and y_{1T} and the equations for the inverse in x_{2T} and y_{2T}.

   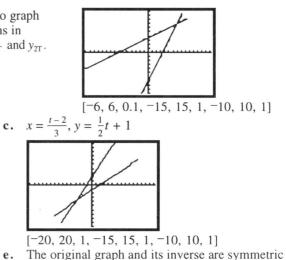

   $[^-6, 6, 0.1, ^-15, 15, 1, ^-10, 10, 1]$

   b. $x = t + 1$, $y = t^2$

   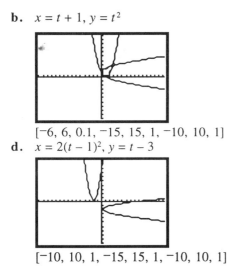

   $[^-6, 6, 0.1, ^-15, 15, 1, ^-10, 10, 1]$

   c. $x = \frac{t-2}{3}$, $y = \frac{1}{2}t + 1$

   $[^-20, 20, 1, ^-15, 15, 1, ^-10, 10, 1]$

   d. $x = 2(t - 1)^2$, $y = t - 3$

   $[^-10, 10, 1, ^-15, 15, 1, ^-10, 10, 1]$

   e. The original graph and its inverse are symmetric with respect to the line $y = x$.

   f. To graph the line $y = x$ in parametric mode, graph $x = t$ and $y = t$.

2. Graph c is the inverse because the x- and y-coordinates have been switched from the original graph and both graphs are symmetric to the line $y = x$.

3. **a.** $x = t + 5$; $t = x - 5$. Now substitute this expression for t into the y equation: $y = 2(x - 5) - 1$; $y = 2x - 11$.
   b. For the inverse, $x = 2t - 1$ and $y = t + 5$.
   c. $y = t + 5$; $t = y - 5$. Now substitute this expression for t into the x-equation: $x = 2(y - 5) - 1$; $x = 2y - 11$.
   d. The nonparametric equations are exactly the same except that the variables have been switched. (See parts a and c.)

4. **a.** $y = t + 3$; $t = y - 3$. Now substitute this expression for t into the x-equation: $x = (y - 3)^2 + 2$; $x - 2 = (y - 3)^2$; $\pm\sqrt{x - 2} = y - 3$; $\pm\sqrt{x - 2} + 3 = y$.
   b. The inverse is $x = t + 3$ and $y = t^2 + 2$.
   c. $x = t + 3$; $t = x - 3$. Now substitute this expression for t into the y-equation: $y = (x - 3)^2 + 2$.
   d. Answers will vary. The original equation contains a radical expression. The inverse equation has a squared quantity. The position of the numbers 2 and 3 have been switched.

5. Answers will vary. To be a function, the graph must pass the vertical line test. So that both the first set of equations and the equations for the inverse to be functions, you must restrict the values of t so that a horizontal line drawn through the original graph only intersects the graph once. $t \geq 3$ or $t \leq 3$ works.

6. Answers will vary. See the answer to Problem 5. $t \leq 0$ or $t \geq 0$ works.

7. **a.** Answers will vary. This equation is a parabola that has been shifted 1 unit to the left and 2 units down. One answer might be $x = t$ and $y = (t + 1)^2 - 2$.
   b. The parametric equations for the inverse are $x = (t + 1)^2 - 2$ and $y = t$.
   c. To find the nonparametric equation for the inverse, substitute y for t in the x-equation: $x = (t + 1)^2 - 2$; $x = (y + 1)^2 - 2$ and $x + 2 = (y + 1)^2$; $\pm\sqrt{x + 2} = y + 1$; $y = \pm\sqrt{x + 2} - 1$.
   d. To find the nonparametric form of the original equation, substitute x for t in the original y-equation: $y = (t + 1)^2 - 2$; $y = (x + 1)^2 - 2$. The inverse is not a function so you can't use $f(x)$ notation. It will take two equations to write the inverse equation: $y = \sqrt{x - 2} - 1$ and $y = -\sqrt{x - 2} - 1$.

8. **a.** The original function is $y = 2x - 3$, so $f(x) = 2x - 3$. To find the inverse, switch the x- and y-coordinates of the original function and solve for y: $x = 2y - 3$; $x + 3 = 2y$; $y = \frac{x+3}{2}$, so $f^{-1}(x) = \frac{x+3}{2}$.

b. The original function is $3x + 2y = 4$. Solve for y: $2y = {}^-3x + 4$; $y = \frac{-3x+4}{2}$, so $f(x) = f(x) = \frac{4-3x}{2}$.
To find the inverse, switch the x- and y-coordinates in the original function and solve for y:
$3y + 2x = 4$; $3y = {}^-2x + 4$; $y = \frac{-2x+4}{3}$, so $f^{-1}(x) = \frac{4-2x}{3}$.

c. The original function is $x^2 + 2y = 3$. Solve for y: $2y = {}^-x^2 + 3$; $y = \frac{-x^2+3}{2}$, so $f(x) = \frac{-x^2+3}{2}$ or
$f(x) = \frac{-1}{2}x^2 + \frac{3}{2}$. Exchange the x- and y-coordinates to find the inverse: $x = \frac{-1}{2}y^2 + \frac{3}{2}$; $\frac{-1}{2}y^2 =$
$x - \frac{3}{2}$; $y^2 = -2\left(x - \frac{3}{2}\right) = -2x + 3$; $y = \pm\sqrt{-2x+3}$. The inverse isn't a function, so $f^{-1}(x)$
notation doesn't apply.

9. a. i. $y = 6.34x - 140$ so for the inverse, $x = 6.34y - 140$; $x + 140 = 6.34y$; $y = \frac{x+140}{6.34}$ or $f^{-1}(x) = \frac{x+140}{6.34}$.

    ii. $f(f^{-1}(15.75)) = 15.75$ iii. $f^{-1}(f(15.75)) = 15.75$ iv. $f(f^{-1}(x)) = f^{-1}(f(x)) = x$

b. i. $y = 1.8x + 32$ so for the inverse, $x = 1.8y + 32$; $x - 32 = 1.8y$; $y = \frac{x-32}{1.8}$ or $f^{-1}(x) = \frac{x-32}{1.8}$.

    ii. $f(f^{-1}(15.75)) = 15.75$ iii. $f^{-1}(f(15.75)) = 15.75$ iv. $f(f^{-1}(x)) = f^{-1}(f(x)) = x$

10. a. Enter the data for meters and temperature in °C into lists and calculate the equation of the least-squares or median-median line. The least-squares equation is $f(x) = {}^-0.0066x + 14.6175$.

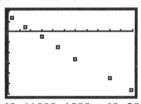

[0, 11000, 1000, ⁻60, 20, 10]

b. Exchange the x- and y-coordinates to find the inverse, $x = {}^-0.0066y + 14.6175$; $x - 14.6175 = {}^-0.0066y$; $y = \frac{x-14.6175}{-0.0066}$ or $f^{-1}(x) = {}^-152.51x + 2229.30$.

c. Enter the data for feet and temperature in °F into lists and calculate the equation of the least-squares or median-median line. The least-squares equation is $f(x) = {}^-0.0036x + 58.5586$.

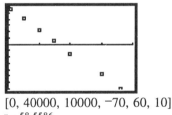

[0, 40000, 10000, ⁻70, 60, 10]

d. To find the inverse, $x = {}^-0.0036y + 58.5586$; $x - 58.5586 = {}^-0.0036y$; $y = \frac{x-58.5586}{-0.0036}$ or $g^{-1}(x) = {}^-281.52x + 16{,}485.41$.

e. Use the $f(x)$ function in part a to find the temperature in °C first. $f(x) = {}^-0.0066(6194) + 14.6175 = {}^-26.26$°C. Then use the function from the beginning of the section to change the °C to °F: $y = 1.8x + 32$ so $y = 1.8({}^-26.26) + 32 = {}^-15.27$°F.

f. Let $f(x) = {}^-0.0066x + 14.6175$ equal the function that relates (altitude in meters, temperature in °C) and let $h(x) = 1.8x + 32$ equal the function that relates (°C, °F). Then $h(f(x))$ with an input of altitude in meters, will give an output in °F.

11. a. Make a table comparing the original Celsius temperatures with today's Celsius temperature.

	Freezing			Boiling
Today's Celsius temperature (°C)	0	25	60	100
Original Celsius temperatures (y)	100	75	40	0

Enter this data into lists and calculate a best-fit line. The equation is $y = 100 - C$.

b. The equation for converting Celsius degrees into Fahrenheit degrees is $F = 1.8C + 32$. Solve the equation from part a for C; $C = 100 - y$. Substitute this expression for C into the equation for F, and solve for y. $F = 1.8(100 - y) + 32$; $F = 180 - 1.8y + 32$; $F = 212 - 1.8y$; $y = \frac{F-212}{-1.8}$.

12. Answers will vary.

13. Answers will vary. Problem 1 is correct. Problem 2 is incorrect. The notation $f^{-1}(x)$ indicates the inverse function related to $f(x)$. Problem 3 is incorrect. The expression $9^{-1/5}$ can be rewritten as $\frac{1}{9^{1/5}}$. Problem 4 is incorrect. The expression 0^0 is not defined.

Take Another Look 7.4

Part 1
(It doesn't matter what seed value is used.)

$f(x) = 2.5x(1 - x)$
The orbit limit is 0.6.

$f(x) = 2.8x(1 - x)$
The orbit limit is 0.642857034.

$f(x) = 3.2x(1 - x)$
The orbit limit is periodic producing a cycle of length two, 0.7994554905 and 0.5130445095.

$f(x) = 3.4x(1 - x)$
The orbit limit is periodic producing a cycle of length two, 0.4519631956 and 0.8421543824.

$f(x) = 3.5x(1 - x)$
The orbit limit is periodic producing a cycle of length four, 0.382819683 and 0.8269407066 and 0.5008842103 and 0.8749972636.

$f(x) = 3.5x(1 - x)$
The orbit has no limit. It is chaotic.

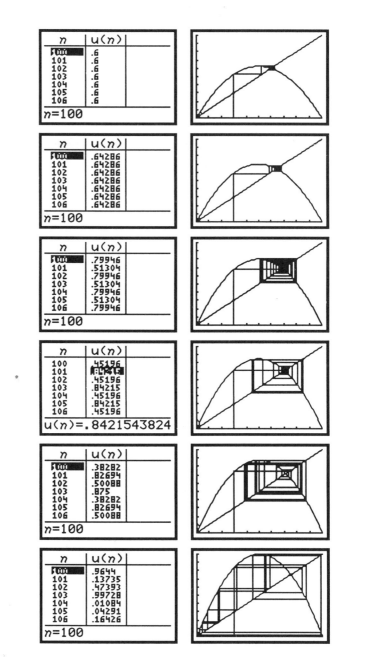

Part 2
$f(x) = \sqrt{x}$ approaches a limit of 1 when $x_0 = 2$.
$f(x) = \sqrt{x}$ approaches a limit of 1 when $x_0 = 10$.
$f(x) = \sqrt{x}$ approaches a limit of 1 when $x_0 = 0.5$.

```
Plot1 Plot2 Plot3
 nMin=0
∙∙u(n)⊟√(u(n-1)
  u(nMin)⊟(2)
∙∙v(n)=
  v(nMin)=
\w(n)=
  w(nMin)=
```

Part 3

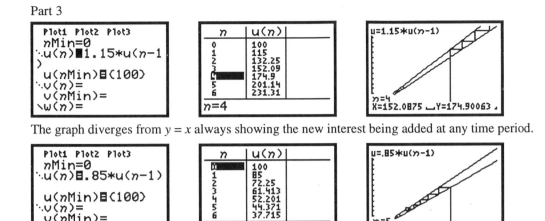

The graph diverges from $y = x$ always showing the new interest being added at any time period.

The graph converges to the limit 0 when $y = x$. This is the long run value when 15% is removed at each time period.

Problem Set 7.5

1. **a.** $x^5 = 50$; $x = 50^{1/5} \approx 2.187$ **b.** $\sqrt[3]{x} = 3.1$; $x = 3.1^3 = 29.791$
    c. $x^2 = {}^-121$; no solution since any real number squared is positive
    d. $x^{1/4} - 2 = 3$; $x^{1/4} = 5$; $x = 5^4 = 625$ **e.** $4x^7 - 6 = {}^-2$; $4x^7 = 4$; $x^7 = 1$; $x = 1^{1/7} = 1$
    f. $3(x^{2/3} + 5) = 207$; $x^{2/3} + 5 = 69$; $x^{2/3} = 64$; $x = 64^{3/2}$; $x = 512$
    g. $1450 = 800\left(1 + \frac{x}{12}\right)^{7.8}$; $1.8125 = \left(1 + \frac{x}{12}\right)^{7.8}$; $1.8125^{1/7.8} = \left(1 + \frac{x}{12}\right)$; $1.0792 = 1 + \frac{x}{12}$; $0.0792 = \frac{x}{12}$; $x \approx 0.951$
    h. $14.2 = 222.1x^{3.5}$; $0.0639 = x^{3.5}$; $0.0639^{1/3.5} = x$; $x = 0.456$

2. **a.** $(27x^6)^{2/3} = 27^{2/3}(x^6)^{2/3} = 9x^4$ **b.** $(16x^8)^{3/4} = 16^{3/4}(x^8)^{3/4} = 8x^6$
    c. $(36x^{-12})^{3/2} = 36^{3/2}(x^{-12})^{3/2} = 216x^{-18}$

3. $y = a^x$ where y is the light intensity coming through the glass and x is the number of sheets of glass. $0.50 = a^6$; $0.50^{1/6} = a$; $a \approx 0.891$. Each sheet will allow 0.891, or 89.1%, of the light intensity through the glass so the reduction rate is 0.109, or 10.9%.

4. **a.** If the population doubles in 35 yr, then $2 = (1 + r)^{35}$; $2^{1/35} = 1 + r$; $r = 0.02$. The equation is $P = 4(1.02)^t$ where t is the number of years since 1975.
    b. Answers will vary (depending on the year). In 1993, the population should have been $4 \cdot 1.02^{(1993 - 1975)} \approx$ 5.7 billion. In 1994, the population should have been $4 \cdot 1.02^{(1994 - 1975)} \approx$ 5.8 billion. In 1995, the population should have been $4 \cdot 1.02^{(1995 - 1975)} \approx$ 5.9 billion.
    c. Answers will vary. The 1993 population was 5.5 billion so the error was $\frac{5.7 - 5.5}{5.5} = 0.036$, or a 3.6% error.

5. $4 = 2(1 + r)^{(2016 - 1994)}$; $4 = 2(1 + r)^{22}$; $2 = (1 + r)^{22}$; $2^{1/22} = 1 + r$; $1.032 = 1 + r$; $r \approx 0.032$ so the inflation rate is 3.2%.

6. **a.**
    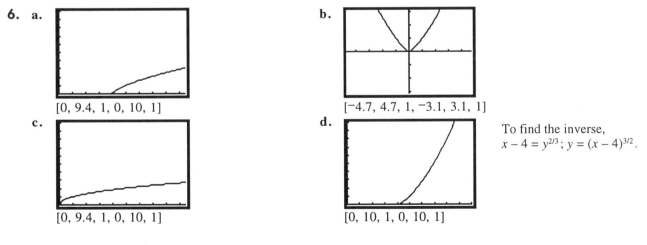
    [0, 9.4, 1, 0, 10, 1]
    b.
    [${}^-4.7$, 4.7, 1, ${}^-3.1$, 3.1, 1]
    c.
    [0, 9.4, 1, 0, 10, 1]
    d.
    [0, 10, 1, 0, 10, 1]

    To find the inverse, $x - 4 = y^{2/3}$; $y = (x - 4)^{3/2}$.

7. a. $y = 2(x^{2/3} - 4)$ so for the inverse, $x = 2(y^{2/3} - 4)$; $\frac{x}{2} = y^{2/3} - 4$; $\frac{x}{2} + 4 = y^{2/3}$; $y = \left(\frac{x}{2} + 4\right)^{3/2}$ or $f^{-1}(x) = \left(\frac{x}{2} + 4\right)^{3/2}$.

    b. Answers will vary but should be equivalent to the line $y = x$. Enter the function into y_1 and the inverse function into y_2. Then to graph $f(f^{-1}(x))$, enter $y_1(y_2)$ into y_3. Another possibility is to enter

$$2\left(\left(\left(\frac{x}{2} + 4\right)^{3/2}\right)^{2/3} - 4\right).$$

    c. Answers will vary. One possibility is to enter the function into y_1 and the inverse function into y_2. Enter $y_3 = x + 2$. Then to graph $f(f^{-1}(x + 2))$, enter $y_1(y_2(y_3))$ into y_4. Another possibility is

$$y = 2\left(\left(\left(\frac{x + 2}{2} + 4\right)^{3/2}\right)^{2/3} - 4\right).$$

8. a.

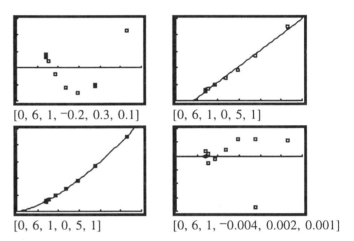

    [0, 6, 1, 0, 5, 1]

    b. The least-squares line of best fit is $y = -0.8118 + 9.681x$. To determine how good the fit is, calculate and graph the residuals. The residuals form a definite pattern, which means the line is not a good fit. You can also see from the graph of the data and the least-squares line that the two are not a good fit.

    [0, 6, 1, −0.2, 0.3, 0.1]   [0, 6, 1, 0, 5, 1]

    c. Answers will vary but should be close to $y = 0.37x^{1.5}$. The graph of the data and the equation appear to be a good fit. The range of the residuals is between −0.004 and 0.001, and there is no pattern in the residuals.

    [0, 6, 1, 0, 5, 1]   [0, 6, 1, −0.004, 0.002, 0.001]

9. a. Answers will vary depending on the equation found in Problem 8.

    $y = 0.37x^{1.5}$; $15.945 = 0.37x^{1.5}$; $43.0946 = x^{1.5}$; $43.0946^{1/1.5} = x$; $x = 12.292 \approx 1{,}229{,}200$ km.

    b. $1{,}295{,}400 = 12.954(100{,}000)$ km; $y = 0.37(12.954)^{1.5} \approx 17.25$ days.

10. Answers will vary.

Take Another Look 7.5

The variable, x, represents the number of years, with 1790 as the base year.

An exponential model might be $y = 3{,}929{,}000 \, (1.024)^x$.

Using this model, the doubling time is approximately 3.2 years. The population would have reached 260 million in the year 1968.

Project: Finding e

Time	Formula	Value
year	$\left(1+\frac{1}{1}\right)^{1}$	2
quarter	$\left(1+\frac{1}{4}\right)^{4}$	2.44
month	$\left(1+\frac{1}{12}\right)^{12}$	2.61
week	$\left(1+\frac{1}{52}\right)^{52}$	2.69
day	$\left(1+\frac{1}{365}\right)^{365}$	2.714
hour	$\left(1+\frac{1}{8760}\right)^{8760}$	2.71812
min	$\left(1+\frac{1}{525600}\right)^{525600}$	2.718279
sec	$\left(1+\frac{1}{31536000}\right)^{31536000}$	2.7182824
x	$\left(1+\frac{1}{x}\right)^{x}$	2.718281828

$e^{0.05} = 1.051271096$

The two functions never differ by much, as seen by the combined graph. Interestingly enough, they become more and more different until almost 11 yr, then they become closer again. At 11 yr the continuous growth differs from the discrete model by 3.44 g. By 50 yr the two differ by only 0.43 g. The first graph shows both $y_1 = 200(1 - 0.09)^x$ and $y_2 = 200e^{-0.09x}$ in the window [0, 50, 10, 0, 200, 25]. The second graph is the difference $y_2 - y_1$ in the window [0, 50, 10, −1, 5, 1]. On the other hand, if you look at the percent error in the third graph by using the discrete model, you see that it continues to increase and reaches nearly 20% error in 50 yr. The function $\frac{y_2 - y_1}{y_2}$ is graphed in the window [0, 50, 10, 0, 0.2, 0.05].

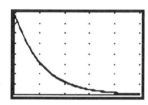 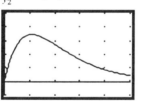 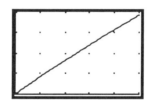

Problem Set 7.6

1. **a.** $10^x = 1000$ **b.** $5^x = 625$ **c.** $7^x = \sqrt{7}$ **d.** $8^x = 2$
   e. $5^x = \frac{1}{25}$ **f.** $6^x = 1$

2. **a.** $10^x = 1000$; $10^x = 10^3$; $x = 3$ **b.** $5^x = 625$; $5^x = 5^4$; $x = 4$
   c. $7^x = \sqrt{7}$; $7^x = 7^{1/2}$; $x = \frac{1}{2}$ **d.** $8^x = 2$; $(2^3)^x = 2^1$; $2^{3x} = 2^1$; $3x = 1$; $x = \frac{1}{3}$
   e. $5^x = \frac{1}{25}$; $5^x = 5^{-2}$; $x = -2$ **f.** $6^x = 1$; $6^x = 6^0$; $x = 0$

3. **a.** $10^3 = 1000$, $10^4 = 10,000$; $3 < \log 1250 < 4$ **b.** $10^2 = 100$, $10^3 = 1000$; $2 < \log 125 < 3$
   c. $10^1 = 10$, $10^2 = 100$; $1 < \log 12.5 < 2$ **d.** $10^0 = 1$, $10^1 = 10$; $0 < \log 1.25 < 1$
   e. $10^{-1} = 0.1$, $10^1 = 10$; $-1 < \log 0.125 < 0$ **f.** $10^{-2} = 0.01$, $10^{-1} = 0.1$; $-2 < \log 0.0125 < -1$

4. The window used for all of the graphs is [−4.7, 4.7, 1, −3.1, 3.1, 1].

a.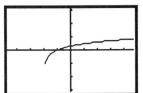

The graph is shifted 2 units to the left of $y = \log x$.

b.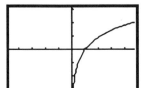

The graph of $y = \log x$ is stretched vertically by a factor of 3.

c.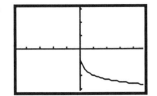

The graph is flipped over the x-axis and then shifted 2 units down from $y = \log x$.

d.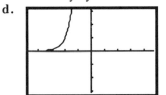

The graph is shifted 2 units to the left of $y = 10^x$.

e.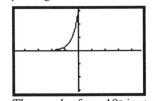

The graph of $y = 10^x$ is stretched vertically by a factor of 3.

f.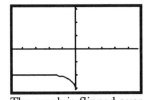

The graph is flipped over the x-axis and then shifted 2 units down from $y = 10^x$.

5. $g(x) = 23(0.94)^x$; $5 = 23(0.94)^x$; $0.2174 = 0.94^x$; $x = \log_{0.94} 0.2174$; $x = \frac{\log 0.2174}{\log 0.94} \approx 24.66$ or approximately 25 min

6. a. $1000 = 0.051517(1.1306727)^x$; $19411.07 = 1.1306727^x$; $x = \log_{1.1306727} 19411.07$; $x = \frac{\log 19411.07}{\log 1.1306727}$; $x = 80.4$. Since x represents years after 1900, according to the model the debt will pass \$1 trillion in the year 1980.

   b. The annual growth rate is approximately 13% [because $(1 + r) = 1.1306727$].

   c. $2 = (1.1306727)^x$; $x = \log_{1.1306727} 2$; $x = \frac{\log 2}{\log 1.1306727}$; $x = 5.64$ or about 5.6 yr to double.

7. a. $523.2 = 261.6(a)^1$; $a = 2$. To get the next frequency multiply 2 by the previous term, or to get a previous term divide by 2. $C_1 = 32.7$, $C_2 = 65.4$, $C_3 = 130.8$, $C_6 = 1046.4$, $C_7 = 2092.8$, $C_8 = 4185.6$.

   b. $y = 16.35(2^x)$ where 16.35 is the starting frequency and the multiplier is 2

   c. Answers will vary, but string lengths are related to the frequencies. Longer lengths have smaller frequencies.

8. a. $100 = ab^0$; $a = 100$; $50 = 100b^{5750}$; $0.5 = b^{5750}$; $b = 0.5^{1/5750}$; $b \approx 0.999879$. The equation is $y = 100(0.999879)^x$.

   b. $48.37 = 100(0.999879)^x$; $0.4837 = 0.999879^x$; $x = \log_{0.999879} 0.4837$; $x = \frac{\log 0.4837}{\log 0.999879}$; $x \approx 6002$ yr ago or the current year − 6025. (In 1997, the year would be 4028 BC.)

9. a. $y = ab^x$ **b.** (0, 88.7), (6, 92.9)   **c.** $88.7 = ab^0$; $88.7 = a$

   d. $92.9 = 88.7b^6$; $1.04735 = b^6$; $b = 1.04735^{1/6}$; $b \approx 1.0077$

   e. $106.3 = 88.7(1.0077)^x$; $1.1984 = 1.0077^x$; $x = \log_{1.0077} 1.1984$; $x = \frac{\log 1.1984}{\log 1.0077}$; $x \approx 23.595$ so 23 or 24 clicks

10. Answers will vary.

Problem Set 7.7

1. a. $\log 2 + \log 5 = \log 10$ **b.** $\log 2 + \log 50 = \log 100$
   c. $\log 30 + \log 30 = \log 900$ **d.** $\log 40 + \log 5 = \log 200$
   e. To get the answer, multiply the arguments.   **f.** Answers are the same as for parts 1a.–1d.
   g. $\log a + \log b = \log ab$
   h. Logs are exponents, and when you multiply exponential expressions with the same base, you add the exponents.

2. a. $\log 30 - \log 6 = \log 5$ **b.** $\log 200 - \log 10 = \log 20$

c. $\log 600 - \log 20 = \log 30$ **d.** $\log 600 - \log 15 = \log 40$

e. To get the answer, divide the arguments.   **f.** Answers are the same as for parts 2a.–2d.

g. $\log a - \log b = \log \frac{a}{b}$

h. Logs are exponents, and when you divide exponential expressions with the same base, you subtract the exponents.

3. a. i. $\log 2 \approx 0.3$ ii. $\log 2^3 = \log 8 \approx 0.9$ **b.** $\log 2^3 = 3 \log 2$

c. i. $\log 50 \approx 1.7$ ii. $\log 50^2 = \log 2500 = 3.4$ **d.** $\log 50^2 = 2 \log 50$

e. Answers are the same.   **f.** $\log a^b = b \log a$

g. Yes; for example, $\log 2 = 0.3$, $\log 2^{-3} = {}^-0.9$, $(0.3)({}^-3) = {}^-0.9$

h. $\log \sqrt{a} = \frac{1}{2} \log a$

4. a. True; logarithm product property   **b.** False; $\log 5 + \log 3 = \log 15$

c. True; $\log 16 = \log 2^4 = 4 \log 2$; logarithm power property

d. True; logarithm quotient property   **e.** False; $\log 9 - \log 3 = \log 3$

f. False; $\log \sqrt{7} = \frac{1}{2} \log 7$ **g.** False; $\log 35 = \log 5 + \log 7$

h. True; $\log \frac{1}{4} = \log 1 - \log 4 = {}^-\log 4$ since $\log 1 = 0$

i. False; $\log 3 - \log 4 = \log \frac{3}{4}$

j. True; $\log 64 = \log 2^6 = \log(2^4)^{6/4} = \log(16)^{3/2} = 1.5 \log 16$

5. Answers will vary. Examples: The log of a product is the sum of the logs. The log of a quotient is the difference of the logs. The log of a number raised to a power is the power times the log of the number.

6. Answers will vary. For example, if a horizontal line will intersect f in more than one point, its inverse is not a function.

7. a. $y = 261.6(2^{x/12})$ since the starting value is 261.6 and there are twelve intermediate frequencies to get to the next C note, which has a frequency of twice the previous C note.

b.

	Note	Frequency			Note	Frequency
Do	C	261.6		**Sol**	G	392.0
	C#	277.2			G#	415.3
Re	D	293.6		**La**	A	440.0
	D#	311.1			A#	466.1
Mi	E	329.6		**Ti**	B	493.8
Fa	F	349.2		**Do**	C	523.2
	F#	370.0				

8. $\log_4 9 \cdot \log_9 12 \cdot \log_{12} 16 = \dfrac{\log 9}{\log 4} \cdot \dfrac{\log 12}{\log 9} \cdot \dfrac{\log 16}{\log 12} = \dfrac{\log 16}{\log 4} = \dfrac{\log 4^2}{\log 4} = \dfrac{2 \log 4}{\log 4} = 2$

9. a. $\log_n 6 = \log_n 2 + \log_n 3 = x + y$ **b.** $\log_n 2.5 = \log_n 5 - \log_n 2 = z - x$

c. $\log_n 125 = \log_n 5 + \log_n 5 + \log_n 5 = 3 \log_n 5 = 3z$

d. $\log_n 100 = \log_n 2 + \log_n 5 + \log_n 2 + \log_n 5 = 2(\log_n 2 + \log_n 5) = 2(x + z)$

10. a. $\log_2 16 = \dfrac{\log 16}{\log 2} = 4$ **b.** $\log_5 8 = \dfrac{\log 8}{\log 5} = 1.292$

c. $\log_8 5 = \dfrac{\log 5}{\log 8} = 0.774$ **d.** $\log_3 15 = \dfrac{\log 15}{\log 3} = 2.465$

11. a. Be sure to graph the functions sequentially. Notice that $y_1(y_2)$ graphs the line $y = x$ in the first quadrant only while $y_2(y_1)$ graphs the entire line $y = x$.

$[-5, 5, 1, -5, 5, 1]$

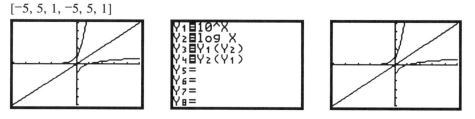

b. $[-5, 5, 1, -5, 5, 1]$

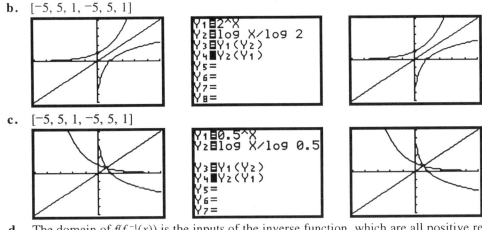

c. $[-5, 5, 1, -5, 5, 1]$

d. The domain of $f(f^{-1}(x))$ is the inputs of the inverse function, which are all positive real numbers. The domain of $f^{-1}(f(x))$ is the inputs of the function, which are all real numbers. The difference is that the inside function in $f(f^{-1}(x))$ is a logarithm, which uses only positive values, while in $f^{-1}(f(x))$ the inside function is an exponential, which can accept any real number as an input.

12. a. True: If you apply the vertical line test, any vertical line will not intersect the curve in more than one point.
   b. False: The curve is always increasing (or decreasing) and never levels off.
   c. True: The vertical asymptote is $x = 0$ since log 0 is undefined.
   d. True: Any number raised to the zero power is 1.
   e. True: There is no vertical, horizontal, or other axis of symmetry.
   f. True: Experiment by graphing logarithms with different bases. Use the change of base property to do this.

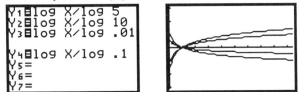

13. Answers will vary.

Problem Set 7.8

1. $9000 = 3000\left(1 + \frac{0.0675}{12}\right)^t$; $3 = 1.005625^t$; $t = \log_{1.005625} 3$; $t = \frac{\log 3}{\log 1.005625}$; $t \approx 195.9$ mo

2. a. $12.85 = 4.2^x$; $x = \log_{4.2} 12.85$; $x = \frac{\log 12.85}{\log 4.2}$; $x \approx 1.779$

   b. By definition, $12.85 = 4.2^x$ is $x = \log_{4.2} 12.85$. Using the change of base property: $x = \frac{\log 12.85}{\log 4.2}$.
   If you took the log of both sides, you would have $\log 12.85 = \log 4.2^x$; using the logarithm power property,
   $\log 12.85 = x\log 4.2$; dividing both sides by $\log 4.2$, $\frac{\log 12.85}{\log 4.2} = x$. Using the definition of logarithms
   or "taking the log" of both sides results in the same solution.

3. a. $800 = 10^x$; $\log 800 = \log 10^x$; $\log 800 = x\log 10$; $x = \frac{\log 800}{\log 10}$; $x \approx 2.903$

   b. $2048 = 2^x$; $\log 2048 = \log 2^x$; $\log 2048 = x\log 2$; $x = \frac{\log 2048}{\log 2}$; $x = 11$

   c. $16 = 0.5^x$; $\log 16 = \log 0.5^x$; $\log 16 = x\log 0.5$; $x = \frac{\log 16}{\log 0.5}$; $x = -4$

   d. $478 = 18.5(10^x)$; $25.8378 = 10^x$; $\log 25.8378 = \log 10^x$; $\log 25.8378 = x\log 10$; $x = \frac{\log 25.8378}{\log 10}$; $x \approx 1.4123$

   e. $155 = 24.0(1.89^x)$; $6.458 = 1.89^x$; $\log 6.458 = \log 1.89^x$; $\log 6.458 = x\log 1.89$; $x = \frac{\log 6.458}{\log 1.89}$; $x \approx 2.93$

   f. $0.0047 = 19.1(0.21^x)$; $2.461 \cdot 10^{-4} = 0.21^x$; $\log 2.461 \cdot 10^{-4} = \log 0.21^x$; $\log 2.461 \cdot 10^{-4} = x\log 0.21$;
   $x = \frac{\log 2.461 \cdot 10^{-4}}{\log 0.21}$; $x = 5.325$

4. a. 5 ft 6 in. = 5.5 ft; $A = 0.657(W^{0.425})(h^{0.725}) = 0.657(120^{0.425})(5.5^{0.725}) \approx 17.3$ ft^2
   b. 5 ft 8 in. = 5.667 ft; $17.49 = 0.657(W^{0.425})(5.75^{0.725})$; $26.62 = (W^{0.425})(5.75^{0.725})$; $7.490 = W^{0.425}$;
   $W = 7.490^{1/0.425}$; $W \approx 114$ lb
   c. Answers will vary.

5. a. Assuming that this is an exponential function, use the model $y = ab^t$ where h represents the number of hours and T the temperature: $h = 192\, b^T$. Now substitute (22°C, 42) into the equation: $42 = 192b^{22}$; $0.21875 = b^{22}$; $\sqrt[22]{0.21875}$; $b \approx 0.93325$. So the exponential function is $h = 192(0.93325^T)$.

   b. $h = 192(0.93325^{30}) \approx 24.2$ hr at 30°C; $h = 192(0.93325^{16}) \approx 63.6$ hr

   c. $147 = 192(0.93325^T)$; $0.765625 = 0.93325^T$; $T = \frac{\log 0.765625}{\log 0.93325}$; $T \approx 3.87$°C

   d.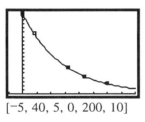

   $[-5, 40, 5, 0, 200, 10]$

   e. A realistic domain is 0°C to 100°C, which are the freezing and boiling points.

6. a. $D = 10 \log\left(\frac{10^{-13}}{10^{-16}}\right)$; $D = 10 \log 10^3$; $D = 10 \cdot 3$; $D = 30$ dB

   b. $D = 10 \log\left(\frac{3.16 \cdot 10^{-13}}{10^{-16}}\right)$; $D = 10 \log(3.16 \cdot 10^6)$; $D = 10 \cdot 6.4997$; $D \approx 65$ dB

   c. $107 = 10 \log\left(\frac{x}{10^{-16}}\right)$; $10.7 = \log\left(\frac{x}{10^{-16}}\right)$; using the definition of logarithms: $10^{10.7} = \frac{x}{10^{-16}}$; $x = 10^{10.7} \cdot 10^{-16}$; $x = 10^{-5.3}$; $x = 5 \cdot 10^{-6}$ W/cm².

   d. $47 = 10 \log\left(\frac{I}{10^{-16}}\right)$ implies $\frac{I}{10^{-16}} = 10^{4.7}$; $42 = 10 \log\left(\frac{I}{10^{-16}}\right)$ implies $\frac{I}{10^{-16}} = 10^{4.2}$. The ratio of the sounds is $\left(\frac{10^{4.7}}{10^{4.2}}\right) = 10^{0.5} \approx 3.16$ times louder.

7. a. $y = ab^x$; $14.7 = ab^0$; $14.7 = a \cdot 1$; $a = 14.7$
   b. $y = 14.7b^x$; $9.46 = 14.7b^2$; $0.643537 = b^2$; $0.8022078 = b$
   c. $12000/5280 = 2.27$ mi; $y = 14.7(0.8022078^{2.27})$; $y = 8.91$ psi
   d. $y = 14.7(0.8022078^x)$; $3.65 = 14.7(0.8022078^x)$; $0.248299 = 0.8022078^x$; $x = \frac{\log 0.248299}{\log 0.8022078}$; $x = 6.32$ mi

8. a. $100 = ab^0$; $a = 100$; $50 = 100b^{5750}$; $0.5 = b^{5750}$; $b = 0.5^{1/5750}$; $b \approx 0.999879$. The equation is $y = 100(0.999879)^x$.
   b. $y = 100(0.999879)^x$; $25 = 100(0.999879)^x$; $0.25 = 0.999879^x$; $x = \frac{\log 0.25}{\log 0.999879}$; $x = 11456.286$ or $x \approx 11,500$ years old
   c. $y = 100(0.999879)^x$; $62.45 = 100(0.999879)^x$; $0.6245 = 0.999879^x$; $x = \frac{\log 0.6245}{\log 0.999879}$; $x = 3890.706$; about $1990 - 3890 \approx 1,900$ BC.
   d. $y = 100(0.999879)^x$; $y = 100(0.999879)^{100000000}$; $y = 0$. There is virtually nothing left to measure so you could not use carbon-14 for dating coal.

9. a. $100\% - 3.5\% = 96.5\%$ remains after 1 min
   b. $y = ab^x$; $100 = ab^0$; $a = 100$; $96.5 = 100b^1$; $b = 0.965$, so $y = 100(0.965)^x$.
   c. $y = 100(0.965)^x$; $50 = 100(0.965)^x$; $0.5 = 0.965^x$; $x = \frac{\log 0.5}{\log 0.965}$; $x \approx 19.456$ min
   d. 60 min(24 hr/day) = 1440 min per day. In one day, $y = 100(0.965)^{1440}$; $y = 5.23 \cdot 10^{-21}$. In one day, the carbon-11 is virtually gone, so you could never use it to date an archaeological find.

10. a.–d. Answers will vary.

Problem Set 7.9

1.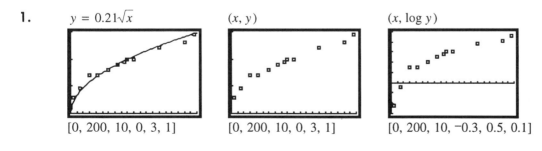

    $y = 0.21\sqrt{x}$ \qquad (x, y) \qquad $(x, \log y)$

    $[0, 200, 10, 0, 3, 1]$ \qquad $[0, 200, 10, 0, 3, 1]$ \qquad $[0, 200, 10, -0.3, 0.5, 0.1]$

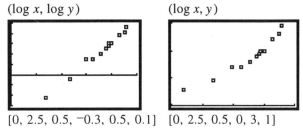

(log *x*, log *y*)   (log *x*, *y*)

[0, 2.5, 0.5, −0.3, 0.5, 0.1]   [0, 2.5, 0.5, 0, 3, 1]

The graph of (log *x*, log *y*) appears to be the most linear.

Use a least-squares regression to find a linear equation, $y = 0.417x - 0.5186$. This is actually the equation $\log y = 0.417 \log x - 0.5186$ or $y = 10^{0.417 \log x - 0.5186}$. So $y = 10^{0.417 \log x} \cdot 10^{-0.5186}$ or $y \approx 0.303x^{0.417}$.

2. a.

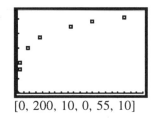

[0, 200, 10, 0, 55, 10]

b. (log *x*, *y*)

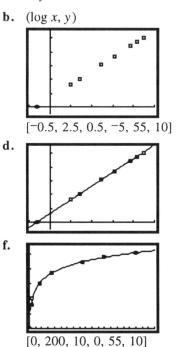

[−0.5, 2.5, 0.5, −5, 55, 10]

c. Choose two points from (log *x*, *y*) to find the equation of the line (or use the calculator to find a line of best fit). The equation should be close to $y = 20x + 6$.

d.

e. $y = 20 \log x + 6$ (Answers will vary depending on the method used to find the equation. Be sure to check your answer graphically to make sure the equation fits.)

f.

[0, 200, 10, 0, 55, 10]

3. a.–e. Answers will vary, but the equation should be close to $y = a(0.5)^x$ where a represents the starting amount of M&Ms.

4. a.

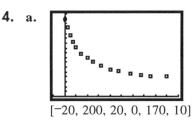

[−20, 200, 20, 0, 170, 10]

b. Subtract 40 from each of the temperatures.

[−20, 200, 20, 0, 170, 10]

c. Graph (*x*, log *y*).

[−20, 200, 20, 0, 3, 1]

d. The least-squares line is $y = -0.0113x + 2.062$.

e. $\log(y - 40) = -0.0113x + 2.062$. Therefore, $y - 40 = (10^{2.062})(10^{-0.0113})^x$. So $y = 115.35(0.9743)^x + 40$.

f.

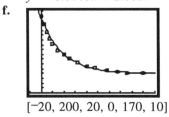

[−20, 200, 20, 0, 170, 10]

5. a.

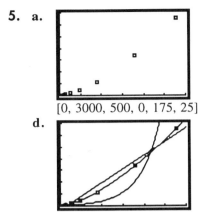

[0, 3000, 500, 0, 175, 25]

b. LinReg($a + bx$): $r = 0.9885$

c. ExpReg: $r = 0.8857$
PwrReg: $r = 0.999999$

d.

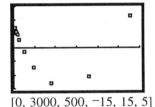

e. Residual plot for the linear regression

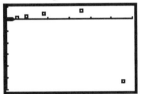

[0, 3000, 500, −15, 15, 5]

The residuals form a definite parabola-like pattern. The range of the residuals is from −13 to +12.

Residual plot for the exponential regression

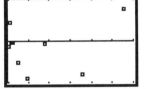

[0, 3000, 500, −300, 50, 50]

Most of the residuals are above the x-axis with the exception of one, which is far below the axis. The range of the residuals is from −265 to +32.

Residual plot for the power regression

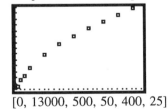

[0, 3000, 500, −0.01, 0.01, 0.01]

Although many of the residuals appear below the axis with one far above, the range is very small—from −0.009 to 0.008.

f. Answers will vary.

6. a.–c. Answers will vary.

7. a. Graph the data. The equation should be close to $y = 3.56x^{0.5}$.

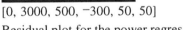

[0, 13000, 500, 50, 400, 25]

b. Answers will vary.

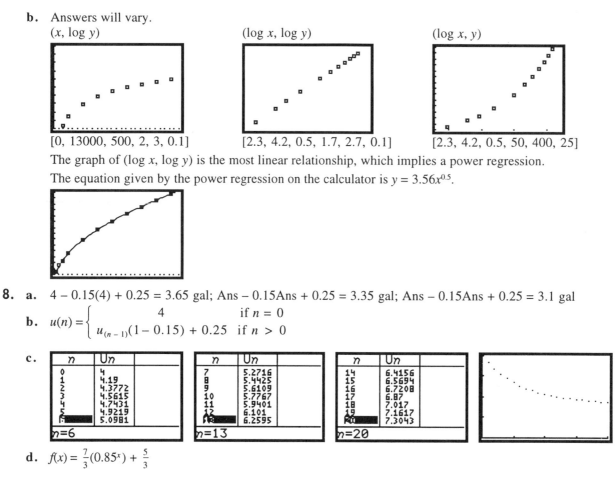

(x, log y)

(log x, log y)

(log x, y)

[0, 13000, 500, 2, 3, 0.1]   [2.3, 4.2, 0.5, 1.7, 2.7, 0.1]   [2.3, 4.2, 0.5, 50, 400, 25]

The graph of (log x, log y) is the most linear relationship, which implies a power regression.
The equation given by the power regression on the calculator is $y = 3.56x^{0.5}$.

8. a. $4 - 0.15(4) + 0.25 = 3.65$ gal; $\text{Ans} - 0.15\text{Ans} + 0.25 = 3.35$ gal; $\text{Ans} - 0.15\text{Ans} + 0.25 = 3.1$ gal

b. $u(n) = \begin{cases} 4 & \text{if } n = 0 \\ u_{(n-1)}(1 - 0.15) + 0.25 & \text{if } n > 0 \end{cases}$

c.

n	Un
0	4
1	4.19
2	4.3772
3	4.5615
4	4.7431
5	4.9219
6	5.0981

n=6

n	Un
7	5.2716
8	5.4425
9	5.6109
10	5.7767
11	5.9401
12	6.101
13	6.2595

n=13

n	Un
14	6.4156
15	6.5694
16	6.7208
17	6.87
18	7.017
19	7.1617
20	7.3043

n=20

d. $f(x) = \frac{7}{3}(0.85^x) + \frac{5}{3}$

Project: Income by Gender

The data is fairly linear through these 18 years, but it is not so linear that someone couldn't argue that it fits a different model. The most logical choice is exponential, but that is actually a much poorer fit than a linear model, showing a real pattern in the residuals. If you look at linear models, you will find *men* = 1174.16*year* – 73,744 and *women* = 813.40*year* – 52,521—or that male salaries are increasing by \$1,174 each year and female salaries are increasing by only \$813 each year. This difference is reflected by the line fitting the data (*time, men – women*), which is *men – women* = 360.76*year* – 21,223.

On the other hand, male salaries have increased by 197% in the 18 years while female salaries have increased by 230%. This is why the ratio of male salaries to female salaries is decreasing over time. A line for this scattered data is *men/women* = –0.013567*year* + 2.71866, which indicates that the ratio decreases by 1.3% each year. Making long-range predictions for any of the equations on this small interval is not going to give very likely results. This last model would predict the ratio to be 1.36 by the turn of the century, but the first two equations give a ratio of 43672/28819 or 1.51. In fact, the ratio of the first two equations predicts that the men's average salary will always be at least 144% of the women's average salary.

Chapter Review

Problem Set 7.10

1. a. $4^{-2} = \frac{1}{4^2} = \frac{1}{16}$

b. $(-3)^{-1} = \frac{1}{-3} = -\frac{1}{3}$

c. $\left(\frac{1}{5}\right)^{-3} = \left(\frac{5}{1}\right)^3 = 125$

d. $49^{1/2} = \sqrt{49} = 7$

e. $64^{-1/3} = \frac{1}{\sqrt[3]{64}} = \frac{1}{4}$

f. $\left(\frac{9}{16}\right)^{3/2} = \left(\sqrt{\frac{9}{16}}\right)^3 = \left(\frac{3}{4}\right)^3 = \frac{27}{64}$

g. $-7^0 = -1$ (Note: Order of operations says to do exponents before multiplying.)

h. $(3)(2)^2 = (3)(4) = 12$

i. $(0.6^{-2})^{-1/2} = 0.6^{(-2 \cdot -1/2)} = 0.6^1 = 0.6$

2. a. $\log x + \log y = \log xy$ **b.** $\log \frac{z}{v} = \log z - \log v$ **c.** $(7x^{2.1})(0.3x^{4.7}) = 2.1x^{(2.1+4.7)} = 2.1x^{6.8}$

d. $\log w^k = k \log w$ **e.** $\sqrt[5]{x} = x^{1/5}$ **f.** $\log_5 t = \frac{\log t}{\log 5}$

3. a. $4.7^x = 28$; $\log 4.7^x = \log 28$; $x\log 4.7 = \log 28$; $x = \frac{\log 28}{\log 4.7} \approx 2.153$

b. $4.7^{x2} = 2209$; $\log 4.7^{x2} = \log 2209$; $x^2\log 4.7 = \log 2209$; $x^2 = \frac{\log 2209}{\log 4.7}$; $x^2 = 4.975757$; $x \approx 2.231$

c. $\log_x 2.9 = 1.25$; $x^{1.25} = 2.9$; $x = \sqrt[1.25]{2.9}$; $x \approx 2.344$

d. $\log_{3.1} x = 47$; $3.1^{47} = x$; $x \approx 1.242 \cdot 10^{23}$

e. $7x^{2.4} = 101$; $x^{2.4} = 14.42857$; $x = \sqrt[2.4]{14.42857}$; $x \approx 3.041$

f. $9000 = 500(1.065)^x$; $18 = 1.065^x$; $x = \log_{1.065} 18$; $x = \frac{\log 18}{\log 1.065}$; $x \approx 45.897$

g. $\log x = 3.771$; $x = 10^{3.771}$; $x \approx 5902$

h. $\sqrt[5]{x^3} = 47$; $(x^3)^{1/5} = 47$; $x^3 = 47^5$; $x = \sqrt[3]{47^5}$; $x \approx 612$

4. a. $y = a + b \log x$; $0.50 = a + b \log 1$; $0.50 = a + b \cdot 0$; $a = 0.50$

b. $y = a + b \log x$; $3.44 = 0.50 + b \log 15$; $2.94 = b \log 15$; $b = \frac{2.94}{\log 15}$; $b = 2.4998$

c. $y = 0.50 + 2.4998 \log x$; to find the x-intercept, set $y = 0$ and solve for x. $0 = 0.50 + 2.4998 \log x$; $-0.50 = 2.4998 \log x$; $\log x = -0.2$; $x = 10^{-0.2} = 0.63$. The real-world meaning of the x-intercept is that the first 0.63 of a minute of calling is free.

d. $y = 0.50 + 2.4998 \log x$; $y = 0.50 + 2.4998 \log 30$; $y = \$4.19$

e. $y = 0.50 + 2.4998 \log x$; $2.00 = 0.50 + 2.4998 \log x$; $1.5 = 2.4998 \log x$; $0.6 = \log x$; $x = 10^{0.6} = 3.98$ min

5. a.

[0, 6, 1, 0, 12000, 1000]

b. $(x, \log y)$ $(\log x, \log y)$ $(\log x, y)$

[0, 6, 1, 2.5, 4.5, 0.5]   [−0.1, 0.8, 0.1, 2.5, 4.5, 0.5]   [−0.1, 0.8, 0.1, 0, 12000, 1000]

c. The graphs of $(x, \log y)$ and $(\log x, \log y)$ both look more linear than $(\log x, y)$ indicating that the best fit for the original data is either a power regression or an exponential regression. The exponential regression on the calculator gives you $y = 249.15(2.20)^x$ with $r = 0.988$. The power regression gives you $y = 398.14x^{1.98}$ with $r = 0.997$. To determine which is indeed the best fit for the original data, you need to calculate the residuals.

Power regression   Residuals

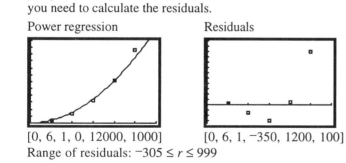

[0, 6, 1, 0, 12000, 1000]   [0, 6, 1, −350, 1200, 100]

Range of residuals: $-305 \le r \le 999$

Exponential regression   Residuals

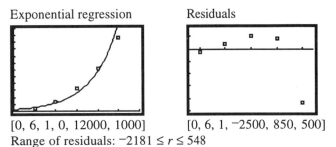

[0, 6, 1, 0, 12000, 1000]   [0, 6, 1, −2500, 850, 500]
Range of residuals: −2181 ≤ r ≤ 548

Both residual plots show patterns that are somewhat similar to each other. The range of the residuals is less for the power regression (13,040) than for the exponential regression (2729). So it seems that the power regression may be the better choice. The *r*-value for the power regression was also slightly better.

d. Using the exponential regression: 1990 = 299,166; 1995 = 15,367,552; 2000 = 789,532,012
Using the power regression: 1990 = 30,787; 1995 = 73,804; 2000 = 135,062

e. Using the power regression, $y = 398.14x^{1.98}$; $1000000 = 398.14x^{1.98}$; $2530.75 = x^{1.98}$; $x = 2530.75^{1/1.98}$; $x \approx 52$. There will be 1,000,000 cases in 1981 + 52 or the year 2033. Using the exponential regression, $y = 249.15(2.20)^x$; $1000000 = 249.15(2.20)^x$; $4013.646 = 2.20^x$; $x \approx 11$ yr; 1981 + 11 or the year 1992.

f. Answers will vary.

6. a. There are many ways to select data points: using midpoints of the intervals, using one point for each year, and other methods. The equations generated will vary depending on the choice of method. However, the answers for parts b and c should be similar. For this solution the point (55, 0.75) was used as the first value, and each time the wage changed a new data point was defined. Answers will vary as to which is the better model for the data.

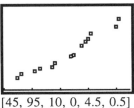

[45, 95, 10, 0, 4.5, 0.5]

Power regression   Exponential regression
(*x*, log *y*)   (log *x*, log *y*)

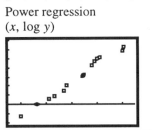   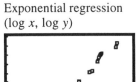

[45, 95, 10, −0.2, 0.7, 0.1]   [1.6, 2, 0.1, −0.2, 0.7, 0.1]
$y = (4.49 \cdot 10^{-6})x^{3.04}$, $r = 0.986$ $y = 0.067(1.05)^x$, $r = 0.989$

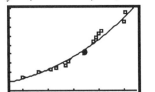   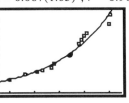

Residuals   Residuals

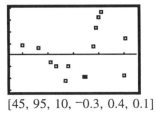   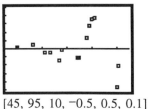

[45, 95, 10, −0.3, 0.4, 0.1]   [45, 95, 10, −0.5, 0.5, 0.1]

Range of the residuals

−0.22 to 0.36   −0.465 to 0.378

Sum of the squared residuals

0.4943   0.6708

The range of the residuals and the sum of the squared residuals are slightly less for the power regression model, so this regression is probably the best model.

b. ✓Substituting $x = 100$, 110, and 120 into the power regression equation gives you $5.40, $7.12, and $9.39 for the years 2000, 2010, and 2020 respectively. Substituting $x = 100$, 110, and 120 into the exponential regression equation gives you $8.81, $14.35, and $23.38 for the years 2000, 2010, and 2020 respectively.

c. Substituting $x = 38$ into the power regression equation gives you $0.28 for the year 1938. Substituting $x = 38$ into the exponential regression equation gives you $0.43 for the year 1938.

7. Answers will vary.

Take Another Look 7.10

Linear model (on semilog paper): $y = 0.052207x - 1.9943$

Exponential model: $y = 0.010132(1.12773)^x$

Chapter 8

Problem Set 8.1

Many of the questions in this section ask the student to devise a method to randomly select an outcome or to generate a set of random numbers. In this solution set, one example is given but is by no means the only method.

1. Answers will vary. The teacher could number 30 chips from 1 to 30 and then put them in a jar. Each day she could select six chips. The students whose roll numbers in the grade book correspond to the number of the chip selected must turn in their homework that day. Each day the six selected chips are returned to the jar.

2. Answers will vary for 2a.–e. Possible answers are given for 2a.–c.

    a. Roll a die for each student. If a 1 is rolled, that student gets on bus 1, if a 2 is rolled, that student gets on bus 2, and so on. If a 6 is rolled, roll the die again.

    b. Roll the die 100 times. Each time you roll a 6, roll the die again. Total the number of students selected for each bus. Theoretically, $\frac{1}{5}$ of the students, or 20 students, should be assigned to each bus.

    c. See Calculator Note 8B. Alter the Random Number Generator Routine to `seq (int 5rand + 1,x,1,99,1)→L`$_1$. Seq is found in the List menu. Note: You can put only 99 numbers into a list on the TI-82. Plot this data in a histogram to see the total number of rolls for each number from 1 to 5. You will need to generate one more random number to get 100 trials. Use trace to determine the number of students that are on each bus.

    d. Answers will vary.   **e.** Answers will vary.

3. Each one of these procedures for producing random numbers has shortcomings.

    a. Middle numbers (3–7) are more common than getting only 1 or 2 or 8 or 9 heads in one trial of dropping pennies.

    b. Very few pencils will be at 0 or 1 in.; students throw away their pencils long before that.

    c. Books tend to open to pages that are used more than others.

    d. Answers will vary. See Calculator Note 8B. Alter the Random Number Generator Routine to `seq (int 9rand + 1,x,1,99,1)→L`$_1$.

4. **a.** Answers will vary.

    b. Alter the Random Number Generator Routine to `seq (int 6rand + 1,x,1,99,1)→L`$_1$. Look at the list generated and count the number of turns needed until you roll a 6 and can start the game. After each 6, assume a turn has started and begin counting for the next turn.

    c. Answers will vary.

    d. Answers will vary. Add the results from the ten trials and divide by 10.

    e. Answers will vary. Long-run averages should tend toward six turns in order to roll a 6.

5. a. Answers will vary.

b. One possible way to do this is to assign each of the letters in the word CHAMPION a number from 1 to 8. Look at the first digit in the Random Number Table. If the first digit is a 0 or a 9 (which would not represent a letter in the cereal, then look at the next digit until you get a digit from 1 to 8. Count down the table until you have at least one of each number.

c. Answers will vary. Using this method with the first column takes 20 boxes, with the second column takes 13 boxes, with the third column takes 14 boxes, with the fourth column takes 24 boxes, and with the fifth column takes 35 boxes.

d. Answers will vary. (20 + 13 + 14 + 24 + 35)/5 = 21.2 boxes.

e. Answers will vary. Average numbers of boxes should be about 22 boxes.

6. a. Alter the Random Number Generator Routine to `seq (int 6rand + 1,x,1,99,1)→L₁`. Plot a histogram and use trace to find the total number of 1's, 2's, 3's, and so on, rolled. Record that data in the table and repeat the process 12 times. (Note: After plotting the histogram, quit and then use $\boxed{\text{2nd}}$ $\boxed{\text{ENTRY}}$ to generate the next set of 99 rolls.) Answers will vary.

b. The long-range pattern should show that $\frac{1}{6}$ of all rolls should be a 3, $\frac{1}{6}$ of all rolls should be a 1, and so on.

c. List the cumulative number of rolls in L_1 and the cumulative proportion of 3's in L_2. Plot using a scatter plot.

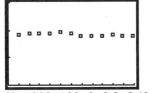

When the data points are added from other classmates, the points should level out to a straight line. If you considered 5's instead of 3's, the data should level out to the same value as with the 3's.

[0, 1200, 100, 0, 0.3, 0.1]

d. Answers will vary.

e. Ideally, $P(3) = \frac{1}{6} \approx 0.167$

7. a. Set window as described in Calculator Note 8C and graph.

    i. $^-2 < y < 4$ ii. {1, 2, 3}

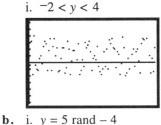

b. i. $y = 5$ rand $- 4$ ii. $y = $ int 4 rand $- 4$ iii. $y = $ int 3 rand $+ 2$

8. a. Answers will vary. In the long run, the average should tend toward 2 children.

b. The long-run average for number of girls should be 1 also.

Problem Set 8.2

1. a. 36 different outcomes (1–6 on the green die with 1–6 on the white die)

    b. 6 different outcomes

Green die

    c. 12 different outcomes

Green die

d. 3 different outcomes

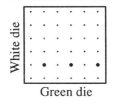
Green die

2. **a.** $x + y = 9$ (4 different outcomes)

b. $x + y = 6$ (5 different outcomes)

c. $x - y = 1$ or $y - x = 1$ (10 different outcomes)

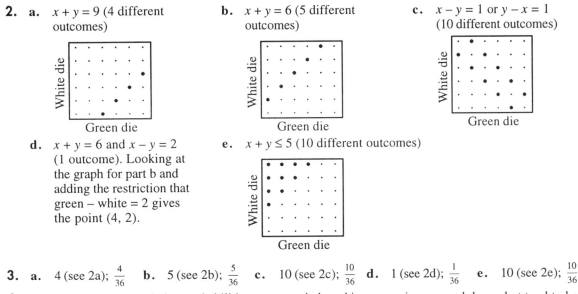

White die / Green die

d. $x + y = 6$ and $x - y = 2$ (1 outcome). Looking at the graph for part b and adding the restriction that green − white = 2 gives the point (4, 2).

e. $x + y \le 5$ (10 different outcomes)

White die / Green die

3. **a.** 4 (see 2a); $\frac{4}{36}$ **b.** 5 (see 2b); $\frac{5}{36}$ **c.** 10 (see 2c); $\frac{10}{36}$ **d.** 1 (see 2d); $\frac{1}{36}$ **e.** 10 (see 2e); $\frac{10}{36}$

4. **a.** Initially the cumulative probabilities are unsettled, making many jogs up and down, but tend to be between 0.5 and 0.7.

b. In the long run, the probabilities tend toward 0.6.

c. If the proportion graph tended toward 1, this would mean that in the long run success was a certainty.

d. If the proportion graph tended toward 0, this would mean that in the long run there is no chance of something happening.

e. The range of values possible for any probabilities is from 0 to 1.

5. **a.** The total area of the square is $12(12) = 144$.

b. Area of shaded region is $\frac{1}{2}bh = \frac{1}{2}(12 - 1)(12 - 4) = \frac{1}{2}(11)(8) = 44$.

c. $\frac{44}{144}$ **d.** $\frac{44}{144} = 0.306$ **e.** $144 - 44 = 100$. Probability is $\frac{100}{144} = 0.694$.

f. The probability that any given random point will land on another specific random point is 0. The probability that any given random point will land on a specific line is also 0.

6. **a.** Use the Average Value program to find the average y-value and multiply that by 10 to find the area under the curve. The average value $2.108(10) = 21.08$ for the area.

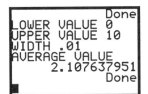

```
                    Done
LOWER VALUE 0
UPPER VALUE 10
WIDTH .01
AVERAGE VALUE
            2.107637951
                    Done
```

b. The area of the rectangle is $10(4) = 40$. **c.** The part of the rectangle under the curve is $\frac{21.08}{40} = 0.527$.

d. Modify the program Ratio of Success in Calculator Note 8D. Change the indicated lines to : $\ulcorner$ x→Y$_1$, :10Rand→X, and 4Rand→B. Then run the program. Answers will vary.

The area under the curve is approximately $0.526(40) = 21.04$. (0.526 represents the ratio of points under the curve to the total points in the rectangle, so multiply this ratio by the total area of the rectangle to find the area under the curve.)

e. Answers will vary.

7. **a.** $x + y \le 6$ **b.** **c.** $\frac{18}{64} \approx 0.28$

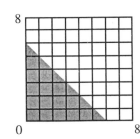

8. a. $x - y \leq 10$ or $y - x \leq 10$ **b.** $\frac{11}{36} = 0.31$

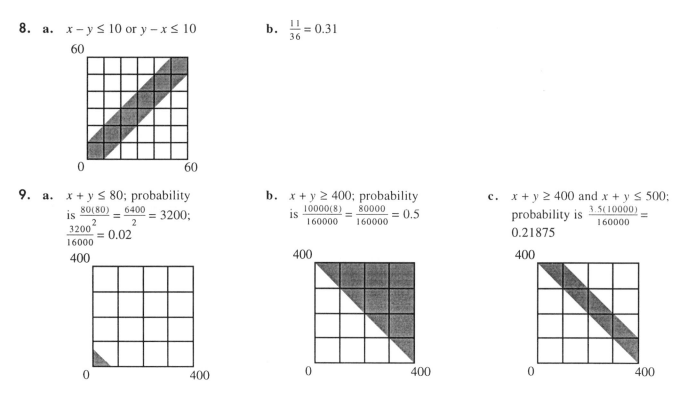

9. a. $x + y \leq 80$; probability is $\frac{80(80)}{2} = \frac{6400}{2} = 3200$; $\frac{3200}{16000} = 0.02$

60

0   60

b. $x + y \geq 400$; probability is $\frac{10000(8)}{160000} = \frac{80000}{160000} = 0.5$

c. $x + y \geq 400$ and $x + y \leq 500$; probability is $\frac{3.5(10000)}{160000} = 0.21875$

400

0   400

400

0   400

400

0   400

Take Another Look 8.2

Make sure students have their calculators set to parametric, dot, and simultaneous modes.

a. Minimum value = 0; maximum value = 1. The values of Tstep and Tmax control the number of points plotted. The number of points equals Tmax divided by Tstep.

b. XT = 6 rand; YT = 6 rand; Window: [0, 500, 1, 0, 6, 1, 0, 6, 1]

c. XT = 6 rand + 1; YT = 6 rand + 1

d. XT = int(6 rand + 1); YT = int (6 rand + 1)

e. XT = int(5 rand) + 2 will include 2 and 6; XT = 4 rand + 2 will give numbers between 2 and 6; YT = 3; Window: [0, 500, 1, 0, 7, 1, 0, 4, 1]

Problem Set 8.3

1. a. There are 24 different arrangements. (Draw a tree diagram or make a list.) To find the answers to 1b–f, count the number of ways the event can occur out of the 24 possible outcomes.

b. The probability that milk is first is $\frac{6}{24}$ or $\frac{1}{4}$.

c. The probability that flour is first and shortening is second is $\frac{2}{24}$ or $\frac{1}{12}$.

d. The probability that the order is FBSM is $\frac{1}{24}$.

e. The probability that the order is not FBSM is $\frac{23}{24}$.

f. The probability that flour and milk are next to each other is $\frac{12}{24}$ or $\frac{1}{2}$.

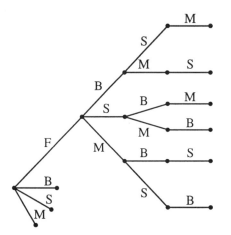

2. a.

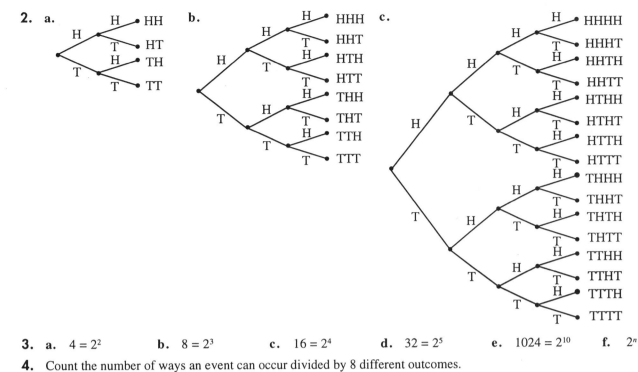

b.

c.

3. a. $4 = 2^2$ **b.** $8 = 2^3$ **c.** $16 = 2^4$ **d.** $32 = 2^5$ **e.** $1024 = 2^{10}$ **f.** 2^n

4. Count the number of ways an event can occur divided by 8 different outcomes.

a. $\frac{1}{8} = 0.125$ **b.** $\frac{3}{8} = 0.375$ **c.** $\frac{2}{3} = 0.667$

5. The diagram is the same as the one for Problem 3c. Count the number of ways an event can occur divided by 16 different ways of answering the four questions.

a. $\frac{1}{16} = 0.0625$ **b.** $\frac{4}{16} = 0.25$ **c.** $\frac{6}{16} = 0.375$ **d.** $\frac{4}{16} = 0.25$ **e.** $\frac{1}{16} = 0.0625$

f. $\frac{1 + 4 + 6 + 4 + 1}{16} = 1$ **g.** $\frac{4 + 1}{16} = 0.313$

6. a. 270 **b.** $180 + 240 + 210 + 300 + 270 + 180 = 1380$

c. $P(80 - 90) = \frac{270}{1380} = 0.196$ **d.** $P(80 - 90)' = \frac{1380 - 270}{1380} = \frac{1110}{1380} = 0.804$

7. First the table totals need to be completed.

	Liberal	Conservative	Totals
Age under 30	210	145	355
Age 30–45	235	220	455
Age over 45	280	410	690
Totals	725	775	1500

a. $\frac{280}{1500} = 0.187$ **b.** $\frac{775}{1500} = 0.517$ **c.** $\frac{145}{355} = 0.408$ **d.** $\frac{145}{775} = 0.187$

8. a.

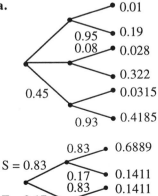

b. P(a site M2 phone is defective) = 0.08
c. P(a random manufactured phone is defective) = (0.01 + 0.028 + 0.0315) = 0.0695
d. P(a phone is manufactured at site M2 if you already know it is defective) = $\frac{0.28}{0.0695} = 0.4029$

9.

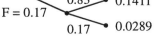

a. P(overtime) = 0.0289 (which means he missed both free throws)
b. P(no overtime & Pistons win) = (0.6889 + 0.1411 + 0.1411) = 0.9711 (which means he made either one or both of the shots)
c. P(no overtime & Pistons win by 2) = 0.6889 (which means he had both free throws)

10. The diagram is the same as the one for Problem 3c.
The branches are FFFF, FFFM, FFMF, FFMM, FMFF, FMFM, FMMF, FMMM, MFFF, MFFM, MFMF, MFMM, MMFF, MMFM, MMMF, MMMM.
P(exactly two girls) = $\frac{6}{16}$ = 0.375

11. For a cube to be cut into 27 smaller cubes, you would slice each face into 9 squares. There would be 8 corner pieces having 3 painted faces, 12 outside noncorner pieces having 2 painted faces, and 6 middle pieces having 1 painted face. The 1 cube in the very center of the original cube will have no painted face.

   a. P(exactly 1 painted face) = $\frac{6}{27}$ ≈ 0.222   **b.** P(exactly 2 painted faces) = $\frac{12}{27}$ ≈ 0.444

   c. P(exactly 3 painted faces) = $\frac{8}{27}$ ≈ 0.296   **d.** P(no painted face) = $\frac{1}{27}$ ≈ 0.037

Project: Permutations and Combinations

a. The solution to the problem is 6! or 720 arrangements. There are six possible choices for what letter you place first. Then there are five possible choices to use in the next position. That makes 30 possibilities for the first two letters, RA, RN, RD, RO, RM, AR, AN, AD, and so on. If you continue this counting method for the next letter and the next, you get 6 • 5 • 4 • 3 • 2 • 1 = 720 arrangements. So the probability that the word is DROMAN is 1 out of 720, or 0.00139.

b. The number of arrangements for three letters would be 3! as in part a, but to arrange three letters when you have six to pick from is different. As in part a for the first position, you have six possible choices, five possible choices for the next position, and four possible choices for the last position. So the answer is 6 • 5 • 4 or 6!/3! or $_6P_3$ = 120. Thus the probability of ARM is 1 out of 120, or 0.00833.

c. The total number of arrangements of three letters chosen from six is 120 as explained in part b, but this total included many different arrangements of the same three items, DNA, DAN, AND, and so on. Because there are 3! ways to arrange three letters (from part a), and there are $_6P_3$ three letter arrangements, you can divide $_6P_3$ by 3!, which is the same as $_6C_3$, and you get 20 possible groups of three letters. The probability that the group is D, N, and A is 1 out of 20, or 0.05.

Problem Set 8.4

1. Answers will vary with the random rolls of the die. One sample problem has been worked out below.

   a.

	Sly	Les
Win	20	25

   b. Using the results from the table in part a, P(Les winning) = $\frac{25}{45}$.

   c. There are 36 different ways to roll two dice, and there are 15 different outcomes that have a sum greater than 7 (for example, 2, 6; 3, 5; 4, 4; 5, 3; 6, 2; and so on).

   d. $\frac{15}{36}(5) + \frac{21}{36}(-4) = -0.25$

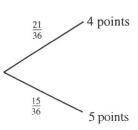

   e. Answers will vary. One possible answer is 7 points if Sly wins and 5 points if Les wins. $\left(\frac{15}{36}(7) + \frac{21}{36}(-5) = 0\right)$

2. a. P(no failures in 10 correct uses) is 0.98^{10} = 0.817, or 81.7%. P(no failures in 20 correct uses) is 0.98^{20} = 0.668, or 66.8%.

   b. 98% effective means 2% failure, or 2 out of every 100 uses will result in a failure. The expected number of uses before one failure is 50.

   c. Answers will vary. Enter and execute the program in Calculator Note 8H. The expected value after 99 trials is 54.27.

   d. Answers will vary. Sort the list generated by the program Protect.

   e. Answers will vary depending on the run of the program in part c.

3. a.

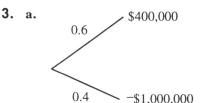

b. The expected value is $0.6(400,000) + 0.4(-1,000,000) = -\$160,000$.

c. Answers will vary. He is better off, not knowing the weather report, to cancel the concert and lose $100,000 because this is less than his expected loss of $160,000.

4. a. P(all four live) $= 0.47^4 = 0.049 = 4.9\%$

b. P(none survive to adulthood) $= 0.53^4 = 0.079 = 7.9\%$

c. The expected value to live is $0.47^4(4) + 4(0.47)^3(0.53)(3) + 6(0.47)^2(0.53)^2(2) + 4(0.47)(0.53)^3(1) = 1.88$ birds.

5. a. P(belongs to a junior) $= \frac{32 + 28}{100} = 0.60 = 60\%$

b. P(belongs to a junior if it belongs to a male) $= \frac{32}{16 + 32} = 0.67 = 67\%$

c. Number of males if there are 100 students would be $16 + 32 = 48$.

d. There are 32 male juniors.

e. Yes; $\frac{32}{48} = 0.67$

6. a. Answers will vary with the data collected in the Medical Testing Investigation.

b. P(testing positive) $= \frac{\text{number of positive tests}}{\text{number of people tested}}$

c. P(having disease if tested positive) $= \frac{\text{number of diseased people testing positive}}{\text{number of people testing positive}}$

d.

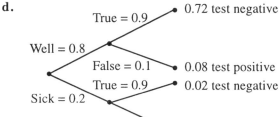

e. Answers will vary.

7. a. Player 1 expected value: $0.25(0.6)(6) + 0.75(0.4)(10) = 3.9$
Player 2 expected value: $0.25(0.4)(8) + 0.75(0.6)x = 3.9$; $0.8 + 0.45x = 3.9$; $0.45x = 3.1$; $x = 6.889$.
A value of 7 points would give a nearly equal value.

b. Answers will vary.

8. Answers will vary.

Project: Coin Toss Game

If you think about where the center of the penny can land, you will envision a small square in the center of each square. Because a penny measures about 0.75 in. in diameter, this means that the square in the center must measure only 0.25 in. squared. The probability that the center of the penny lands in this region is the area of the small square divided by the area of the larger square, which is 0.0625 or about a 6.25% chance. If the length of the side of the square was changed to a inches, then the probability becomes $\frac{(a - 0.75)^2}{a^2}$, so for 2 in. this expression equals about 0.39 or 39% chance. If the coin changes to a coin of radius r, then the probability is $\frac{(a - r)^2}{a^2}$. The area inside the square should actually be decreased by the thickness of the line (actually half the thickness on each side). Now the probability is $\frac{(a - r - t)^2}{a^2}$. Using a line thickness of 0.1 in. and solving the equation $\frac{(a - 0.951 - 0.1)^2}{a^2} = 0.01$ for a gives 1.17 in.

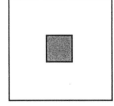

Problem Set 8.5

1. a. 3 colors

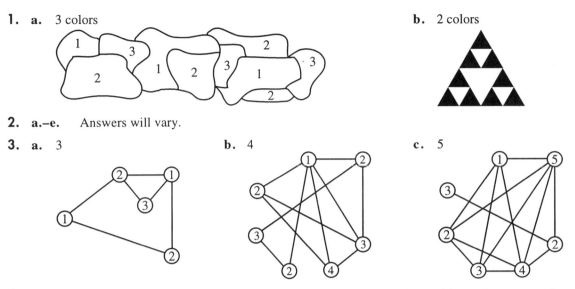

b. 2 colors

2. a.–e. Answers will vary.

3. a. 3   **b.** 4   **c.** 5

4. Draw the diagram as suggested in the problem. Connect each vertex (class) with an edge to any other class with which they should not be grouped. Any two vertices (classes) that are connected by an edge must be different colors or numbers. The best schedule will have 5 exam periods. The following is one possible solution.

Period 1: L1, L2, L3, L5, H3, P3, S3
Period 2: M1, M2, M4, S2, S4, P1
Period 3: E1, E2, E3, E4
Period 4: H1, H2, M3, M5, P2
Period 5: S1, L4, L6, H3, P3

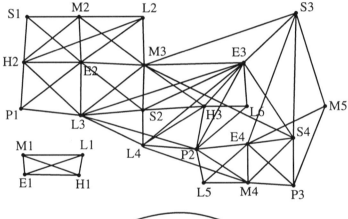

5. 5 storage areas: A (1, 2, 10); B (3, 11); C (4, 8); D (9, 12); E (5, 6, 7)

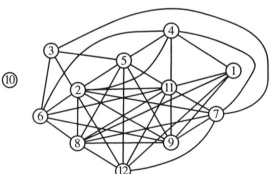

Take Another Look 8.5

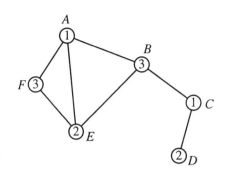

a. The vertices represent radio stations.

b. The edges will connect radio stations that are less than 150 miles apart.

c. Vertices A and B are connected because they are only 88 miles apart and cannot have the same frequency.

d. Two vertices (radio stations) can have the same frequency if they are the same color. If they are different colors, they must have different frequencies.

e. There must be at least three frequencies because A, B, and E cannot have the same frequency.

Problem Set 8.6

1.

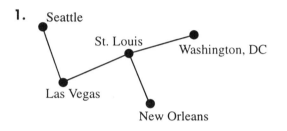

2. a.

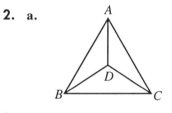

b.

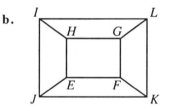

3. a. 10 edges

b.

	1	2	3	4	5
1	0	250	300	200	350
2	250	0	300	350	200
3	300	300	0	200	200
4	200	350	200	0	150
5	350	200	200	150	0

c. 24 different routes. Make a tree diagram is one way to solve this. When you leave city 1 you have 4 choices of cities to go to, then you'll have 3 choices of cities to go to, then 2 choices of cities, and then you will go to the last city and finally back to city 1. 4(3)(2)(1)(1) = 24.

d. There are a variety of strategies to use to solve this problem. One strategy is to choose the cheapest fare each time you make a choice. Another is to choose the cheapest fare in the matrix and continue choosing the next cheapest fare until a loop is formed. At this point you will have to choose the next cheapest fare. Two possible solutions are 1-2-5-4-3-1 or 1-2-3-5-4-1, which both add up to $1,100. Notice that both of these routes can also be reversed.

4. a. In Calif.: 20 − 20(0.10) + 220(0.05) = 29; Out of Calif.: 240 − 29 = 211; [29 211]

b. In Calif.: 29 − 29(0.10) + 211(0.05) = 36.65; Out of Calif.: 240 − 36.65 = 203.35; [36.65 203.35]

c. In Calif.: 36.65 − 36.65(0.10) + 203.35(0.05) = 43.1525; Out of Calif.: 240 − 43.1525 = 196.8475; [43.1525 196.8475]

5. a.

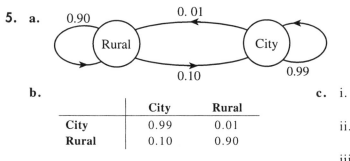

0.90   0. 01   Rural   City   0.10   0.99

b.

	City	Rural
City	0.99	0.01
Rural	0.10	0.90

c. i. City: $16 - 16(0.01) + 9(0.10) = 16.74$;
Rural: $25 - 16.74 = 8.26$; $[16.74 \quad 8.26]$

ii. City: $16.74 - 16.74(0.01) + 8.26(0.10) = 17.3986$;
Rural: $25 - 17.3986 = 7.6014$; $[17.3986 \quad 7.6014]$

iii. City: $17.3986 - 17.3986(0.01) + 7.6014(0.10) = 17.984754$; Rural: $25 - 17.984754 = 7.015246$;
$[17.984754 \quad 7.015246]$

6. $0.125 + 0.25 + 0.25 = 0.625$

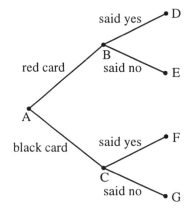

		0.5	cat	0.125
0.5	3			
		0.5	cheese	0.125
0.5	2	0.5	cheese	0.25
0.5	3	0.5	cat	0.25
		0.5	cheese	0.25

Project: Sensitive Survey

Eric knows that there were 70 people at point A. The theoretical probability of a red card is 4 over 10, or 0.4, which means that $70(0.4) = 28$ people theoretically took red cards. Since 28 people went from A to B, then the other 42 people went to C. Of the 28 people at B, 50% will theoretically have an even digit on their social security number. So $28(0.5) = 14$ of them arrive at point D and the same number at point E. The results of Eric's survey had 47 yeses; this means D plus F must add to 47. Since we theorize there were 14 at D, there must be $47 - 14 = 33$ people at F. Likewise, of the 23 noes there were 14 at E so there are 9 at G. The probability of yes on the sensitive question is 33 over 42, or 0.786, or 78.6%.

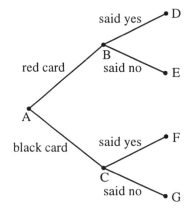

red card — B — said yes → D; said no → E
A
black card — C — said yes → F; said no → G

Problem Set 8.7

1. $[36.65 \quad 203.35]\begin{bmatrix} 0.90 & 0.10 \\ 0.05 & 0.95 \end{bmatrix} = [43.15 \quad 196.84]$

2. a.

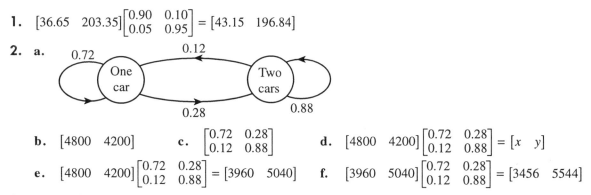

0.72   0.12   One car   Two cars   0.28   0.88

b. $[4800 \quad 4200]$

c. $\begin{bmatrix} 0.72 & 0.28 \\ 0.12 & 0.88 \end{bmatrix}$

d. $[4800 \quad 4200]\begin{bmatrix} 0.72 & 0.28 \\ 0.12 & 0.88 \end{bmatrix} = [x \quad y]$

e. $[4800 \quad 4200]\begin{bmatrix} 0.72 & 0.28 \\ 0.12 & 0.88 \end{bmatrix} = [3960 \quad 5040]$

f. $[3960 \quad 5040]\begin{bmatrix} 0.72 & 0.28 \\ 0.12 & 0.88 \end{bmatrix} = [3456 \quad 5544]$

3. Answers will vary. For example, there are 20 million people living in California and 220 million people living in the United States outside of California. Each year 2 million people immigrate to California and 11 million people immigrate to the United States outside of California.

4. a. $[13 \quad 23] + [-6 \quad 31] = [x \quad y]$

$x = 13 + {}^-6 = 7$; $y = 23 + 31 = 54$ so the sum of the matrices is $[7 \quad 54]$

b. $\begin{bmatrix} 0.90 & 0.10 \\ 0.05 & 0.95 \end{bmatrix}\begin{bmatrix} 0.90 & 0.10 \\ 0.05 & 0.95 \end{bmatrix} = \begin{bmatrix} 0.815 & 0.185 \\ 0.0925 & 0.9075 \end{bmatrix}$

$0.90(0.90) + 0.10(0.05) = 0.815$; $0.10(0.90) + 0.10(0.95) = 0.185$; $0.05(0.90) + 0.95(0.05) = 0.0925$; $0.05(0.10) + 0.95(0.95) = 0.9075$

c. $\begin{bmatrix} 18 & -23 \\ 5.4 & 32.2 \end{bmatrix} + \begin{bmatrix} -2.4 & 12.2 \\ 5.3 & 10 \end{bmatrix} = \begin{bmatrix} 18 - 2.4 & -23 + 12.2 \\ 5.4 + 5.3 & 32.2 + 10 \end{bmatrix} = \begin{bmatrix} 15.6 & -10.8 \\ 10.7 & 42.2 \end{bmatrix}$

d. $10\begin{bmatrix} 18 & -23 \\ 5.4 & 32.2 \end{bmatrix} = \begin{bmatrix} 180 & -230 \\ 54 & 322 \end{bmatrix}$

5. Enter $[20 \quad 220]$ into matrix A and $\begin{bmatrix} 0.90 & 0.10 \\ 0.05 & 0.95 \end{bmatrix}$ into matrix B.

a. $[20 \quad 220]\begin{bmatrix} 0.90 & 0.10 \\ 0.05 & 0.95 \end{bmatrix} = [29 \quad 211]$ **b.** $[29 \quad 211]\begin{bmatrix} 0.90 & 0.10 \\ 0.05 & 0.95 \end{bmatrix} = [36.65 \quad 203.35]$

c. $[36.65 \quad 203.35]\begin{bmatrix} 0.90 & 0.10 \\ 0.05 & 0.95 \end{bmatrix} = [43.1525 \quad 196.8475]$

d. In the long run, you will get $[80 \quad 160]$.

6. a. $\begin{bmatrix} 0.815 & 0.185 \\ 0.0925 & 0.9075 \end{bmatrix}$ **b.** $\begin{bmatrix} 0 & 0 & 0 \\ 0 & 4 & 0 \\ 0 & 0 & 0 \end{bmatrix}$

7. a.

	Low	Average	High
Low	0.5	0.45	0.05
Average	0.25	0.5	0.25
High	0.3	0.3	0.4

b. After one generation: $[0.25 \quad 0.60 \quad 0.15]\begin{bmatrix} 0.5 & 0.45 & 0.05 \\ 0.25 & 0.5 & 0.25 \\ 0.3 & 0.3 & 0.4 \end{bmatrix} = [0.32 \quad 0.4575 \quad 0.2225]$

After two generations: $[0.32 \quad 0.4575 \quad 0.2225]\begin{bmatrix} 0.5 & 0.45 & 0.05 \\ 0.25 & 0.5 & 0.25 \\ 0.3 & 0.3 & 0.4 \end{bmatrix} = [0.341125 \quad 0.4395 \quad 0.219375]$

After three generations: $[0.341125 \quad 0.4395 \quad 0.219375]\begin{bmatrix} 0.5 & 0.45 & 0.05 \\ 0.25 & 0.5 & 0.25 \\ 0.3 & 0.3 & 0.4 \end{bmatrix}$

$= [0.34625 \quad 0.43906875 \quad 0.21468125]$

In the long run: $[0.3474903475 \quad 0.4401544402 \quad 0.2123552124]$

8. The transition matrix:

	1	2	3
1	0	0.5	0.5
2	0.5	0	0.5
3	0.5	0.5	0

Since the squirrel starts in Room 1, matrix $A = [1 \quad 0 \quad 0]$.

After one room change:

$[1 \quad 0 \quad 0]\begin{bmatrix} 0 & 0.5 & 0.5 \\ 0.5 & 0 & 0.5 \\ 0.5 & 0.5 & 0 \end{bmatrix} = [0 \quad 0.5 \quad 0.5]$

After two room changes:

$[0 \quad 0.5 \quad 0.5]\begin{bmatrix} 0 & 0.5 & 0.5 \\ 0.5 & 0 & 0.5 \\ 0.5 & 0.5 & 0 \end{bmatrix} = [0.5 \quad 0.25 \quad 0.25]$

After three room changes:

$$[0.5 \quad 0.25 \quad 0.25] \begin{bmatrix} 0 & 0.5 & 0.5 \\ 0.5 & 0 & 0.5 \\ 0.5 & 0.5 & 0 \end{bmatrix} = [0.25 \quad 0.375 \quad 0.375]$$

After four room changes:

$$[0.25 \quad 0.375 \quad 0.375] \begin{bmatrix} 0 & 0.5 & 0.5 \\ 0.5 & 0 & 0.5 \\ 0.5 & 0.5 & 0 \end{bmatrix} = [0.375 \quad 0.3125 \quad 0.3125]$$

P(in Room 1 after four room changes) = 0.375

9. **a.** $\begin{bmatrix} 7 & 3 & 0 \\ -19 & -7 & 8 \\ 5 & 2 & -1 \end{bmatrix}$ **b.** $\begin{bmatrix} -2 & 5 \\ 8 & 7 \end{bmatrix}$ **c.** $[13 \quad 29]$ **d.** This is not possible because the number of columns in [A] does not match the number of rows in [B].

e. $\begin{bmatrix} 4 & -1 \\ 4 & -2 \end{bmatrix}$ **f.** This is not possible because the dimensions aren't the same. The dimensions must be the same in order to add or subtract.

10. Answers will vary.

Take Another Look 8.7

a.

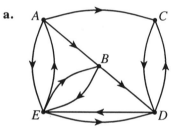

b. See completed matrix below.

c. See completed matrix below.

M	A	B	C	D	E
A	1	1	0	3	1
B	1	1	1	1	1
C	0	0	1	0	1
D	1	1	0	2	0
E	0	1	2	1	3

d. T^2 and M are identical. See completed matrix below.

T^2	A	B	C	D	E
A	1	1	0	3	1
B	1	1	1	1	1
C	0	0	1	0	1
D	1	1	0	2	0
E	0	1	2	1	3

e. See matrix of $T + T^2$ below. The entry in row 1, column 4 tells you that for computers A and D to communicate, you need a third computer. This matrix shows the number of ways two computers can communicate via one or two computers.

$T + T_2$	A	B	C	D	E
A	1	2	1	3	2
B	1	1	1	2	2
C	0	0	1	1	1
D	1	1	1	2	1
E	1	2	2	2	3

f. T^3 gives the number of ways that two computers can communicate via two computers.

g. The product provides the percentage left after 2 years or 2 trials.

Chapter Review

Problem Set 8.8

1. Answers will vary. You might number 10 chips or slips of paper and select one. You might look at the random number table and select the first digit of each number. You could alter the program Generate to :Int 10 Rand + 1.

2. Answers will vary. Possible answers are given.
  a. Look for a well-shuffled full deck after each draw to ensure a random pick each time.
  b. A painfully slow method if you need many numbers. Will people really know how many eggs are left in the carton? Will randomness depend on who is called?
  c. This depends on the randomness involved in falling off. Besides, the numbers 1–12 aren't equally likely. The number 7 is the most likely number to come up, with 1 and 12 the least likely.

3. a. Int 10 rand + 3; Int 10 rand gives an integer between 0 and 9, so adding 3 gives an integer between 3 and 12.
  b. Int 10 rand – 7; Int 10 rand gives an integer between 0 and 9, so subtracting 7 gives an integer between $^-$7 and 2.
  c. 5 rand – 2; 5 rand gives a number between 0 and 4.99, so subtracting 2 gives a number between $^-$2 and 2.99.

4. a. The area of the entire rectangle is lw, so $6(9) = 54$. The area of the shaded region (a trapezoid) is $\frac{1}{2}h(b_1 + b_2) = \frac{1}{2}(6)(6 + 3) = 27$. P(falling in shaded region) $= \frac{27}{54} = \frac{1}{2}$

  b. The area of the rectangle is $lw = 5(9.5) = 47.5$. $\frac{\text{area of shaded region}}{\text{area of entire region}} = \frac{374}{1000}$; $\frac{x}{47.5} = \frac{374}{1000}$; $1000x = 47.5(374)$; $x = 17.765$

5. a. There are 64 possible outcomes

	1	2	3	4	5	6	7	8
1	1, 1	1, 2	1, 3	1, 4	1, 5	1, 6	1, 7	1, 8
2	2, 1	2, 2	2, 3	2, 4	2, 5	2, 6	2, 7	2, 8
3	3, 1	3, 2	3, 3	3, 4	3, 5	3, 6	3, 7	3, 8
4	4, 1	4, 2	4, 3	4, 4	4, 5	4, 6	4, 7	4, 8
5	5, 1	5, 2	5, 3	5, 4	5, 5	5, 6	5, 7	5, 8
6	6, 1	6, 2	6, 3	6, 4	6, 5	6, 6	6, 7	6, 8
7	7, 1	7, 2	7, 3	7, 4	7, 5	7, 6	7, 7	7, 8
8	8, 1	8, 2	8, 3	8, 4	8, 5	8, 6	8, 7	8, 8

  b. There are 10 possible outcomes for which the sum is less than 6.

	1	2	3	4
1	1, 1	1, 2	1, 3	1, 4
2	2, 1	2, 2	2, 3	
3	3, 1	3, 2		
4	4, 1			

  c. P(sum is less than 6) $= \frac{10}{64} \approx 0.156$

  d. P(sum is more than 6) $= \frac{49}{64} \approx 0.766$

6. **a.** There are 32 branches.
 b. There are 10 ways of getting three Trues and two Falses.
 c. If the first two questions are true, then there are only three ways to get three Trues and two Falses: TFF, FTF, and FFT. There are eight different possibilities to answer the last three questions (look at the first three sets of choices on the tree diagram).
P(three Trues and two Falses) = $\frac{3}{8}$ = 0.375.

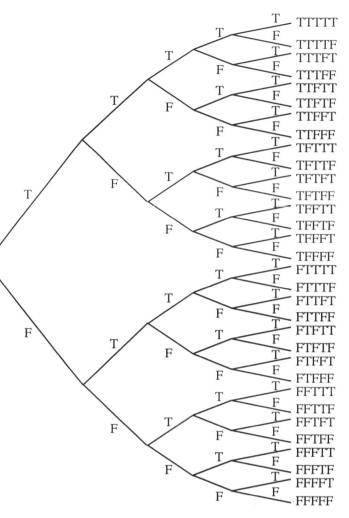

7. **a.**

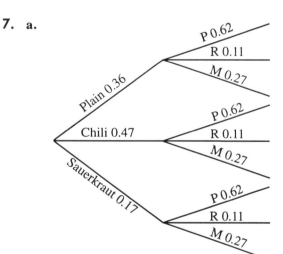

 b. P(chili dog on rye) = 0.47(0.11) = 0.0517
 c. P(sauerkraut on plain) = 0.17(0.62) = 0.1054 so P(**not** sauerkraut on plain) = 1 − 0.1054 = 0.8946
 d. P(plain on plain or chili on multigrain) = 0.36(0.62) + 0.47(0.27) = 0.3501

8. **a.**

	9th grade	10th grade	11th grade	12th grade	Total
Ice cream	18	37	85	114	254
Whipped cream	5	18	37	58	118
Total	23	55	122	172	372

 b. P(sophomore prefer ice cream) = $\frac{37}{55}$ ≈ 0.673 **c.** P(junior prefer whipped cream) = $\frac{37}{122}$ ≈ 0.303

 d. P(prefer ice cream is freshman) = $\frac{18}{254}$ ≈ 0.071 **e.** P(student prefer whipped cream) = $\frac{118}{372}$ ≈ 0.317

9. Her expected score is 20(0.3) + 10(0.4) + 5(0.2) + 1(0.05) = 11.05. To calculate the expected score, find the sum of the products of the value of the score and the percentage of predicted hits.

10. Set up a transition matrix to present the changes:

	Detroit	Chicago
Detroit	$\frac{7}{8}$	$\frac{1}{8}$
Chicago	$\frac{1}{12}$	$\frac{11}{12}$

After first month:

$$[500 \quad 500]\begin{bmatrix} \frac{7}{8} & \frac{1}{8} \\ \frac{1}{12} & \frac{11}{12} \end{bmatrix} = [479.167 \quad 520.833]$$

After second month:

$$[479.167 \quad 520.833]\begin{bmatrix} \frac{7}{8} & \frac{1}{8} \\ \frac{1}{12} & \frac{11}{12} \end{bmatrix} = [462.674 \quad 537.326]$$

After third month:

$$[462.674 \quad 537.326]\begin{bmatrix} \frac{7}{8} & \frac{1}{8} \\ \frac{1}{12} & \frac{11}{12} \end{bmatrix} = [449.617 \quad 550.383]$$

After fourth month:

$$[449.617 \quad 550.383]\begin{bmatrix} \frac{7}{8} & \frac{1}{8} \\ \frac{1}{12} & \frac{11}{12} \end{bmatrix} = [439.280 \quad 560.720]$$

In the long run: $[400 \quad 600]$

11. Answers will vary.

12. Answers will vary.

Chapter 9

Problem Set 9.1

1. a. Enter the two functions into the calculator and look for the points of intersection. You might need to adjust the range in order to see all these points. To find the coordinates of each point of intersection, trace and zoom on the graph or the table, or use the Calc Intersect function.

There are three points of intersections. They are (0, 1), (1, 2), and (5, 26).

Another way to find the points of intersection is to turn off the graphs of Y1 and Y2 and plot Y3 = Y1 – Y2. The *x*-intercept(s) of this graph will be the *x*-coordinate(s) of the point(s) of intersection of the two original equations. To find the *y*-coordinate(s), substitute each *x*-value into either of the original equations.

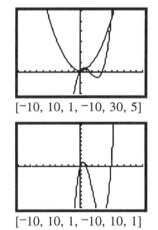

[−10, 10, 1, −10, 30, 5]

[−10, 10, 1, −10, 10, 1]

b. Look at the second graph in part a. To find the values that make Y1 < Y2, look at where the *y*-values are negative, which is when *x* < 0 or when 1 < *x* < 5. To find the values that make Y1 > Y2, look at where the graph is positive, which is when 0 < *x* < 1 or when *x* > 5.

2. a. Answers will vary, depending on how the students zoom in and look at their graph.

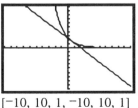

[−10, 10, 1, −10, 10, 1]

b. Graph Y3 = Y1 – Y2: Y1(1) = 1.25; Y2(1) = 1.176470588; Y3(1) = 0.0735294118

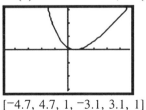

[−4.7, 4.7, 1, −3.1, 3.1, 1]

c. If the *y*-values are equal at the point of intersection, then Y3 = Y1 – Y2 = 0. This point will appear as an *x*-intercept of the graph of Y3.

d. The graph never crosses the *x*-axis.

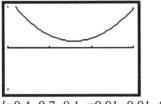

[⁻0.4, 0.7, 0.1, ⁻0.01, 0.01, 0.01]

e. The graphs of the two equations never intersect.

3. Enter the functions into Y₁ and Y₂ and graph Y₃ = Y₁ − Y₂. Trace and zoom in on the graph or the table to find the *x*-intercept of the graph. The *x*-intercept is 9.063. Substitute this value into either Y₁ or Y₂ to find the *y*-value of the point of intersection. (9.063, 2.393)

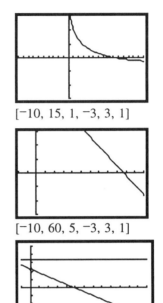

[⁻10, 15, 1, ⁻3, 3, 1]

4. **a.** Enter the functions into Y₁ and Y₂ and graph Y₃ = Y₁ − Y₂. Trace and zoom in on the graph or the table to find the *x*-intercept of the graph. The *x*-intercept is 48.57, so the springs are the same length when 48.57 g of mass are added.

[⁻10, 60, 5, ⁻3, 3, 1]

b. There are many ways to find the solution. You could graph Y₄ = 10 and Y₅ = ⁻10 and look for the intersection of those lines with Y₃, which will represent when one spring is 10 cm longer than the other. When 120 g have been added, the second spring is 10 cm longer. You could also solve this problem algebraically.

[⁻10, 130, 10, ⁻15, 15, 3]

c. Answers will vary: The first spring, which is longer without any attached mass, has less stretch than the second spring. The second spring, which is shorter without any attached mass, will stretch further with additional amounts of added mass.

5. Answers will vary.

6. **a.** No. When 25 pogo sticks are sold, the cost line is above the income line.
b. Yes. When 200 pogo sticks are sold, the income line is above the cost line. The profit is approximately $120. (Approximate the difference between the *y*-values for income and cost for 200 pogo sticks.)
c. The break-even point is about 120 pogo sticks. (Look for the point where the cost and income lines intersect.)
d. The profit is approximately $80. (Approximate the difference between the *y*-values for income and cost for 150 pogo sticks.)

7. **a.–b.** Enter the years, using a reference year of 1900, in list 1, the men's times in seconds in list 2, and the women's times in seconds in list 3. Answers will vary depending on the regression equations used. The answers given below are based on least-squares lines. When the data has been entered into the three lists, calculate the linear regressions for (*year, men's time*) and (*year, women's time*), enter these regressions into y_1 and y_2, and plot the lines.

(*year, men's time*): $y = 162.04 − 0.54x$

(*year, women's time*): $y = 198.76 − 0.84x$

The point of intersection is (122.45, 94.4). In about the year 1900 + 122 or ≈ 2022, winning times for men and women will be about the same.

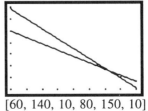

[60, 140, 10, 80, 150, 10]

c. Answers will vary.

d. For the 1994 Olympics, $x = 94$. Using the men's model, the predicted time would be $y = 162.04 - 0.54(94) = 111.28$ sec $= 1.85$ min or 1:51. The model is off $1:51.29 - 1:51 = 0.29$ sec. Using the women's model, the predicted time would be $y = 198.76 - 0.84(94) = 119.8$ sec ≈ 2.00 min. The model is off by $2:02.19 - 2:00 = 2.19$ sec. The actual times are close to the predicted times of the models. The residual for the 1994 men's time is 0.005 min and for the 1994 women's time is 0.0365 min.

8. a. A cost equation modeling the Phrequent Phoner plan is $Cost = 20 + 17(\text{int } x - 1)$ and a cost equation modeling the Pals and Buddies plan is $Cost = 50 + 11(\text{int } x - 1)$.

b.

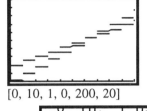

[0, 10, 1, 0, 200, 20]

c. If the time of the phone call is less than 6 min, the Phrequent Phoner plan is less expensive. For times between 6 and 7 min, the plans charge the same rate. If the time of the phone call is greater than or equal to 7 min, the Phrequent Phoner plan is more expensive than the Pals and Buddies plan. (You could look at the table to see these results.)

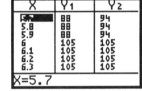
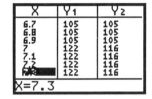

Take Another Look 9.1

$\pi^{10} > 10^{\pi}$; $\log \pi^{10} > \log 10^{\pi}$; $10 \log \pi > \pi \log 10$; $4.97 > 3.14$.
$100^{100} > 1000^{10}$ because $\log 100^{100} > \log 1000^{10}$; $100 \log 100 > 10 \log 1000$; $200 > 30$.
100^x intersects with x^{100} at the point (1.0495, 125.614); $100^x \geq x^{100}$ when $x < 1.0495$.

Problem Set 9.2

1. Answers will vary for the approximate solution before zooming.

a. $y = 3.2x + 44.61$
$y = {}^-5.1x + 5.60$
$3.2x + 44.61 = {}^-5.1x + 5.60$
$8.3x = {}^-39.01$
$x = {}^-4.7$
$y = 3.2({}^-4.7) + 44.61 = 29.57$
$({}^-4.7, 29.57)$

[${}^-10$, 0, 1, 0, 40, 10]

b. $y = \frac{2}{3}x - 3$
$y = \frac{{}^-5}{6}x + 7$
$\frac{2}{3}x - 3 = \frac{{}^-5}{6}x + 7$
$\frac{3}{2}x = 10$
$x = \frac{20}{3} = 6\frac{2}{3}$
$y = \left(\frac{2}{3}\right)\left(\frac{20}{3}\right) - 3 = 1\frac{4}{9}$
$\left(6\frac{2}{3}, 1\frac{4}{9}\right)$

[0, 10, 1, ${}^-5$, 5, 1]

c. $y = 4.7x + 25.1$
$3.1x + 2y = 8.2$
$3.1x + 2(4.7x + 25.1) = 8.2$
$3.1x + 9.4x + 50.2 = 8.2$
$12.5x = {}^-42$
$x = {}^-3.36$
$y = 4.7({}^-3.36) + 25.1 = 9.308$
$({}^-3.36, 9.308)$

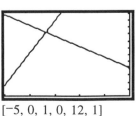

[${}^-5$, 0, 1, 0, 12, 1]

2. Answers will vary for the approximate solution before zooming.

  a. Graph both equations:

$$y = +\sqrt{\dfrac{x^2}{4} - 25}$$

$$y = -\sqrt{\dfrac{x^2}{4} - 25}$$

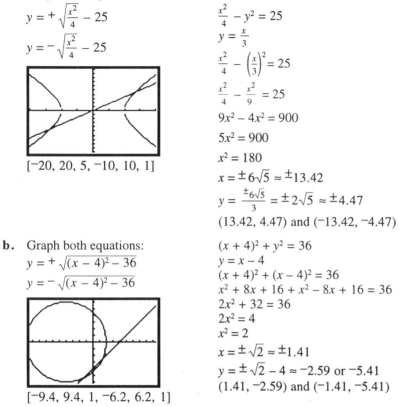

$[-20, 20, 5, -10, 10, 1]$

$$\dfrac{x^2}{4} - y^2 = 25$$
$$y = \dfrac{x}{3}$$
$$\dfrac{x^2}{4} - \left(\dfrac{x}{3}\right)^2 = 25$$
$$\dfrac{x^2}{4} - \dfrac{x^2}{9} = 25$$
$$9x^2 - 4x^2 = 900$$
$$5x^2 = 900$$
$$x^2 = 180$$
$$x = \pm 6\sqrt{5} \approx \pm 13.42$$
$$y = \dfrac{\pm 6\sqrt{5}}{3} = \pm 2\sqrt{5} \approx \pm 4.47$$
$(13.42, 4.47)$ and $(-13.42, -4.47)$

  b. Graph both equations:
$$y = +\sqrt{(x-4)^2 - 36}$$
$$y = -\sqrt{(x-4)^2 - 36}$$

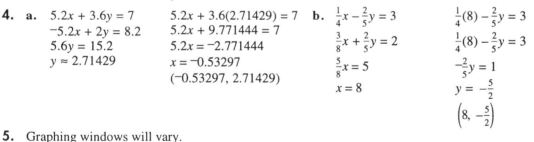

$[-9.4, 9.4, 1, -6.2, 6.2, 1]$

$$(x+4)^2 + y^2 = 36$$
$$y = x - 4$$
$$(x+4)^2 + (x-4)^2 = 36$$
$$x^2 + 8x + 16 + x^2 - 8x + 16 = 36$$
$$2x^2 + 32 = 36$$
$$2x^2 = 4$$
$$x^2 = 2$$
$$x = \pm\sqrt{2} \approx \pm 1.41$$
$$y = \pm\sqrt{2} - 4 \approx -2.59 \text{ or } -5.41$$
$(1.41, -2.59)$ and $(-1.41, -5.41)$

3. **a.** Cost for first camera: $y = 47 + 11.5x$
     Cost for second camera: $y = 59 + 4.95x$
  b. $47 + 11.5x = 59 + 4.95x$; $6.55x = 12$; $x \approx 1.83$ yr
  c. Answers will vary. You could graph each cost function and zoom in for the intersection point; you could use substitution to find the intersection point, or you could look at a table to find the break-even point where the cost for both cameras is the same.

4. **a.**

$5.2x + 3.6y = 7$ $5.2x + 3.6(2.71429) = 7$
$-5.2x + 2y = 8.2$ $5.2x + 9.771444 = 7$
$5.6y = 15.2$ $5.2x = -2.771444$
$y \approx 2.71429$ $x = -0.53297$
             $(-0.53297, 2.71429)$

  b.

$\dfrac{1}{4}x - \dfrac{2}{5}y = 3$ $\dfrac{1}{4}(8) - \dfrac{2}{5}y = 3$
$\dfrac{3}{8}x + \dfrac{2}{5}y = 2$ $\dfrac{1}{4}(8) - \dfrac{2}{5}y = 3$
$\dfrac{5}{8}x = 5$ $-\dfrac{2}{5}y = 1$
$x = 8$ $y = -\dfrac{5}{2}$
           $\left(8, -\dfrac{5}{2}\right)$

5. Graphing windows will vary.

  a.

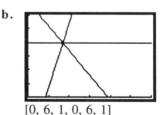

$[0, 6, 1, 0, 6, 1]$

  b.

$[0, 6, 1, 0, 6, 1]$

  c. $1.8y_1 = 8.46x - 7.2$
       $4.7y_2 = -8.46x + 32.9$
  d. $6.5y = 25.7$
       $y = \dfrac{25.7}{6.5} \approx 3.954$
  e. Answers will vary.

6. a. Multiply the first equation by 3.
$$3(2.1x + 3.6y = 7)$$
$$6.3x + 10.8y = 21$$

Add this result to the second equation.
$$6.3x + 10.8y = 21$$
$$-6.3x + y = 8.2$$
$$11.8y = 29.2$$

Solve for y.
$$y = \frac{29.2}{11.8} \approx 2.4746$$

Substitute this y-value into one of the equations and solve for x.
$$-6.3x + 2.4746 = 8.2$$
$$-6.3x = 5.7254$$
$$x = \frac{5.7254}{-6.3} \approx -0.9088$$

The solution is $(-0.9088, 2.4746)$.

b. Multiply the first equation by -3.
$$-3\left(\frac{1}{4}x - \frac{4}{5}y = 7\right) \rightarrow \frac{-3}{4}x + \frac{12}{5}y = -21$$

Add this result to the second equation.
$$\frac{-3}{4}x + \frac{12}{5}y = -21$$
$$\frac{3}{4}x + \frac{2}{5}y = 2$$
$$\frac{14}{5}y = -19$$

Solve for y.
$$y = \frac{-95}{14} \approx -6.786$$

Substitute this y-value into one of the equations and solve for x.
$$\frac{1}{4}x - \frac{4}{5}(-6.786) = 7$$
$$\frac{1}{4}x + 5.4288 = 7: \frac{1}{4}x = 1.5712$$
$$x \approx 6.286$$

The solution is $(6.286, -6.786)$.

7. a. Multiply the second equation by -3.6.
$$-3.6(-6.3x + y = 8.2)$$
$$22.68x - 3.6y = -29.52$$

Add this result to the first equation.
$$22.68x - 3.6y = -29.52$$
$$2.1x + 3.6y = 7$$
$$24.78x = -22.52$$

Solve for x.
$$x = \frac{-22.52}{24.78} \approx -0.9088$$

Substitute this x-value into one of the equations and solve for y.
$$2.1(-0.9088) + 3.6y = 7$$
$$-1.908 + 3.6y = 7$$
$$3.6y = 8.908$$
$$y = \frac{8.908}{3.6} \approx 2.4746$$

The solution is $(-0.9088, 2.4746)$.

b. Multiply the second equation by 2.
$$2\left(\frac{3}{4}x + \frac{2}{5}y = 2\right) \rightarrow \frac{6}{4}x + \frac{4}{5}y = 4$$

Add this result to the first equation.
$$\frac{6}{4}x + \frac{4}{5}y = 4$$
$$\frac{1}{4}x - \frac{4}{5}y = 7$$
$$\frac{7}{4}x = 11$$

Solve for x.
$$x = \frac{44}{7} \approx 6.286$$

Substitute this x-value into one of the equations and solve for y.
$$\frac{1}{4}(6.286) - \frac{4}{5}y = 7$$
$$1.5714 - \frac{4}{5}y = 7$$
$$-\frac{4}{5}y = 5.4286$$
$$y \approx -6.786$$

The solution is $(6.286, -6.786)$.

8. a. Multiply the first equation by 5.
$$5(3x + 2y = 7) \rightarrow 15x + 10y = 35$$

Multiply the second equation by 3.
$$3(-5x + 4y = 6) \rightarrow -15x + 12y = 18$$

Add the first equation to the second equation.
$$22y = 53$$

Solve for y.
$$y = \frac{53}{22} \approx 2.409$$

Substitute this y-value into one of the equations and solve for x.
$$3x + 2(2.409) = 7$$
$$3x + 4.818 = 7$$
$$3x = 2.1818$$
$$x = \frac{2.1818}{3} \approx 0.727$$

The solution is $(0.727, 2.409)$.

b. Multiply the first equation by 2.
$$2(y = x^2 - 4) \rightarrow 2y = 2x^2 - 8$$

Add the first equation to the second equation.
$$2y = 2x^2 - 8$$
$$y = -2x^2 + 2$$
$$3y = -6$$

Solve for y.
$$y = \frac{-6}{3} = -2$$

Substitute this y-value into one of the equations and solve for x.
$$-2 = x^2 - 4$$
$$2 = x^2$$
$$x = \pm\sqrt{2} \approx \pm1.41$$

The solutions are $(1.41, -2)$ and $(-1.41, -2)$.

9. The conversion formula is $C = \frac{5}{9}(F - 32)$. We want $F = 3C$. Substitute into the conversion formula: $C = \frac{5}{9}(3C - 32)$; $9C = 15C - 160$; $160 = 6C$; $C \approx 26.67$ so $F = 3C = 3(26.67) \approx 80°$.

10. Answers will vary.

11. The first sequence has the equation $y = 11.7 + 0.3x$, and the second sequence has the equation $y = 14.8 + 0.2x$. Using substitution, $11.7 + 0.3x = 14.8 + 0.2x$; $0.1x = 3.1$; $x = 31$. For the 31st term, both sequences have the same value, which is $11.7 + 0.3(31) = 21$.

Take Another Look 9.2

C represents the city population and R represents the rural population.

$$[C \ R] = [C \ R],$$
$$[0.99C + 0.10R \quad 0.01C + 0.90R] = [C \ R].$$

$$0.99C + 0.10R = C \quad \Rightarrow \quad 0.10R = 0.01C$$
$$0.01C + 0.90R = R \quad \Rightarrow \quad 0.01C = 0.10R$$

Notice that the two resulting equations are the same. Confirm that both are equivalent to $C = 10R$.

The populations approach 22.7 million in the city and 2.27 million in rural areas.

Problem Set 9.3

1. a. i.

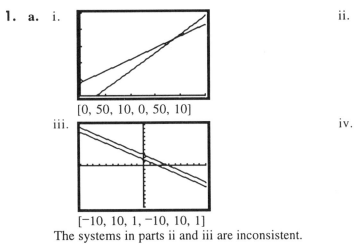

[0, 50, 10, 0, 50, 10]

ii.

[−10, 10, 1, −10, 10, 1]

iii.

[−10, 10, 1, −10, 10, 1]

iv.

[−10, 10, 1, −10, 10, 1]

The systems in parts ii and iii are inconsistent.

b. The graphs of the systems that are inconsistent are parallel and do not intersect.

c. ii. $y = \frac{3}{4}x - 4$

$y = 0.75x + 3$

$\frac{3}{4}x - 4 = 0.75x + 3$

$^-4 = 3$

iii. $3(4x + 6y = 9) \rightarrow 12x + 18y = 27$

$^-10(1.2x + 1.8y = 4.7) \rightarrow ^-12x - 18y = ^-47$

$0 = ^-20$

When you try to solve an inconsistent system, you reach a numerical impossibility.

d. You can recognize an inconsistent linear system without graphing it because the lines have the same slope. In standard form, $Ax + By = C$, the slope is $-\frac{A}{B}$.

2. Answers will vary. Samples are given below.

a. $y = 2x + b$ where b is any number except 4.

b. $y = \frac{-1}{3}x + b$ where b is any number except $^-3$.

c. $2x + 5y = b$ where b is any number except 10.

d. $x - 2y = b$ where b is any number except $^-6$.

3. a. i.

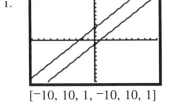

[−10, 10, 1, −10, 10, 1]

ii.

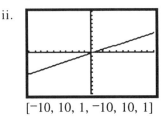

[−10, 10, 1, −10, 10, 1]

iii.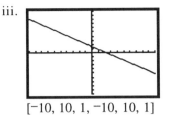

[−10, 10, 1, −10, 10, 1]

iv.

[−10, 10, 1, −10, 10, 1]

Parts ii and iii are dependent linear systems.

b. The graphs of dependent linear systems are the same line—one is graphed on top of the other.

c. ii. $y = \frac{1}{4}(2x - 1)$

$y = 0.5x - 0.25$

$\frac{1}{4}(2x - 1) = 0.5x - 0.25$

$\frac{1}{2}x - \frac{1}{4} = 0.5x - 0.25$

$0 = 0$

iii. $3(4x + 6y = 9) \rightarrow 12x + 18y = 27$

$-10(1.2x + 1.8y = 2.7) \rightarrow -12x - 18y = -27$

$0 = 0$

When you try to solve a dependent system, you get a true statement like $0 = 0$.

d. A dependent linear system (having multiple solutions) will have the same slope and the same intercept, or the equations are multiples of each other.

4. Answers will vary. Samples are given below.

a. $2y = 4x + 8$, or multiply the original equation by any other number.

b. $3y = -x - 9$, or multiply the original equation by any other number.

c. $4x + 10y = 20$, or multiply the original equation by any other number.

d. $2x - 4y = -12$, or multiply the original equation by any other number.

5. a. Because $x = 3t + 1$ and $x = 2 - 4t^2$,

$3t + 1 = 2 - 4t^2$.

Solve for t.

$4t^2 + 3t - 1 = 0$

$(t + 1)(t - 0.25) = 0$

$t = -1$ or 0.25

At $t = 0.25$:

$x = 3(0.25) + 1 = 1.75$ and

$y = 8(0.25)^2 - 2 = -1.5$

$x = 2 - 4(0.25)^2 = 1.75$ and

$y = 6(0.25) - 3 = -1.5$ so at $t = 0.25$

the intersection is $(1.75, -1.5)$.

At $t = -1$:

$x = 3(-1) + 1 = -2$ and $y = 8(-1)^2 - 2 = 6$.

$x = 2 - 4(-1)^2 = -2$ and $y = 6(-1) - 3 = -9$.

So at $t = -1$ the graphs do not intersect.

b. Because $x = 3t + 1$ and $x = 2 - 3t$,

$3t + 1 = 2 - 3t$.

Solve for t.

$6t = 1$

$t = \frac{1}{6}$

At $t = \frac{1}{6}$, $x = 3\left(\frac{1}{6}\right) + 1 = 1.5$ and $y = 4\left(\frac{1}{6}\right) + 2 = 2\frac{2}{3}$;

$x = 2 - 3\left(\frac{1}{6}\right) = 1.5$ and $y = 4 - 2\left(\frac{1}{6}\right) = 3\frac{2}{3}$ so there is

no solution or intersection point for this system.

6. $x_{1t} = 200t \cos 45$, $y_{1t} = 200t \sin 45$; $x_{2t} = -180t \cos 30 + 200$,

$y_{2t} = 180t \sin 30$ (Since the second plane is starting 200 mi east of the first plane, add 200 to the x-value. Remember to change from a navigation angle to a trigonometric angle.)

To find out if they are in danger of hitting each other, set a third equation as $x = t$ and $y = \sqrt{(x_1 - x_2)^2 + (y_1 - y_2)^2}$.

Trace to find the nearest the two planes are to each other.

The two planes never get closer than 34.1 mi, so they do not seem to be in any danger of hitting each other.

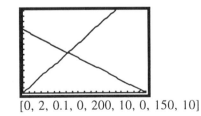

[0, 2, 0.1, 0, 200, 10, 0, 150, 10]

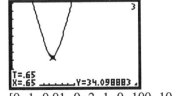

T=.65
X=.65 ....Y=34.098883

[0, 1, 0.01, 0, 2, 1, 0, 100, 10]

7. $34.3 = ab^3$ and $8.2 = ab^7$. Solve the first equation for a and substitute the result into the second equation: $a = \frac{34.3}{b^3}$; $8.23543 = \frac{34.3}{b^3}(b^7)$; $8.23543 = 34.3(b^4)$; $b^4 = 0.24$; $b = (0.24)^{(1/4)} \approx 0.7$; $a = \frac{34.3}{0.7^3}$; $a = 100$.

8. For the first service, $y_1 = 6 - 23$ int (^-x) and for the second service, $y_2 = 550 - 175$ int $\left(\frac{-x}{26}\right)$.
   (Note: 1 lb equals 16 oz.) Graph and trace to find out for which weights each service is cheaper.

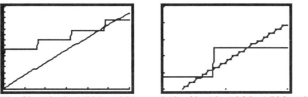

[0, 60, 10, 0, 1500, 100]   [40, 60, 10, 1000, 1500, 100]

Now trace to find which cost is cheaper. y_1 is more expensive when $46 < x \le 48$ or $x > 54$ oz.

9. Tan $50° = \frac{h}{x}$; tan $40° = \frac{h}{x + 10}$. Solve the first equation for h and substitute into the second equation: $h = x$ tan 50; tan $40 = \frac{x \tan 50}{x + 10}$; $0.839 = \frac{1.192x}{x + 10}$; $0.839x + 8.39 = 1.192x$; $8.39 = 0.353x$; $x = 23.8$ m. To find h, substitute in the value for x: $h = x$ tan $50 = 23.8(1.192) = 28.36$ m.

10. a. Answers will vary. Enter the time from 1900 in the first list, the San Jose population in the second list, and the Detroit population in the third list. Using the least-squares model (linear regression), graph the two functions and look for the intersection of the lines. The populations will be the same in the year 1900 + 96 or 1996.

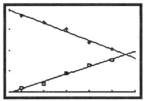

[45, 100, 10, 0, 2000000, 500000]

   b. According to the model, the populations will both be 903,634.
   c. The equations used (from linear regressions) are $y = ^-830,011.6 + 18,051.82x$ and $y = 2,930,012.7 - 21,099.93x$.

11. There are two possible answers: 12 peacocks, 16 pigeons, 20 swans, and 24 *sārasa* birds or 0 peacocks, 32 pigeons, 40 swans, and 0 *sārasa* birds.

Project: Bifurcation and Systems

There are many ways to find the solution, both computationally and visually. One very interesting way to find a cycle of two is to graph the function and its inverse. From your work with inverses, you should recognize that $x = 3.2y(1 - y)$ is the inverse of $y = 3.2x(1 - x)$. So when the function is equal to its inverse, you have a cycle of two.

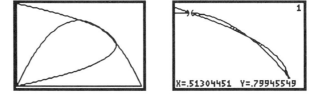

One way to look at the second function is to ask when $f(f(f(x)))$ comes back to x. You can see that there are four points of intersection on the graph. One of these points is the single-cycle point, which always returns its own value. The other three points form the tri-cycle. The uni-cycle occurs at $x = 0.7389033943$, and the bi-cycle for the second equation is {0.3691613885, 0.8919352172}. Note that this equation has a bi-cycle but the first equation has no tri-cycle (see the third picture below).

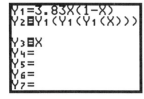 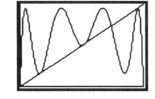 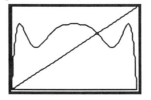

Problem Set 9.4

1. a. $\begin{bmatrix} 5 & 2 \\ 7 & 3 \end{bmatrix}\begin{bmatrix} 1 & -3 \\ 5 & -2 \end{bmatrix} = \begin{bmatrix} 5(1) + 2(5) & 5(-3) + 2(-2) \\ 7(1) + 3(5) & 7(-3) + 3(-2) \end{bmatrix} = \begin{bmatrix} 15 & -19 \\ 22 & -27 \end{bmatrix}$

b. $\begin{bmatrix} 4 & -1 \\ 3 & 6 \\ 2 & -3 \end{bmatrix} \begin{bmatrix} 2 & -5 & 0 \\ 1 & -2 & 7 \end{bmatrix} \begin{bmatrix} 4(2) + {}^-1(1) & 4(-5) + {}^-1(-2) & 4(0) + {}^-1(7) \\ 3(2) + 6(1) & 3(-5) + 6(-2) & 3(0) + 6(7) \\ 2(2) + {}^-3(1) & 2(-5) + {}^-3(-2) & 2(0) + {}^-3(7) \end{bmatrix} = \begin{bmatrix} 7 & -18 & -7 \\ 12 & -27 & 42 \\ 1 & -4 & -21 \end{bmatrix}$

c. This is not possible because you need the same number of rows in the second matrix as you have columns in the first matrix.

2. a. $\begin{bmatrix} 1 & 5 \\ 6 & 2 \end{bmatrix} \begin{bmatrix} a & b \\ c & d \end{bmatrix} = \begin{bmatrix} 1a + 5c & 1b + 5d \\ 6a + 2c & 6b + 2d \end{bmatrix} = \begin{bmatrix} -7 & 33 \\ 14 & -26 \end{bmatrix}$

$2(a + 5c = {}^-7) \quad \rightarrow \quad 2a + 10c = {}^-14 \qquad\qquad {}^-28a = {}^-84$

$-5(6a + 2c = 14) \quad \rightarrow \quad -30a - 10c = {}^-70 \qquad\qquad a = 3, c = {}^-2$

$2(b + 5d = 33) \quad \rightarrow \quad 2b + 10d = 66 \qquad\qquad {}^-28b = 196$

$-5(6b + 2d = {}^-26) \quad \rightarrow \quad -30b - 10d = 130 \qquad\qquad b = {}^-7, d = 8$

b. $\begin{bmatrix} 1 & 5 \\ 6 & 2 \end{bmatrix} \begin{bmatrix} a & b \\ c & d \end{bmatrix} = \begin{bmatrix} 1a + 5c & 1b + 5d \\ 6a + 2c & 6b + 2d \end{bmatrix} = \begin{bmatrix} 1 & 0 \\ 0 & 1 \end{bmatrix}$

$2(a + 5c = 1) \quad \rightarrow \quad 2a + 10c = 2 \qquad\qquad {}^-28a = 2$

$-5(6a + 2c = 0) \quad \rightarrow \quad -30a - 10c = 0 \qquad\qquad a = \frac{-1}{14}, c = \frac{3}{14}$

$b + 5d = 0 \quad \rightarrow \quad 2b + 10d = 0 \qquad\qquad {}^-28b = {}^-5$

$6b + 2d = 1 \quad \rightarrow \quad -30b - 10d = {}^-5 \qquad\qquad b = \frac{5}{28}, d = \frac{-1}{28}$

3. a. $\begin{bmatrix} 5 & 2 \\ 7 & 3 \end{bmatrix} \begin{bmatrix} 3 & -2 \\ -7 & 5 \end{bmatrix} = \begin{bmatrix} 5(3) + 2(-7) & 5(-2) + 2(5) \\ 7(3) + 3(-7) & 7(-2) + 3(5) \end{bmatrix} = \begin{bmatrix} 1 & 0 \\ 0 & 1 \end{bmatrix}$

b. $\begin{bmatrix} 1 & 5 & 4 \\ 6 & 2 & -2 \\ 0 & 3 & 1 \end{bmatrix} \begin{bmatrix} 0.16 & 0.14 & -0.36 \\ -0.12 & 0.02 & 0.52 \\ 0.36 & -0.06 & -0.56 \end{bmatrix} = \begin{bmatrix} 1 & 0 & 0 \\ 0 & 1 & 0 \\ 0 & 0 & 1 \end{bmatrix}$

c. Answers will vary. Two matrices are inverses if when you multiply them together you get the identity matrix as the answer.

4. a. $\begin{bmatrix} 4 & -3 \\ -5 & 4 \end{bmatrix}$ **b.** $\begin{bmatrix} -0.5555 & 1.4444 & 0.1111 \\ 0.5 & -1 & 0 \\ -1.6666 & 2.3333 & 0.3333 \end{bmatrix}$ or $\begin{bmatrix} \frac{-5}{9} & \frac{13}{9} & \frac{1}{9} \\ 0.5 & -1 & 0 \\ \frac{-7}{6} & \frac{7}{3} & \frac{1}{3} \end{bmatrix}$

c. $\begin{bmatrix} 1.4 & -0.6 \\ -2 & 1 \end{bmatrix}$ **d.** $\begin{bmatrix} -0.1190 & 0.1905 & 0.1667 \\ -0.0238 & 0.2381 & -0.1667 \\ -0.3095 & 0.0952 & -0.1667 \end{bmatrix}$ or $\begin{bmatrix} \frac{-5}{42} & \frac{13}{9} & \frac{1}{9} \\ \frac{-1}{42} & \frac{5}{21} & \frac{-1}{6} \\ \frac{-13}{42} & \frac{2}{21} & \frac{-1}{6} \end{bmatrix}$

5. a. $\begin{bmatrix} 5.2 & 3.6 \\ -5.2 & 2 \end{bmatrix} \begin{bmatrix} x \\ y \end{bmatrix} = \begin{bmatrix} 7 \\ 8.2 \end{bmatrix}$ **b.** $\begin{bmatrix} \frac{1}{4} & \frac{-2}{5} \\ \frac{3}{8} & \frac{2}{5} \end{bmatrix} \begin{bmatrix} x \\ y \end{bmatrix} = \begin{bmatrix} 3 \\ 2 \end{bmatrix}$

6. Enter the coefficients of the variables into matrix A and the constant terms into matrix B. To find the solution to the system, multiply $[A]^{-1} [B]$.

a. $[A] = \begin{bmatrix} 8 & 3 \\ 6 & 5 \end{bmatrix}$; $[B] = \begin{bmatrix} 41 \\ 39 \end{bmatrix}$; $[A]^{-1}[B] = \begin{bmatrix} 4 \\ 3 \end{bmatrix}$ **b.** $[A] = \begin{bmatrix} 11 & -5 \\ 9 & 2 \end{bmatrix}$; $[B] = \begin{bmatrix} -38 \\ -25 \end{bmatrix}$; $[A]^{-1}[B] = \begin{bmatrix} -3 \\ 1 \end{bmatrix}$

c. $[A] = \begin{bmatrix} 2 & 1 & -2 \\ 6 & 2 & -4 \\ 4 & -1 & 3 \end{bmatrix}$; $[B] = \begin{bmatrix} 1 \\ 3 \\ 5 \end{bmatrix}$; $[A]^{-1}[B] = \begin{bmatrix} 0.5 \\ 6 \\ 3 \end{bmatrix}$

d. $[A] = \begin{bmatrix} 4 & 1 & 2 & -3 \\ -3 & 3 & -1 & 4 \\ 5 & 4 & 3 & -1 \\ -1 & 2 & 5 & 1 \end{bmatrix}$; $[B] = \begin{bmatrix} -16 \\ 20 \\ -10 \\ -4 \end{bmatrix}$; $[A]^{-1}[B] = \begin{bmatrix} -1 \\ 1 \\ -2 \\ 3 \end{bmatrix}$

7. a. $2l + 2w = 44$, $l = 2 + 2w$; $2(2 + 2w) + 2w = 44$; $4 + 4w + 2w = 44$; $6w = 40$; $w = \frac{20}{3}$ cm, $l = \frac{46}{3}$ cm

   b. $2l + b = 40$, $b = l - 2$; $2l + l - 2 = 40$; $3l = 42$; $l = 14$ cm, $b = 12$ cm

   c. $f = 3c - 0.4$, $f = 1.8c + 32$; $3c - 0.4 = 1.8c + 32$; $1.2c = 32.4$; $c = 27°C$, $f = 80.6°F$

8. a. The three equations are: $7t + 3a + 9s = 19.55$; $9t + 10a = 13$; $8t + 7a + 10s = 24.95$

$$\begin{bmatrix} 7 & 3 & 9 \\ 9 & 10 & 0 \\ 8 & 7 & 10 \end{bmatrix}\begin{bmatrix} t \\ a \\ s \end{bmatrix} = \begin{bmatrix} 19.55 \\ 13 \\ 24.95 \end{bmatrix}; \begin{bmatrix} t \\ a \\ s \end{bmatrix} = \begin{bmatrix} 0.5 \\ 0.85 \\ 1.5 \end{bmatrix}$$

   b. $5 + 10(0.5 + 0.85 + 1.5) = 28.50$

   c. Carey would have been better off buying a ticket book for $28.50 because it cost her $24.95 + $5.00 or $29.95.

9. a. First plan: $12,500 + 0.05(12)(3500) = \$14,600$
   Second plan: $6800 + 0.15(12)(3500) = \$13,100$

   b. $y = 12,500 + 0.05(12)x = 12,500 + 0.6x$ **c.** $y = 6800 + 0.15(12)x = 6800 + 1.8x$

   d. $12,500 + 0.6x = 6800 + 1.8x$; $5700 = 1.2x$; $x = 4750$. The second plan will be the better choice if they sell more than 4750 tickets.

   e. Answers will vary. Since the hall holds 2200 people, and the series will run for three consecutive nights, the company can sell a potential of 6600 seats.

10. Write equations to represent each class, using s to represent the number of students in the second-hour class, t to represent the number of students in the third-hour class, and v to represent the number of students in the seventh-hour class.

$\frac{1}{2}s + \frac{1}{3}t + \frac{1}{4}v = 18$

$\frac{1}{4}s + \frac{1}{2}t + \frac{1}{6}v = 16$

$\frac{1}{4}s + \frac{1}{6}t + \frac{7}{12}v = 20$

$$\begin{bmatrix} \frac{1}{2} & \frac{1}{3} & \frac{1}{4} \\ \frac{1}{4} & \frac{1}{2} & \frac{1}{6} \\ \frac{1}{4} & \frac{1}{6} & \frac{7}{12} \end{bmatrix}^{-1} \begin{bmatrix} 18 \\ 16 \\ 20 \end{bmatrix} = \begin{bmatrix} s \\ t \\ v \end{bmatrix}; \begin{bmatrix} s \\ t \\ v \end{bmatrix} = \begin{bmatrix} 12 \\ 18 \\ 24 \end{bmatrix}$$

There are 12 students in the second hour, 18 in the third hour, and 24 in the seventh hour.

11. The two equations are $9c + 7w = 107$ and $7c + 9w = 101$.

$$\begin{bmatrix} 9 & 7 \\ 7 & 9 \end{bmatrix}^{-1}\begin{bmatrix} 107 \\ 101 \end{bmatrix} = \begin{bmatrix} c \\ w \end{bmatrix}; \begin{bmatrix} c \\ w \end{bmatrix} = \begin{bmatrix} 8 \\ 5 \end{bmatrix}$$

The price of a citron is 8; the price of a fragrant wood apple is 5.

Project: Nonlinear Systems with Three Variables

a. The given solution uses substitution to reduce the equations to one variable. Solve for that variable by graphing. Then use that value to further reduce the equations. The two points of intersection at $(x, y, z) = (2.179113745, -0.3623730567, 7.262087348)$ and $(0.2415820378, -3.268670617, 7.262087348)$.

$z = 9x^2 + 4y^2 - 36$

$z + 36 = 9x^2 + 4y^2$

$z = 6xy + 12$

$z - 12 = 6xy$

$z = 3x - 2y$

$z^2 = (3x - 2y)^2$

$z^2 = 9x^2 - 12xy + 4y^2$

$z^2 = (9x^2 + 4y^2) - 2(6xy)$

$z^2 = (z + 36) - 2(z - 12)$

$z^2 = z + 36 - 2z + 24$

$z^2 = 60 - z$

$z = 7.262087348, -8.262087348$

$7.26\cdots = 3x - 2y$

$2y(7.26\cdots = 3x - 2y)$

$14.52\cdots y = 6xy - 4y^2$

$4y^2 + 14.52\cdots y = 6xy$

$7.26\cdots - 12 = 6xy$

$4.73\cdots = 6xy$

$4.73\cdots = 4y^2 + 14.52\cdots y$

$y = -0.3623730567, -3.268670617$

$7.26\cdots = 3x - 2(-0.362\cdots)$

$7.26\cdots = 3x + 0.724\cdots$

$6.53\cdots = 3x$

$x = 2.179113745$

$7.26\cdots = 3x - 2(-3.26\cdots)$

$7.26\cdots = 3x + 6.53\cdots$

$0.724\cdots = 3x$

$x = 0.2415820378$

b. The authors were able to find only one point of solution for this system at $(x, y, z) = (-70.98456354, 80.015080061, 348.41143848)$. One procedure is to put the three functions into Y = using X for x, Y for z, and A for y. Then store a value for $A(y)$ and find a window to view all three intersections. Continue to change the A-value to move the intersections closer together. If there is another point of intersection, the authors would like to know about it.

Problem Set 9.5

1. $y \geq 2.4x + 2$ and $y \leq -x^2 - 2x + 6.4$
All inequations are shaded so that the feasible region is not shaded.

2.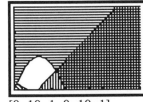

[0, 10, 1, 0, 10, 1]

Vertex points: $(0, 2)$, $(0, 5)$, $(2.752, 3.596)$, $(3.529, 2.353)$

3.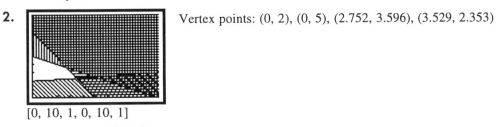

[0, 10, 1, 0, 10, 1]

Vertex points: $(1, 0)$, $(1.875, 0)$, $(3.307, 2.291)$, $(0.209, 0.791)$

4.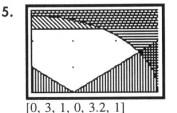

[0, 5, 1, 0, 5, 1]

$y \leq (12 - 4x)/3$, $y \leq (8 - 1.6x)/2$, $y \leq 2 - 2x$

Vertex points: $(0, 4)$, $(3, 0)$, $(1, 0)$, $(0, 2)$

5.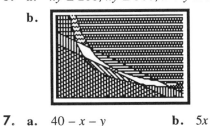

[0, 3, 1, 0, 3.2, 1]

Vertex points: $(1, 0)$, $(2.562, 1.562)$, $(1.658, 2.5)$, $(0, 2.5)$, $(0, 1)$

6. **a.** $xy \geq 200$, $xy \leq 300$, $x + y \geq 33$, $x + y \leq 40$ or $y \geq \frac{200}{x}$, $y \leq \frac{300}{x}$, $y \geq 33 - x$, $y \leq 40 - x$

b.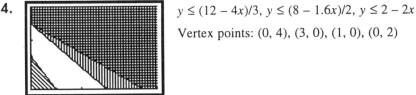

c. Use the trace to locate the picture measurements to see if they are in the feasibility region or not.
12.4 by 16.3, no; 16 by 17.5, yes; 14.3 by 17.5, no.

7. **a.** $40 - x - y$ **b.** $5x$ **c.** $5x + 2y > 100$ **d.** $x + y < 30$; $5x + 2y > 100$; $y \geq 0$

e. $5x + 2y > 100 \Rightarrow y > \frac{100 - 5x}{2}$;

$x + y < 30 \Rightarrow y < 30 - x; y \geq 0; x \geq 0$

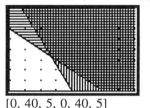

[0, 40, 5, 0, 40, 5]

f. (20, 0), (30, 0), (13.33, 16.67)

8. a. First, substitute the given point values for x and y in the generic equation. There will be three equations in three variables, a, b, and c. Set up a matrix equation in the form $[A][X] = [B]$ and find $[X]$.

$$\begin{aligned} -32 &= 4a - 2b + c \\ 7 &= a + b + c \\ 63 &= 9a + 3b + c \end{aligned} \quad \begin{bmatrix} 4 & -2 & 1 \\ 1 & 1 & 1 \\ 9 & 3 & 1 \end{bmatrix} \begin{bmatrix} a \\ b \\ c \end{bmatrix} = \begin{bmatrix} -32 \\ 7 \\ 63 \end{bmatrix}; \begin{bmatrix} a \\ b \\ c \end{bmatrix} = \begin{bmatrix} 3 \\ 16 \\ -12 \end{bmatrix}$$

b. The equation of the parabola is $y = 3x^2 + 16x - 12$.

c. Answers will vary. Substitute each point in the equation to verify that they lie on the parabola.

$$\begin{aligned} -32 &= 3(-2)2 + 16(-2) - 12 \\ &= 3(4) - 32 - 12 \\ &= -32 \end{aligned}$$

Do the same for the other two points.

9. Answers will vary.

Problem Set 9.6

Change the window format to Grid On in order to see the integer points in the feasible region. All inequations are shaded such that the feasible region is not shaded. Points on the border are part of the interior also because the inequations are not strict inequations.

1. i. a. $y \leq \frac{-2x + 6}{3}$, $y \leq 6 - 4x$, $x > 0$, $y > 0$

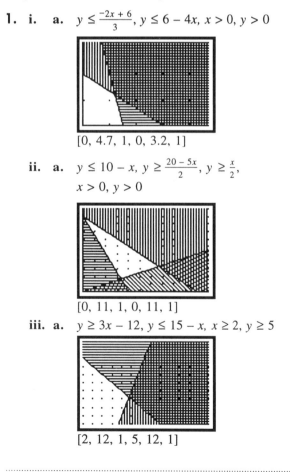

[0, 4.7, 1, 0, 3.2, 1]

b. (0, 0), (1.5, 0), (1.2, 1.2), (0, 2)

c. The possible integer points are (0, 0), (0, 1), (0, 2), (1, 0), (1, 1). The maximum value of $5x + 2y$ for interior points occurs at (1, 1): $5(1) + 2(1) = 7$.

d. The maximum value of $5x + 2y$ for vertex points occurs at (1.2, 1.2): $5(1.2) + 2(1.2) = 12$.

ii. a. $y \leq 10 - x$, $y \geq \frac{20 - 5x}{2}$, $y \geq \frac{x}{2}$, $x > 0$, $y > 0$

[0, 11, 1, 0, 11, 1]

b. (3.3333, 1.6667), (6.6667, 3.3333), (0, 10)

c. The possible integer points are (0, 10), (1, 8), (1, 9), (2, 6), (2, 7), (2, 8), (3, 3), (3, 4), (3, 5), (3, 6), (3, 7), (4, 2), (4, 3), (4, 4), (4, 5), (4, 6), (5, 3), (5, 4), (5, 5), (6, 3), (6, 4). The minimum value of $x + 3y$ for interior points occurs at (4, 2): $4 + 3(2) = 10$.

d. The minimum value of $x + 3y$ for vertex points occurs at (3.3333, 1.6667): $3.3333 + 3(1.6667) = 8.3333$.

iii. a. $y \geq 3x - 12$, $y \leq 15 - x$, $x \geq 2$, $y \geq 5$

[2, 12, 1, 5, 12, 1]

b. (2, 5), (5.6667, 5), (6.75, 8.25), (2, 13)

c. (2, 5), (2, 6) . . . (2, 13); (3, 5), (3, 6) . . . (3, 12) (4, 5), (4, 6) . . . (4, 11); (5, 5), (5, 6) . . . (5, 10) (6, 6), (6, 7) . . . (6, 9) The maximum value of $2x + y$ for interior points occurs at (6, 9): $2(6) + 9 = 21$.

d. The maximum value of $2x + y$ for vertex points occurs at (6.75, 8.25): $2(6.75) + 8.25 = 21.75$.

iv. a. $y \geq \frac{10 - x}{2}$, $y \geq 12 - 2x$, $y \geq x - 8$

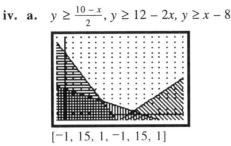

$[-1, 15, 1, -1, 15, 1]$

b. (4.6667, 2.6667), (8.6667, 0.6667)

c. There are an infinite set of possible interior points. The minimum value of $3x + 2y$ for interior points occurs at (4, 4): $3(4) + 2(4) = 20$.

d. The minimum value of $3x + 2y$ for vertex points occurs at (4.6667, 2.6667): $3(4.6667) + 2(2.6667) = 19.3333$.

Conclusion: Answers will vary. The optimal value is always located at the vertex of a region closest to or at the interior integer point with the optimal value.

2. a.

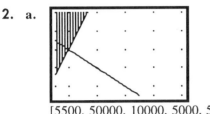

$[5500, 50000, 10000, 5000, 50000, 10000]$

The solution is the portion of the line $x + y = 40,000$ that lies between the shaded portions of the graph.

b. The integer point providing the maximum value is (10,000, 30,000), which is at the intersection of the line and the border equation $y = 3x$. The maximum value is $0.08(10,000) + 0.10(30,000) = 3,800$.

3. a. There are zero or more of each species in the region. (There cannot be a negative number of birds.)

b. The area required by species X plus the area required by species Y is no more than 180,000 m².

c. The total food requirements of species X plus the total food requirements of species Y is no more than 72,000 kg.

d.

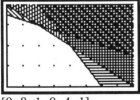

$[0, 1600, 100, 0, 1600, 100]$

$x \geq 0$, $y \geq 0$, $y \leq (180,000 - 120x)/90$, $y \leq (72,000 - 39.6x)/69.6$

The vertices of the region are (0, 0), (1500, 0), (1263.2, 315.8), and (0, 1034.5).

e. The maximum number of nesting pairs is 1578. Any of the points (1261, 317), (1262, 316), (1263, 315), (1264, 314), or (1265, 313) give this total.

4. Answers will vary.

Problem Set 9.7

1.

	Number of shawls (x)	Number of afghans (y)	Constraining value
Spinning (hr)	1	2	≤ 8
Dyeing (hr)	1	1	≤ 6
Weaving (hr)	1	4	≤ 14
Profit	\$16	\$20	

$x + 2y \leq 8$, $x + y \leq 6$, $x + 4y \leq 14$, $x \geq 0$, $y \geq 0$ or $y \leq \frac{8 - x}{2}$, $y \leq 6 - x$, $y \leq \frac{14 - x}{4}$: Profit = $16x + 20y$

Vertices: (0, 0), (6, 0), (4, 2), (2, 3), (0, 3.5)
The maximum profit occurs at (4, 2) or $16(4) + 20(2) = \$104$.
They should make four shawls and two afghans.

$[0, 8, 1, 0, 4, 1]$

2.

	Siberians	Poodles	Constraining value
Number of poodles		y	≤ 20
Number of Siberians	x		≤ 15
Food	6	2	≤ 100
Training	250	1000	≤ 10000
Profit	80	200	

$y \le 20$, $x \le 15$, $6x + 2y \le 100$, $250x + 1{,}000y \le 10{,}000$, $x \ge 0$, $y \ge 0$ or $y \le 20$, $x \le 15$, $y \le \frac{100 - 6x}{2}$, $y \le \frac{10{,}000 - 250x}{1000}$, $x \ge 0$, $y \ge 0$: Profit $= 80x + 200y$

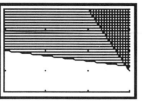

The vertices of the feasible region are (0, 0), (15, 0), (15, 5), (14.5455, 6.3636), and (0, 10).

To maximize profits, they should raise 14 Siberians and 6 poodles: $80(14) + 200(6) = \$2{,}320$.

[0, 15, 5, 0, 20, 5]

3. x = the number of newspaper ads; y = the number of radio ads. Newspaper minimum: $x \ge 4$; radio minimum: $y \ge 5$; cost: $50x + 100y \le 1000$ or $y \le \frac{1000 - 50x}{100}$; optimize number of people reached: $8{,}000x + 15{,}000y$

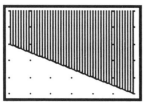

The vertices of the feasible region are (4, 5), (4, 8), and (10, 5).
To maximize the number of people reached, place ten radio ads and five newspaper ads: $8{,}000(10) + 15{,}000(5) = 155{,}000$ people.
Answers will vary. One assumption may be that people who listen to the radio are independent of people who read the newspaper.

[0, 10, 1, 5, 10, 1]

4.

	Hectares of coffee (x)	Hectares of cocoa (y)	Constraining values
Available land	x	y	≤ 500,000
Hectares of coffee (x)	x		≥ 100,000
Hectares of cocoa (y)		y	≥ 200,000
Production		y	≤ 270,000
Available workers	$2x$	$5y$	≤ 1,750,000
Profit	$220x$	$310y$	

$x + y \le 500{,}000$ or $y \le 500{,}000 - x$, $x \ge 100{,}000$, $y \ge 200{,}000$, $y \le 270{,}000$, $2x + 5y \le 1{,}750{,}000$ or $y \le \frac{1{,}750{,}000 - 2x}{5}$: Profit $= 220x + 310y$

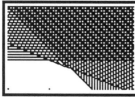

The vertices of the feasible region are (100,000, 200,000), (300,000, 200,000), (250,000, 250,000), (100,000, 270,000), and (200,000, 270,000).
The maximum profit occurs when you plant 250,000 hectares of coffee and 250,000 hectares of cocoa: Profit $= 220x + 310y = 220(250{,}000) + 310(250{,}000) = \$132{,}500{,}000$.

[100000, 400000, 100000, 200000, 400000, 100000]

5.

	Number of barrels of low-sulfur oil	Number of barrels of high-sulfur oil	Constraining values
Total barrels	x	y	≥ 1200
Percentage	$0.02x$	$0.06y$	$\leq 0.04(x + y)$
Cost	$18.50x$	$14.70x$	

$x + y \geq 1200$ or $y \geq 1200 - x$; $0.02x + 0.06y \leq 0.04(x + y)$ or $y \leq x$: Cost $= 18.50x + 14.70y$

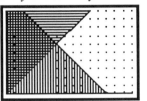

The vertices of the feasible region are (1200, 0) and (600, 600). The minimum cost will occur when you use 600 barrels of the low-sulfur and 600 barrels of the high-sulfur oil. Cost $= 18.50(600) + 14.70(600) = \$19{,}920$.

[0, 1500, 100, 0, 1000, 100]

Take Another Look 9.7

As you graph each of the lines representing the cost function, you should notice that they are all parallel with a slope of $^-0.6$ regardless of the cost value used.

The feasible region contains all the x-y pairs that satisfy all the inequalities but the maximum or minimum always occurs at one of the vertices.

Visually, this can be modeled using the *Geometer's Sketchpad*. (See the Linear Programming activity in *Integrating Algebra and Geometry*.)

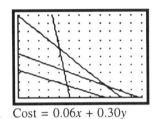

Cost $= 0.06x + 0.30y$

After graphing all the inequalities and determining the feasible region, graph a line $P = Ax + By$ such as $1.20 = 0.06x + 0.30y$. Then use *Sketchpad* to actually slide the line up or down across the feasible region (keeping the slope at a constant value). This shows the maximum or minimum cost occurring at a vertex of the region. This process could also show that two points could be on the same line for a maximum or minimum cost.

Other explanations might include: In three-dimensional space, the cost equation is a plane. The feasible portion of this plane lies directly above the feasible region in the x-y plane. The maximum or minimum points are at the vertex of the plane that is farthest from or closest to the x-y plane.

Project: Nonlinear Programming

The last inequation in this set should be changed to $0.5x - 10^y \leq 4$ or you don't get the right region when you graph it. Intersections occur at (6.8915844, 12.831312); (4.4874274, 3.712335); (10, 0); and (22.83942, 0.87038873). The maximum value for k is 181.9059791 when the circle contacts the last point listed.

 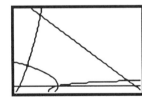 

Problem Set 9.8

1. Enter the coefficients of the variables into matrix A. If the determinant is not equal to 0, the system has a unique solution.
   a. determinant $= 0$
   b. determinant $= 124.4625$
   c. determinant $= 0$
   d. determinant $= 773.381$
   e. determinant $= 0$
   f. determinant $= 0$
   Only parts b and d have unique solutions. (Note: Be sure to enter the 0's for the missing variables in part e.)

2. Replace the first row of the matrix of the coefficients with a 1 followed by 0's for the rest of the row. Then multiply $[A]^{-1}[B]$ where $[B]$ consists of the answers to the equations. The solution to this new system will provide one point on the line of intersection. Test this point into the other equations in the system. If it works for all equations, the system is dependent. If the point does not work in all equations, the system is inconsistent.

   a. Dependent; the point $(16, {}^-5.333)$ works in both equations.

   c. Dependent; the point $(21, {}^-17, 1)$ works in all three equations.

   e. Inconsistent; the point $(16, 15.667, {}^-3.862)$ does not work in the first equation, but does work in the last two equations.

   f. Inconsistent; the point $(1, 1.209, 1.116, 0.256)$ does not work in the first equation, but does work in the last three equations.

3.

	True/false (w)	Fill in the blank (x)	Matching (y)	Essay (z)	Constraints
Points	$2w$	$4x$	$6y$	$10z$	$= 100$
Time	$1w$	$2x$	$5y$	$6z$	$= 60$
Lines	$4w$	$3x$	$15y$	$9z$	$= 110$

The equations are: $2w + 4x + 6y + 10z = 100$, $1w + 2x + 5y + 6z = 60$, and $4w + 3x + 15y + 9z = 110$.

Since there are four variables and only three equations, there are many solutions. The question is if there is an integer solution. Try different numbers for one of the variables. For example, create a new equation, $w = 1$. Use this equation to create a $4 \cdot 4$ system. The solution for this system is $(1, 7.667, 2.333, 5.333)$. Repeat this procedure with $w = 2$. The solution for this system is an integer solution, $(2, 6, 2, 6)$. There is another solution with $w = 5$: $(5, 1, 1, 8)$.

For $w = 1$: $[A] = \begin{bmatrix} 1 & 0 & 0 & 0 \\ 2 & 4 & 6 & 10 \\ 1 & 2 & 5 & 6 \\ 4 & 3 & 15 & 9 \end{bmatrix}$, $[B] = \begin{bmatrix} 1 \\ 100 \\ 60 \\ 110 \end{bmatrix}$, $[A]^{-1}[B] = \begin{bmatrix} 1 \\ 7.667 \\ 2.333 \\ 5.333 \end{bmatrix}$

4. a.–b. Answers will vary.

5. Answers will vary.

6. Answers will vary.

Take Another Look 9.8

a. The minimum number of coins is 3 dimes and 154 quarters. The maximum number of coins is 388 dimes and 0 quarters.

b. The number of dimes can start with 3 and increment by 5 up to 388. The number of quarters can start with 154 and decrease by 2 down to 0. There are 78 different solutions.

c. It is not possible for dimes to equal quarters.

d. To have 250 coins she has to have 158 dimes and 92 quarters.

e. Answers may vary but some possibilities may include:

   1. x = dimes; y = quarters: $0.10x + 0.25y = 38.80$. Use your calculator and graph the equation in a "friendly" window. Use TRACE to find possible values. You can use the "table" feature of your calculator to determine the values.

   2. Use parametric equations, $XT = t$ and $YT = \frac{38.80 - 0.1t}{0.25}$. Set the window values to $[3, 400, 5, 0, 400, 10, 0, 170, 5]$. Using TRACE with a Tstep of 5 will jump to exact values.

Project: Inverse by Hand

One way is to find the determinant of the matrix shown visually at the right. Make five columns by repeating the first two. Take the product of each of the three downward diagonals and the three upward diagonals. Sum all of the down diagonal products and all of the up diagonal products. Finally, subtract the upward sum from the downward sum and you have the determinant.

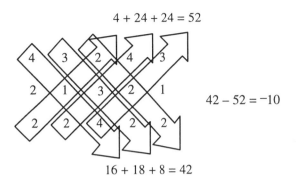

$$4 + 24 + 24 = 52$$

$$42 - 52 = {}^-10$$

$$16 + 18 + 8 = 42$$

Create a new matrix by replacing each element with the determinant of its minor, the minor being a matrix of the four values left after eliminating the row and column of the element to be replaced. If the row number plus the column number is odd, then change the sign of the minor.

Transpose the matrix of minors, that is, move element (a, b) to position (b, a) and divide by the determinant. The result is the inverse of the 3×3 matrix.

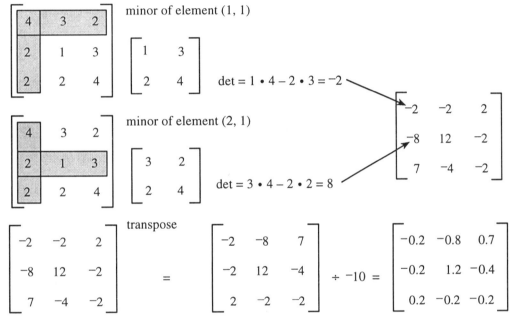

Another method is to create a 3×6 matrix by combining the original matrix with an identity matrix. By adding and multiplying rows, you can change the matrix until the first three columns become the identity matrix.

combined matrix

$$\begin{bmatrix} {}^-1 & 4 & 3 & 1 & 0 & 0 \\ {}^-0.5 & {}^-3 & 2 & 0 & 1 & 0 \\ {}^-2 & 6 & 7 & 0 & 0 & 1 \end{bmatrix}$$

${}^-1 \cdot R1$

$$\begin{bmatrix} 1 & {}^-4 & {}^-3 & {}^-1 & 0 & 0 \\ {}^-0.5 & 3 & 2 & 0 & 1 & 0 \\ {}^-2 & 6 & 7 & 0 & 0 & 1 \end{bmatrix}$$

$0.5 \cdot R1 + R2$

$$\begin{bmatrix} 1 & {}^-4 & {}^-3 & {}^-1 & 0 & 0 \\ 0 & {}^-5 & 0.5 & {}^-0.5 & 1 & 0 \\ {}^-2 & 6 & 7 & 0 & 0 & 1 \end{bmatrix}$$

$2 \cdot R1 + R3$

$$\begin{bmatrix} 1 & {}^-4 & {}^-3 & {}^-1 & 0 & 0 \\ 0 & {}^-5 & 0.5 & {}^-0.5 & 1 & 0 \\ 0 & {}^-2 & 1 & {}^-2 & 0 & 1 \end{bmatrix}$$

$0.2 \cdot R2$

$$\begin{bmatrix} 1 & {}^-4 & {}^-3 & {}^-1 & 0 & 0 \\ 0 & 1 & {}^-0.1 & 0.1 & {}^-0.2 & 0 \\ 0 & {}^-2 & 1 & {}^-2 & 0 & 1 \end{bmatrix}$$

$2 \cdot R2 + R3$

$$\begin{bmatrix} 1 & {}^-4 & {}^-3 & {}^-1 & 0 & 0 \\ 0 & 1 & {}^-0.1 & 0.1 & {}^-0.2 & 0 \\ 0 & 0 & 0.8 & {}^-1.8 & {}^-0.4 & 1 \end{bmatrix}$$

$1.25 \cdot R3$

$$\begin{bmatrix} 1 & {}^-4 & {}^-3 & {}^-1 & 0 & 0 \\ 0 & 1 & {}^-0.1 & 0.1 & {}^-0.2 & 0 \\ 0 & 0 & 1 & {}^-2.25 & {}^-0.5 & 1.25 \end{bmatrix}$$

$0.1 \cdot R3 + R2$

$$\begin{bmatrix} 1 & -4 & -3 & -1 & 0 & 0 \\ 0 & -5 & 0.5 & -0.5 & 1 & 0 \\ -2 & 6 & 7 & 0 & 0 & 1 \end{bmatrix}$$

$4 \cdot R2 + R1$

$$\begin{bmatrix} 1 & 0 & -3 & -1.5 & -1 & 0.5 \\ 0 & 1 & 0 & 0.125 & -0.25 & 0.125 \\ 0 & 0 & 1 & -2.25 & -0.5 & 1.25 \end{bmatrix}$$

$3 \cdot R3 + R1$

$$\begin{bmatrix} 1 & 0 & 0 & -8.25 & -2.5 & 4.25 \\ 0 & 1 & 0 & 0.125 & -0.25 & 0.125 \\ 0 & 0 & 1 & -2.25 & -0.5 & 1.25 \end{bmatrix}$$

The last three columns of the final matrix are the inverse of the original matrix.

Chapter Review

Problem Set 9.9

1. $(0.634, -0.598)$ and $(2.366, 4.598)$

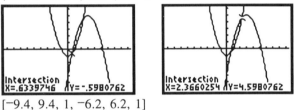

$[-9.4, 9.4, 1, -6.2, 6.2, 1]$

2. a. Answers will vary. No window is really good to see the intersection, but one possible window is $[0, 20, 2, 0, 45, 5]$.

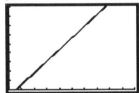

b. Turn off Y1 and Y2 and graph Y3 = Y1 – Y2. A good window is $[0, 20, 2, -1, 1, 0.1]$.

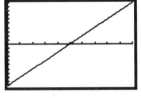

c. $3.2x - 4 = 3.1x - 3$

d. $0 = 0.1x - 1$; $1 = 0.1x$; $x = 10$

e. Equation 1 can be rewritten as $0 = 3.2x - 4 - y$. Now substitute the second equation, which equals y, into the above equation, resulting in $0 = 3.2x - 4 - (3.1x - 3)$. Solving this resulting equation for x will give you the x-intercept for y_3.

3. a. $6.2x + 18.4 = -2.1x + 7.40$; $8.3x = -11$; $x = -1.3253$
Now substitute the x-value into one of the original equations and solve for y;
$y = 6.2(-1.3253) + 18.4 = 10.1831$. The solution is $(-1.3253, 10.1831)$.

b. $\frac{7}{10}x + \frac{2}{5}\left(\frac{3}{4}x - 1\right) = 8$

$\frac{7}{10}x + \frac{3}{10}x - \frac{2}{5} = 8$

$7x + 3x - 4 = 80$

$10x = 84$

$x = 8.4$

Now substitute this result for the x-value in one of the original equations:

$y = \frac{3}{4}(8.4) - 1 = 5.3$.

The solution is $(8.4, 5.3)$.

Or change fractions to decimal equivalents.
$0.7x + 0.4(0.75x - 1) = 8$
$0.7x + 0.3x - 0.4 = 8$
$1x = 8 + 0.4$
$x = 8.4$

4. a. $3x + 2y = 4$
    $-3x + 5y = 3$
    $7y = 7$
    $y = 1$
    $3x + 2(1) = 4$
    $3x = 2$
    $x = \frac{2}{3}$
    $\left(\frac{2}{3}, 1\right)$

b. $5x - 4y = 5$ $25x - 20y = 25$
    $2x + 10y = 2$ $4x + 20y = 4$
                $29x = 29$
                $x = 1$
                $5(1) - 4y = 5$
                $-4y = 0$
                $y = 0$
                $(1, 0)$

5. Graph the equations. If the lines are parallel and do not intersect, the system is inconsistent. If the lines graph on top of each other, the system is dependent. If the lines intersect in one point, the system is consistent.

a. consistent

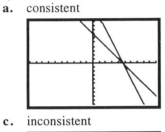

b. dependent

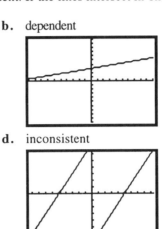

c. inconsistent

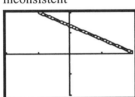

d. inconsistent

6. Enter the matrix into the calculator, and then find $[A]^{-1}$.

a. $[A]^{-1} = \begin{bmatrix} 0.8 & -0.6 \\ 0.2 & -0.4 \end{bmatrix}$

b. $[A]^{-1} = \begin{bmatrix} -0.0353 & 0.1882 & -0.0235 \\ 0.2118 & -0.1294 & 0.1412 \\ -0.3765 & 0.3412 & 0.0824 \end{bmatrix}$

c. $[A]^{-1}$ does not exist

d. $[A]^{-1} = \begin{bmatrix} -0.0893 & 0.1429 & 0.125 \\ -0.0536 & 0.2857 & -0.125 \\ -0.5179 & 0.4286 & 0.125 \end{bmatrix} = \begin{bmatrix} \frac{-5}{56} & \frac{1}{7} & \frac{1}{8} \\ \frac{-3}{56} & \frac{2}{7} & \frac{-1}{8} \\ \frac{-29}{56} & \frac{3}{7} & \frac{1}{8} \end{bmatrix}$

7. Enter the coefficients of the variables into $[A]$ and the constant terms into $[B]$. To find the solution, multiply $[A]^{-1} [B]$.

a. $[A] = \begin{bmatrix} 8 & -5 \\ 6 & 4 \end{bmatrix}$, $[B] = \begin{bmatrix} 17 \\ 33 \end{bmatrix}$, $[A]^{-1} [B] = \begin{bmatrix} 3.758 \\ 2.613 \end{bmatrix}$

b. $[A] = \begin{bmatrix} 4 & 1 & 2 & -3 \\ -3 & 2 & -1 & 4 \\ 5 & 4 & 6 & -1 \\ -2 & 3 & 5 & 7 \end{bmatrix}$, $[B] = \begin{bmatrix} -11 \\ 20 \\ -10 \\ -45 \end{bmatrix}$, $[A]^{-1} [B] = \begin{bmatrix} -39.143 \\ 24.592 \\ 8.816 \\ -34.449 \end{bmatrix}$

8. a. $y \leq \frac{12 - 2x}{3}$, $y \leq 18 - 6x$, $y \geq \frac{2 - x}{2}$, $x > 0$, $y \geq 0$

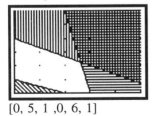

[0, 5, 1 ,0, 6, 1]

The vertices are $(0, 4)$, $(2.625, 2.25)$, $(3, 0)$, $(2, 0)$, and $(0, 1)$. The maximum value occurs at $(0, 4)$: $1.65(0) + 5.2(4) = 20.8$.

b. $y \le 50 - x$, $y \le \frac{440 - 10x}{5}$, $y \le \frac{2400 - 40x}{60}$

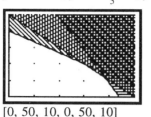

[0, 50, 10, 0, 50, 10]

The vertices are (0, 40), (30, 20), (38, 12), and (44, 0).
The maximum value occurs at (30, 20): 6(30) + 7(20) = 320.

9. Cost for old unit: $y = 300 + 75x$ where x is the number of years
Cost for new unit: $y = 500 + 0.40(75x)$

A new heater will pay for itself in about 4.4 yr.

Intersection
X=4.4444444 _Y=633.33333
[0, 10, 1, 0, 1000, 100]

10. **a.** $2x + 1y + 3z = 5$

b. $4x + 0y + 1z = 6$ for yellow; $0x + 2y + 1z = 2$ for black

c. $[A] = \begin{bmatrix} 2 & 1 & 3 \\ 4 & 0 & 1 \\ 0 & 2 & 1 \end{bmatrix}$, $[B] = \begin{bmatrix} 5 \\ 6 \\ 2 \end{bmatrix}$, $[A]^{-1}[B] = \begin{bmatrix} 1.375 \\ 0.75 \\ 0.5 \end{bmatrix}$

d. Convert the matrix entries to fractions, $\begin{bmatrix} \frac{11}{8} \\ \frac{3}{4} \\ \frac{1}{2} \end{bmatrix}$.
The lowest common denominator
is 8. Multiply each fraction by 8
to get 11, 6, and 4.

e. You would use 11 parts of mixture 1, 6 parts of mixture 2, and 4 parts of mixture 3 to provide the particular color.

11. Answers will vary.

12. Answers will vary.

Chapter 10

Problem Set 10.1

1. **a.** $y = 10{,}000x^4 + 5{,}000x^2 + 2{,}000$ **b.** Answers will vary. One posssible answer is $0 \le x \le 1.5$.

c. Put the expression from part a into y_1 and 17,300 into y_2. Graph and trace, look at a table, or use the calculator intersect function to find the x-value. $x = 1.006$

Intersection
X=1.0059537 _Y=17300
[0, 1.5, 0.1, 0, 18000, 1000]

d. The annual interest rate is 0.006(12) = 0.072 or 7.2%.

2. **a.** The multiplier is $\left(1 - \frac{p}{100}\right)$. The variable p is a percent **decrease** because the drug will eventually disappear from the blood.

b. $30x^3$

c. Put the expression from part a into y_1 and 5 into y_2. Graph and trace, look at a table, or use the calculator intersect function to find the x-value. $x = 55$

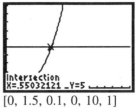

[0, 1.5, 0.1, 0, 10, 1]

d. $\left(1 - \frac{p}{100}\right) = 0.55$; $p = 0.45$ or 45% of the drug is removed each day.

3. a. $50x^3 + 70x^2 + 90x$

b. Put the expression from part a into y_1 and 50 into y_2. Graph and trace, look at a table, or use the calculator intersect function to find the x-value. $x = 0.3976$

[0, 1.5, 0.1, 0, 80, 10]

c. $\left(1 - \frac{q}{100}\right) = 0.3976$; $q = 60.24$ or 60.24% of the drug is removed each day.

4. a.–b.

n	1	2	3	4	5	6	7
s	1	3	6	10	15	21	28

D_1	2	3	4	5	6	7

D_2	1	1	1	1	1

c. The degree of the polynomial is 2. The second finite differences are all the same nonzero number.

d. The numbers are called triangular because they are the number of pieces needed to build a triangle with n rows.

5. a.

Time in sec (t)	0	1	2	3	4	5	6
Height in m (h)	80	95.1	100.4	95.9	81.6	57.5	23.6

D_1	15.1	5.3	−4.5	−14.3	−24.1	−33.9

D_2	−9.8	−9.8	−9.8	−9.8	−9.8

b.

Time in sec (t)	0	1	2	3	4	5	6
Height in m (h)	4	63.1	112.4	151.9	181.6	201.5	211.6

D_1	59.1	49.3	39.5	29.7	19.9	10.1

D_2	−9.8	−9.8	−9.8	−9.8	−9.8

c. The degree of the equation that could be used to model each data set is a second-degree equation because the second finite differences are all the same nonzero number.

d. Select three data points, not all together, and substitute them into the second-degree equation $y = ax^2 + bx + c$. This results in three equations with three unknowns. Use a matrix to solve for the coefficients, a, b, and c.

$\begin{aligned} 80 &= 0a + 0b + c \\ 100.4 &= 4a + 2b + c \\ 81.6 &= 16a + 4b + c \end{aligned}$
$[A] = \begin{bmatrix} 0 & 0 & 1 \\ 4 & 2 & 1 \\ 16 & 4 & 1 \end{bmatrix}$, $[B] = \begin{bmatrix} 80 \\ 100.4 \\ 81.6 \end{bmatrix}$, $[A]^{-1}[B] = \begin{bmatrix} -4.9 \\ 20 \\ 80 \end{bmatrix}$

Therefore, $h = -4.9t^2 + 20t + 80$.

6. a.

Layers (n)	1	2	3	4	5	6
Blocks (b)	1	5	14	30	55	91

D_1	4	9	16	25	36

D_2	5	7	9	11

D_3	2	2	2

b. The relationship has a degree of 3.

c. Select four data points, which are spread out, and substitute them into the third-degree equation $y = ax^3 + bx^2 + cx + d$. This results in four equations with four unknowns. Use a matrix to solve for the coefficients, a, b, c, and d.

$$1 = 1a + 1b + 1c + d$$
$$5 = 8a + 4b + 2c + d$$
$$30 = 64a + 16b + 4c + d$$
$$91 = 216a + 36b + 6c + d$$

Therefore, $b = \frac{1}{3}n^3 + \frac{1}{2}n^2 + \frac{1}{6}n$.

$$[A] = \begin{bmatrix} 1 & 1 & 1 & 1 \\ 8 & 4 & 2 & 1 \\ 64 & 16 & 4 & 1 \\ 216 & 36 & 6 & 1 \end{bmatrix}, [B] = \begin{bmatrix} 1 \\ 5 \\ 30 \\ 91 \end{bmatrix}, [A]^{-1}[B] = \begin{bmatrix} \frac{1}{3} \\ \frac{1}{2} \\ \frac{1}{6} \\ 0 \end{bmatrix}$$

d. $b(8) = \frac{1}{3}(8)^3 + \frac{1}{2}(8)^2 + \frac{1}{6}(8) = 204$ blocks

e. Put the expression from part a into y_1 and 650 into y_2. Graph and trace, look at a table, or use the calculator intersect function to find the x-value. You would have 12 layers to use 650 blocks.

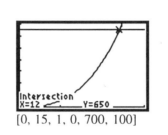

Intersection
X=12   Y=650
[0, 15, 1, 0, 700, 100]

Problem Set 10.2

1. **a.** $y = (x - 2)^2 + 3$
$y = x^2 - 4x + 4 + 3$
$y = x^2 - 4x + 7$

b. $y = (x + 4)^2 - 2$
$y = x^2 + 8x + 16 - 2$
$y = x^2 + 8x + 14$

c. $y = 2(x - 5)^2 - 4$
$y = 2(x^2 - 10x + 25) - 4$
$y = 2x^2 - 20x + 46$

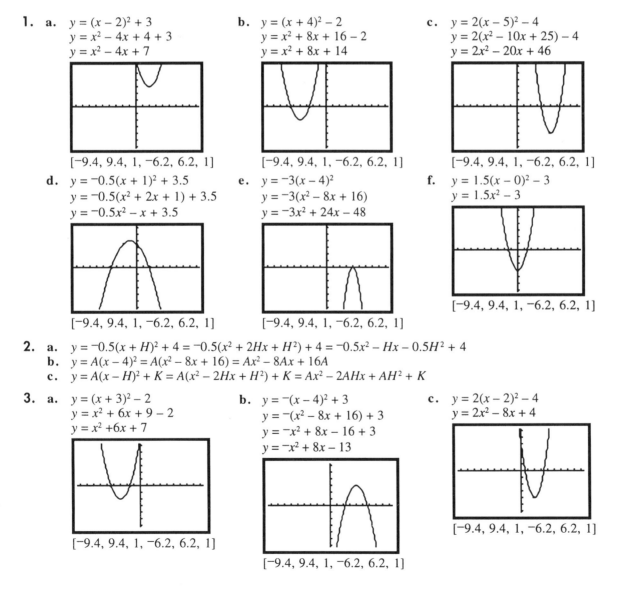

[−9.4, 9.4, 1, −6.2, 6.2, 1]   [−9.4, 9.4, 1, −6.2, 6.2, 1]   [−9.4, 9.4, 1, −6.2, 6.2, 1]

d. $y = -0.5(x + 1)^2 + 3.5$
$y = -0.5(x^2 + 2x + 1) + 3.5$
$y = -0.5x^2 - x + 3.5$

e. $y = -3(x - 4)^2$
$y = -3(x^2 - 8x + 16)$
$y = -3x^2 + 24x - 48$

f. $y = 1.5(x - 0)^2 - 3$
$y = 1.5x^2 - 3$

[−9.4, 9.4, 1, −6.2, 6.2, 1]

[−9.4, 9.4, 1, −6.2, 6.2, 1]   [−9.4, 9.4, 1, −6.2, 6.2, 1]

2. **a.** $y = -0.5(x + H)^2 + 4 = -0.5(x^2 + 2Hx + H^2) + 4 = -0.5x^2 - Hx - 0.5H^2 + 4$
b. $y = A(x - 4)^2 = A(x^2 - 8x + 16) = Ax^2 - 8Ax + 16A$
c. $y = A(x - H)^2 + K = A(x^2 - 2Hx + H^2) + K = Ax^2 - 2AHx + AH^2 + K$

3. **a.** $y = (x + 3)^2 - 2$
$y = x^2 + 6x + 9 - 2$
$y = x^2 + 6x + 7$

b. $y = -(x - 4)^2 + 3$
$y = -(x^2 - 8x + 16) + 3$
$y = -x^2 + 8x - 16 + 3$
$y = -x^2 + 8x - 13$

c. $y = 2(x - 2)^2 - 4$
$y = 2x^2 - 8x + 4$

[−9.4, 9.4, 1, −6.2, 6.2, 1]

[−9.4, 9.4, 1, −6.2, 6.2, 1]

[−9.4, 9.4, 1, −6.2, 6.2, 1]

d. $y = -0.5(x + 1.5)^2 + 3$
$y = -0.5x^2 - 1.5x + 1.875$

e. $y = A(x - H)^2 + K$
$y = Ax^2 - 2AHx + AH^2 + K$

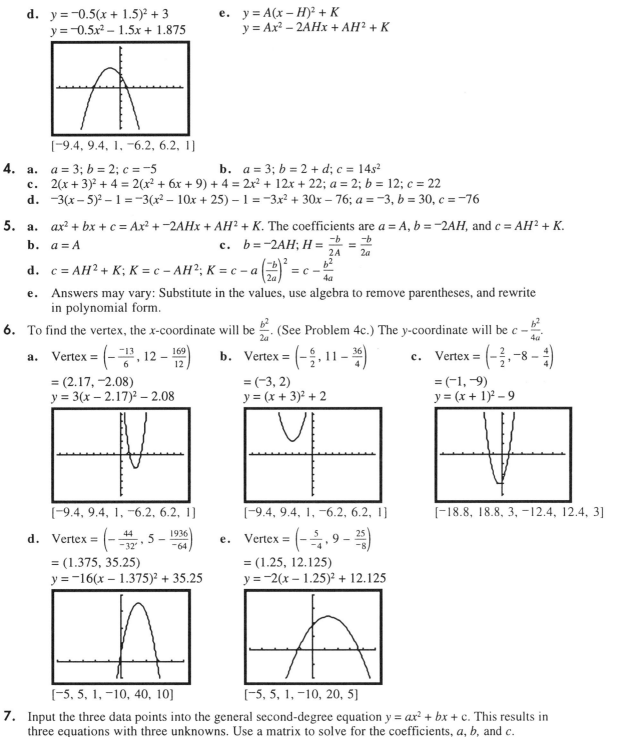

$[-9.4, 9.4, 1, -6.2, 6.2, 1]$

4. **a.** $a = 3; b = 2; c = -5$ **b.** $a = 3; b = 2 + d; c = 14s^2$
    c. $2(x + 3)^2 + 4 = 2(x^2 + 6x + 9) + 4 = 2x^2 + 12x + 22; a = 2; b = 12; c = 22$
    d. $-3(x - 5)^2 - 1 = -3(x^2 - 10x + 25) - 1 = -3x^2 + 30x - 76; a = -3, b = 30, c = -76$

5. **a.** $ax^2 + bx + c = Ax^2 + -2AHx + AH^2 + K$. The coefficients are $a = A, b = -2AH,$ and $c = AH^2 + K$.
    b. $a = A$ **c.** $b = -2AH; H = \frac{-b}{2A} = \frac{-b}{2a}$

    d. $c = AH^2 + K; K = c - AH^2; K = c - a\left(\frac{-b}{2a}\right)^2 = c - \frac{b^2}{4a}$

    e. Answers may vary: Substitute in the values, use algebra to remove parentheses, and rewrite in polynomial form.

6. To find the vertex, the x-coordinate will be $\frac{b^2}{2a}$. (See Problem 4c.) The y-coordinate will be $c - \frac{b^2}{4a}$.

    a. Vertex $= \left(-\frac{13}{6}, 12 - \frac{169}{12}\right)$ **b.** Vertex $= \left(-\frac{6}{2}, 11 - \frac{36}{4}\right)$ **c.** Vertex $= \left(-\frac{2}{2}, -8 - \frac{4}{4}\right)$

       $= (2.17, -2.08)$ $= (-3, 2)$ $= (-1, -9)$
       $y = 3(x - 2.17)^2 - 2.08$ $y = (x + 3)^2 + 2$ $y = (x + 1)^2 - 9$

       $[-9.4, 9.4, 1, -6.2, 6.2, 1]$ $[-9.4, 9.4, 1, -6.2, 6.2, 1]$ $[-18.8, 18.8, 3, -12.4, 12.4, 3]$

    d. Vertex $= \left(-\frac{44}{-32}, 5 - \frac{1936}{-64}\right)$ **e.** Vertex $= \left(-\frac{5}{-4}, 9 - \frac{25}{-8}\right)$

       $= (1.375, 35.25)$ $= (1.25, 12.125)$
       $y = -16(x - 1.375)^2 + 35.25$ $y = -2(x - 1.25)^2 + 12.125$

       $[-5, 5, 1, -10, 40, 10]$ $[-5, 5, 1, -10, 20, 5]$

7. Input the three data points into the general second-degree equation $y = ax^2 + bx + c$. This results in three equations with three unknowns. Use a matrix to solve for the coefficients, a, b, and c.

$27 = 25a + 5b + c$
$4 = 400a + 20b + c$ $[A] = \begin{bmatrix} 25 & 5 & 1 \\ 400 & 20 & 1 \\ 1600 & 40 & 1 \end{bmatrix}$, $[B] = \begin{bmatrix} 27 \\ 4 \\ -5 \end{bmatrix}$, $[A]^{-1}[B] = \begin{bmatrix} 0.03 \\ -2.31 \\ 37.76 \end{bmatrix}$
$-5 = 1600a + 40b + c$

$T = 0.031w^2 - 2.31w + 37.8$

Vertex $= \left(-\frac{-2.31}{0.06}, 37.8 - \frac{5.29}{0.12}\right) = (37.3 \text{ mi/hr}, -5.23°F)$

8. **a.–b.**

Selling price (x)		2.00	2.10	2.20	2.30	2.40
Number sold (y)		200	195	190	185	180
Revenue		400	409.50	418	425.50	432
	D_1		9.50	8.50	7.50	6.50
	D_2			$^-1$	$^-1$	$^-1$

c. Since the second finite differences are all the same nonzero number, the model must be a second-degree equation. Select three data points and input them into the general second-degree equation $y = ax^2 + bx + c$. This results in three equations with three unknowns. Solve for the coefficients, a, b, and c.

$400 = 4a + 2b + c$
$409.50 = 4.41a + 2.1b + c$
$432 = 5.76a + 2.4b + c$
$y = {}^-50x^2 + 300x$

$[A] = \begin{bmatrix} 4 & 2 & 1 \\ 4.41 & 2.1 & 1 \\ 5.76 & 2.4 & 1 \end{bmatrix}$, $[B] = \begin{bmatrix} 400 \\ 409.5 \\ 432 \end{bmatrix}$, $[A]^{-1}[B] = \begin{bmatrix} {}^-50 \\ 300 \\ 0 \end{bmatrix}$

d.

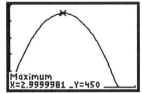

[0, 7, 1, 0, 500, 100]
A selling price of $3 provides the maximum revenue ($450).

9. **a.**

Width	5	10	15	20	25
Length	35	30	25	20	15
Area	175	300	375	400	375

b. Select three data points and input them into the general second-degree equation, $y = ax^2 + bx + c$. This results in three equations with three unknowns. Solve for the coefficients, a, b, and c.

$175 = 25a + 5b + c$
$300 = 100a + 10b + c$
$375 = 625a + 25b + c$
$a = {}^-w^2 + 40w$

$[A] = \begin{bmatrix} 25 & 5 & 1 \\ 100 & 10 & 1 \\ 625 & 25 & 1 \end{bmatrix}$, $[B] = \begin{bmatrix} 175 \\ 300 \\ 375 \end{bmatrix}$, $[A]^{-1}[B] = \begin{bmatrix} {}^-1 \\ 40 \\ 0 \end{bmatrix}$

c.

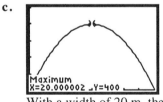

With a width of 20 m, the area is maximized at 400 m².

d. With a width of 0 or of 40 m, there would be no area.

e. With a width less than 0 or greater than 40, there would be negative area.

10. **a.–c.** Answers will vary.

Problem Set 10.3

1. **a.** The x-intercepts are 7.5, $^-2.5$, and 3.2. To find the y-intercept, substitute 0 for x:
$y = 2.5(0 - 7.5)(0 + 2.5)(0 - 3.2) = 2.5(^-7.5)(2.5)(^-3.2) = 150$

b. $y = 2.5(x - 7.5)(x + 2.5)(x - 3.2) = (2.5x - 18.75)(x^2 - 0.7x - 8) = 2.5x^3 - 1.75x^2 - 20x - 18.75x^2$
$+ 13.125x + 150 = 2.5x^3 - 20.5x^2 - 6.875x + 150$

c.

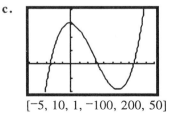

[$^-5$, 10, 1, $^-100$, 200, 50]

2. a. $y = {}^-4.9(x - 0.7)(x - 2.8)$

  b. The x-coordinate of the vertex is halfway between the intercepts. $\frac{0.7 + 2.8}{2} = 1.75$. Substitute this value into the equation to find the y-coordinate of the vertex. $y = {}^-4.9(1.75 - 0.7)(1.75 - 2.8) = {}^-4.9(1.05)({}^-1.05) = 5.40225$. The vertex is (1.75, 5.4). This means that at 1.75 sec the ball reaches its highest point of 5.4 m.

  c. To find the y-intercept, substitute 0 for x: $y = {}^-4.9({}^-0.7)({}^-2.8) = {}^-9.604$. This means that at time 0, the ball is at the bottom of the well, which is 9.604 m deep.

  d. The maximum height will change, but the x-intercepts or the roots will stay the same.

3. a. The x-intercepts are ${}^-1.5$ and ${}^-6$. The y-intercept is ${}^-0.25(1.5)(6) = {}^-2.25$. The x-coordinate of the vertex is $\frac{{}^-1.5 + {}^-6}{2} = {}^-3.75$; the y-coordinate of the vertex is ${}^-0.25({}^-3.75 + 1.5)({}^-3.75 + 6) = 1.265625$, so the vertex is $({}^-3.75, 1.265625)$.

  b. The x-intercept is 4; the y-intercept is $3({}^-4)({}^-4) = 48$. The x-coordinate of the vertex is $\frac{4 + 4}{2} = 4$; the y-coordinate of the vertex is $3(4 - 4)(4 - 4) = 0$, so the vertex is (4, 0).

  c. The x-intercepts are 3, ${}^-2$, and ${}^-5$; the y-intercept is ${}^-2({}^-3)(2)(5) = 60$. The equation does not represent a parabola, so there isn't a vertex.

  d. The x-intercepts are ${}^-3$ and 3; the y-intercept is $5(3)(3)({}^-3) = {}^-135$. The equation does not represent a parabola, so there isn't a vertex.

4. Answers will vary, but the graphs will have the following shapes and number of intercepts. Each window is $[{}^-9.4, 9.4, 1, {}^-6.2, 6.2, 1]$.

  a. $y = (x - 3)^2$

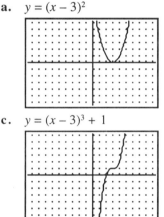

  b. $y = (x - 3)^2 + 1$

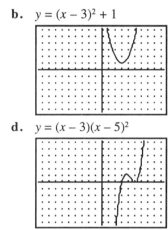

  c. $y = (x - 3)^3 + 1$

  d. $y = (x - 3)(x - 5)^2$

5. a. **i.** First write the equation in the form $y = A(x - R_1)(x - R_2)$ using the known roots or x-intercepts and then substitute in a point to find the value of A: $y = A(x - 2)(x - 4)$. Now substitute in a point (3, ${}^-2$): ${}^-2 = A(3 - 2)(3 - 4)$; ${}^-2 = A(1)({}^-1)$ so $A = 2$. The equation is $y = 2(x - 2)(x - 4)$.

   ii. For the second graph, $y = A(x - {}^-6)(x - {}^-1.5) = A(x + 6)(x + 1.5)$. Now substitute in a point $({}^-2, 0.5)$: $0.5 = A({}^-2 + 6)({}^-2 + 1.5)$; $0.5 = A(4)({}^-0.5)$; $A = {}^-0.25$. The equation is $y = {}^-0.25(x + 6)(x + 1.5)$.

  b. **i.** $y = 2(x - 2)(x - 4) = 2(x^2 - 6x + 8) = 2x^2 - 12x + 16$

   ii. $y = {}^-0.25(x + 6)(x + 1.5) = {}^-0.25(x^2 + 7.5x + 9) = {}^-0.25x^2 - 1.875x - 2.25$

  c. **i.** The x-coordinate of the vertex is $\frac{2 + 4}{2} = 3$; the y-coordinate is $2(3 - 2)(3 - 4) = {}^-2$, so the vertex of the first graph is (3, ${}^-2$). The vertex form of the equation is $y = 2(x - 3)^2 - 2$.

   ii. The x-coordinate of the vertex is $\frac{{}^-6 + {}^-1.5}{2} = {}^-3.75$; the y-coordinate is ${}^-0.25({}^-3.75 + 6)({}^-3.75 + 1.5) = {}^-0.25(2.25)({}^-2.25) = 1.265625$, so the vertex of the graph is $({}^-3.75, 1.265625)$. The vertex form of the equation is $y = {}^-0.25(x + 3.75)^2 + 1.265625$.

6. Answers will vary. When both lines are above the x-axis or below the x-axis, the curve of y_3 is above the x-axis. When one of the lines is above the x-axis and one below the x-axis, the curve is below the x-axis. The lines have the same roots as the curve. The vertex of the curve occurs when both lines are the same distance from the x-axis.

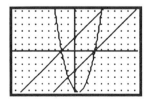

7. a. $y = A(x + 5)(x - 3)(x - 6)$

  b. To find A, substitute the point (0, 180) into the equation: $180 = A(5)({}^-3)({}^-6)$; $A = 2$.

c. $y = 2(x + 5)(x - 3)(x - 6) + 100$

d. $y = 2(x + 5 + 4)(x - 3 + 4)(x - 6 + 4) = y = 2(x + 9)(x + 1)(x - 2)$

8. a. i. $A = (x + 4)(x + 6)$ ii. $A = x^2 + 10x + 24$

    b. i. $A = (x + 5)(x + 5) = (x + 5)^2$ ii. $A = x^2 + 10x + 25$

9. a. i.

ii.

    b. For the figure in 9a.i: $A = (x + 4)^2$; $A = x^2 + 8x + 16$. For the figure in 9a.ii: $A = (2x + 6)(x + 3)$; $A = 2x^2 + 12x + 18$.

10. a. $(x - 6)(x - 4)$ **b.** $(x - 3)(x - 3) = (x - 3)^2$

    c. $(x + 8)(x - 8)$ **d.** $(x + 10)(x - 12)$

    e. $4(x^2 - 22x + 120) = 4(x - 12)(x - 10)$ **f.** $(3x - 5)(2x + 1)$

    g. $(x - R_1)(x - R_2)$ **h.** $(a + b)^2$

11. a. Input the three data points into the general second-degree equation: $y = ax^2 + bx + c$. This results in three equations with three unknowns. Solve for the coefficients, a, b, and c.

$$16a - 4b + c = -2$$
$$a - b + c = 7$$
$$4a + 2b + c = 16$$

$$[A] = \begin{bmatrix} 16 & -4 & 1 \\ 1 & -1 & 1 \\ 4 & 2 & 1 \end{bmatrix}, [B] = \begin{bmatrix} -2 \\ 7 \\ 16 \end{bmatrix}, [A]^{-1}[B] = \begin{bmatrix} 0 \\ 3 \\ 10 \end{bmatrix}$$

The equation is not quadratic because the coefficient, a, is 0. Therefore, this is a line. The equation of the line is $y = 3x + 10$.

    b. $y = A(x + 2)^2 + 3$; to find A, substitute the point $(4, 12)$ into the equation: $12 = A(4 + 2)^2 + 3$; $12 = 36A + 3$; $9 = 36A$; $A = 0.25$, so the equation is $y = 0.25(x + 2)^2 + 3$ or $y = 0.25x^2 + x + y$.

Problem Set 10.4

1. a. $4x^2 - 12x + 9 = (2x - 3)^2$ **b.** $x^2 + 5x + \frac{25}{4} = \left(x + \frac{5}{2}\right)^2$ **c.** $x^2 - 2xy + y^2 = (x - y)^2$

2. a. $(x - 2.3)^2 = 25$ **b.** $(x + 4.45)^2 = 12.25$ **c.** $\left(x - \frac{3}{4}\right)^2 = \frac{25}{16}$

       $x - 2.3 = \pm\sqrt{25}$ $x + 4.45 = \pm\sqrt{12.25}$ $x - \frac{3}{4} = \pm\sqrt{\frac{25}{16}}$

       $x = 2.3 \pm 5$ $x = -4.45 \pm 3.5$ $x = \frac{3}{4} \pm \frac{5}{4}$

       $x = -2.7, 7.3$ $x = -7.95, -0.95$ $x = -\frac{1}{2}, 2$

3. a. $3x^2 - 13x - 10 = 0$ **b.** $x^2 - 5x - 13 = 0$ **c.** $3x^2 + 5x + 1 = 0$

      $a = 3, b = -13, c = -10$ $a = 1, b = -5, c = -13$ $a = 3, b = 5, c = 1$

      $x = \frac{-13 \pm \sqrt{13^2 - 4(3)(-10)}}{2(3)}$ $x = \frac{-(-5) \pm \sqrt{5^2 - 4(1)(-13)}}{2(1)}$ $x = \frac{-5 \pm \sqrt{5^2 - 4(3)(1)}}{2(3)}$

      $x = \frac{-13 \pm \sqrt{17}}{6}$ $x = \frac{5 \pm \sqrt{77}}{2}$ $x = \frac{-5 \pm \sqrt{13}}{6}$

      $x = \frac{-2}{3}, 5$ or $-0.667, 5$ $x \approx -1.887, 6.887$ $x \approx -1.434, -0.232$

    d. $3x^2 - 3x - 2 = 0$ **e.** $14(x - 4) - (x + 2) = (x + 2)(x - 4)$

      $a = 3, b = -3, c = -2$ $14x - 56 - x - 2 = x^2 - 2x - 8$

      $x = \frac{-(-3) \pm \sqrt{3^2 - 4(3)(-2)}}{2(3)}$ $13x - 58 = x^2 - 2x - 8$

                                    $0 = x^2 - 15x + 50$

      $x = \frac{3 \pm \sqrt{33}}{6}$ $a = 1, b = -15, c = 50$

      $x \approx -0.457, 1.457$ $x = \frac{-(-15) \pm \sqrt{15^2 - 4(1)(50)}}{2(1)}$

                                    $x = \frac{15 \pm 5}{2}$

                                    $x = 5, 10$

4. a. $0 = -4.9t^2 + 5t + 7$

$a = -4.9, b = 5, c = 7$

$t = \dfrac{-5 \pm \sqrt{5^2 - 4(-4.9)(7)}}{2(-4.9)}$

$t = \dfrac{-5 \pm \sqrt{162.2}}{-9.8}$

$t \approx -0.789,\ 1.81$

Since the negative solution does not make sense, it will take the projectile 1.81 sec to hit the ground. Substitute this value into the x-equation to find the position when the projectile hits the ground: $x = 5(1.81) - 3 = 6.05$ m. At time $t = 1.81$ sec, the projectile is located approximately at $(6.05, 0)$.

b. $0 = -16t^2 + 2t + 100$

$a = -16, b = 2, c = 100$

$t = \dfrac{-2 \pm \sqrt{2^2 - 4(-16)(100)}}{2(-16)}$

$t = \dfrac{-2 \pm \sqrt{6404}}{-32}$

$t \approx -2.438,\ 2.563$

It will take the projectile 2.56 sec to hit the ground. Substitute this value into the x-equation to find the position when the projectile hits the ground: $x = 7(2.56) + 2 = 19.9$ ft. At time $t = 2.56$ sec, the projectile is located approximately at $(19.9, 0)$.

c. $0 = -4.9t^2 - 3.17t + 470$

$a = -4.9, b = -3.17, c = 470$

$x = \dfrac{-(-3.17) \pm \sqrt{3.17^2 - 4(-4.9)(470)}}{2(-4.9)}$

$x = \dfrac{3.17 \pm \sqrt{9222.049}}{-9.8}$

$x = -10.123,\ 9.476$

It will take the projectile 9.48 sec to hit the ground. Because the x-position is always 9, at time $t = 9.48$ sec the projectile is located approximately at $(9, 0)$.

5. Multiple answers are correct. Answers will vary depending on the multiplier A, which can be placed in front of the factors or within the factors. Those listed below are only examples.

a. $(x - 3)(x + 3) = 0$

b. $(x - 4)(5x + 2) = 0$ or $(x - 4)\left(x + \dfrac{2}{5}\right) = 0$

c. $(x - R_1)(x - R_2) = 0$

d. $-4.9(x - 1.1)(x - 4.7) = 0$

6. Answers will vary.

$x = \dfrac{-2 \pm \sqrt{4 - 4(2)(5)}}{2(2)} = \dfrac{-2 \pm \sqrt{-36}}{4}$

There are no x-intercepts because $\sqrt{-36}$ is not a real number. Without using the formula, you might have graphed the function and seen that the function did not cross the x-axis. Another equation without x-intercepts is $y = x^2 + 1$.

7. a. Many solutions are possible depending on which points are selected. The example below uses points $(10, 19)$, $(40, 116)$, and $(60, 248)$. Form a matrix by substituting the above points into the general equation $y = ax^2 + bx + c$: $19 = 100a + 10b + c$; $116 = 1600a + 40b + c$; $248 = 3600a + 60b + c$.

[0, 80, 10, 0, 350, 50]

$[A] = \begin{bmatrix} 100 & 10 & 1 \\ 1600 & 40 & 1 \\ 3600 & 60 & 1 \end{bmatrix}$, $[B] = \begin{bmatrix} 19 \\ 116 \\ 248 \end{bmatrix}$, $[A]^{-1}[B] = \begin{bmatrix} 0.07 \\ -0.13 \\ 13.6 \end{bmatrix}$

$y = 0.07x^2 - 0.13x + 13.6$

b. Answers will vary depending on which three points were chosen. With real data, the point selection is very important.

c. Answers will vary. Choose points that are spread out rather than ones that are close together.

8.

$\left(7 + 0.5\sqrt{300}\right)^2 - 14\left(7 + 0.5\sqrt{300}\right) - 26$

$49 + 7\sqrt{300} + 75 - 98 - 7\sqrt{300} - 26$

$49 + 75 - 98 - 26 + 7\sqrt{300} - 7\sqrt{300}$

$124 - 124 = 0$

$\left(7 - 0.5\sqrt{300}\right)^2 - 14\left(7 - 0.5\sqrt{300}\right) - 26$

$49 - 7\sqrt{300} + 75 - 98 + 7\sqrt{300} - 26$

$49 + 75 - 98 - 26 - 7\sqrt{300} + 7\sqrt{300}$

$124 - 124 = 0$

9. a. $y = \sqrt{400 - x^2}$

b. $y = \sqrt{400 - 10^2} = \sqrt{300} \approx 17.3$ ft

c. $18 = \sqrt{400 - x^2}$; $324 = 400 - x^2$; $-76 = -x^2$; $76 = x^2$; $x \approx 8.7$ ft

d. Pythagorean theorem: $a^2 + b^2 = c^2$

10. `Pr9m3:QUADFORM`
   `:Disp "A"`
   `:Input A`
   `:Disp "B"`
   `:Input B`
   `:Disp "C"`
   `:Input C`
   `:B²-4AC→D`
   `:(-B+√D)/2A→X`
   `:(-B-√D)/2A→R`
   `:Disp X`
   `:Disp R`

11. $x = 40t \cos 60°$; $y = -16t^2 + 40t \sin 60°$
The net would stretch from 30 to 40 ft from the cannon. When Gonzo is within the distance of the net, he is 10 ft above in the air. Yes, he lands in the net.

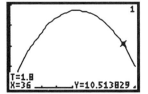

12. Answers will vary.

Take Another Look 10.4

1. a. $h(t) = -4.9t^2 + 23t + 2$. When a ball is thrown straight up at 23 m/sec from an initial height of 2 m, it reaches its maximum height of 28.98 meters after approximately 2.35 sec.

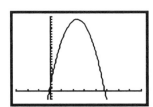

b.

Planet	Acceleration due to gravity	Time to maximum height (sec)	Maximum height (m)
Mercury	3.92	5.87	69.47
Venus	8.82	2.61	31.99
Earth	9.80	2.35	28.99
Mars*	3.92	–?–	–?–
Jupiter	26.46	0.87	12
Saturn	11.76	1.96	24.49
Uranus*	9.80	–?–	–?–
Neptune*	9.80	–?–	–?–
Pluto*	not available	–?–	–?–
Our moon	1.67	13.77	160.38
Our sun	274.4	0.08	2.96

c. Least-squares regression model: $y = 11.50x + 1.98$

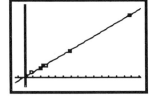

2. Given $h(t) = {}^-4.9t^2 + v_0t + 2$ with $5 \leq v_0 \leq 50$

v_0	t	$h(t)$
5	0.51	3.28
10	1.02	7.10
15	1.53	13.48
20	2.04	22.41
25	2.55	33.89
30	3.06	47.92
35	3.57	64.5
40	4.08	83.63
45	4.59	105.32
50	5.10	129.55

The quadratic regression is $y = 4.9x^2 - 0.0008 + 2.0023$.

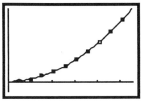

Problem Set 10.5

1. Because the object is dropped, there is no initial velocity.
$y = {}^-4.9x^2 = {}^-4.9(6.8)^2$; $y = {}^-226.576$; height ≈ 227 m
$y = {}^-16x^2 = {}^-16(6.8)^2$; $y = {}^-739.84$; height ≈ 740 ft

2. a. Use the equation $H(t) = {}^-4.9t^2 + v_0t + h_0$ where v_0 is the initial velocity and h_0 is the initial height. Select two points to substitute into the equation, and solve for v_0 and h_0.

$120.1 = {}^-4.9(1)^2 + v_0(1) + h_0$ $346.6 = {}^-4.9(4)^2 + v_0(4) + h_0$
$125 = v_0(1) + h_0$ $425 = v_0(4) + h_0$

$[A] = \begin{bmatrix} 1 & 1 \\ 4 & 1 \end{bmatrix}$, $[B] = \begin{bmatrix} 125 \\ 425 \end{bmatrix}$, $[A]^{-1}[B] = \begin{bmatrix} 100 \\ 25 \end{bmatrix}$

$H(t) = {}^-4.9t^2 + 100t + 25$

b. The initial height was 25 m; the initial velocity was 100 m/sec.

c. $x = \dfrac{{}^-100 \pm \sqrt{10000 - 4({}^-4.9)(25)}}{2({}^-4.9)} = \dfrac{{}^-100 \pm \sqrt{10,490}}{{}^-9.8} \approx {}^-0.247$ and 20.655. The vertex, or maximum height, must be halfway between the x-values. $\dfrac{{}^-0.247 + 20.655}{2} = 10.2$ sec

d. To find the maximum height, substitute the time of 10.2 sec into the equation:
$H(t) = {}^-4.9(10.2)^2 + 100(10.2) + 25 \approx 535$ m.

e. $300 = {}^-4.9t^2 + 100t + 25$; $0 = {}^-4.9t^2 + 100t - 275$; $t = \dfrac{{}^-100 \pm \sqrt{10000 - 4({}^-4.9)({}^-275)}}{2({}^-4.9)} = t = \dfrac{{}^-100 \pm \sqrt{4610}}{{}^-9.8} \approx$ 3.28 sec and 17.1 sec

f. The object hits the ground at 20.7 sec. (See part c. Throw out the extraneous negative solution.)

3. a.

Number of flashlights	200	190	180
Cost (x)	6.60	7.10	7.60
Income (y)	1320	1349	1368

$1320 = 6.60^2a + 6.60b + c$; $1349 = 7.10^2a + 7.10b + c$; $1368 = 7.60^2a + 7.60b + c$

$[A] = \begin{bmatrix} 43.56 & 6.6 & 1 \\ 50.41 & 7.1 & 1 \\ 57.76 & 7.6 & 1 \end{bmatrix}$, $[B] = \begin{bmatrix} 1320 \\ 1349 \\ 1368 \end{bmatrix}$, $[A]^{-1}[B] = \begin{bmatrix} {}^-20 \\ 332 \\ 0 \end{bmatrix}$

$y = {}^-20x^2 + 332x + 0$

b. $x = \dfrac{{}^-332 \pm \sqrt{332^2 - 4({}^-20)(0)}}{2({}^-20)} = 0, 16.6$. The maximum, or vertex, will occur halfway between these x-values or at \$8.30 each for a total of ${}^-20(8.30)^2 + 332(8.30) + 0 = \$1,377.80$.

4. a.

Width (x)	10	20	30	40
Length	60	40	20	0
Area (y)	600	800	600	0

Width = x, length = $80 - 2x$; area $y = x(80 - 2x)$ or $y = -2x^2 + 80x$

b. $x = \dfrac{-80 \pm \sqrt{6400 - 4(-2)(0)}}{2(-2)} = \dfrac{-80 \pm \sqrt{6400}}{-4} = 0$ or 40. The maximum will occur halfway between,

at a width of 20 ft. The area would be $20(80 - 2(20)) = 20(40) = 800$ ft².

5. a.

Number of cuts (x)	1	2	3	4	5
Number of pieces (y)	2	4	7	11	16

Choose three points, substitute them into the general quadratic equation, and solve using matrices.

$2 = a + b + c$
$4 = 4a + 2b + c$ $\qquad [A] = \begin{bmatrix} 1 & 1 & 1 \\ 4 & 2 & 1 \\ 9 & 3 & 1 \end{bmatrix}$, $[B] = \begin{bmatrix} 2 \\ 4 \\ 7 \end{bmatrix}$, $[A]^{-1}[B] = \begin{bmatrix} 0.5 \\ 0.5 \\ 1 \end{bmatrix}$
$7 = 9a + 3b + c$
$y = 0.5x^2 + 0.5x + 1$

b. $y = 0.5(5)^2 + 0.5(5) + 1 = 16$ pieces; $y = 0.5(10)^2 + 0.5(10) + 1 = 56$ pieces
There is no greatest number of pieces. The graph goes up forever.

6. a. $y = (26 - 2x)(21 - 2x)$

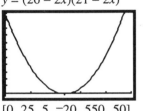

[0, 25, 5, −20, 550, 50]

b. $0 \le x \le 10.5$ in. (See the root in the graph in part a.) $0 \le A \le 546$ m². (If $x = 0$, area = $26(21) = 546$; if $x = 10.5$, area = $5(0) = 0$.)

c. Area of rectangle = $26(21) = 546$. To make the two areas equal, the area of the shaded region and the area of the unshaded region should both be $\frac{546}{2} = 273$. Enter $y_2 = 273$, and look for the intersection point. The areas are equal when $x = 3.395$ in.

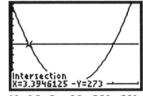

[0, 25, 5, −20, 550, 50]

7. $y = 11{,}000x^2 - Mx - M$

8.

Price ($)	8.00		8.50		9.00		9.50		10.00		10.50		11.00
Number of students	400		373		344		313		280		245		208
Profit	600		746		860		939		980		980		936
D₁		146		114		79		41		0		−44	
D₂			−32		−35		−38		−41		−44		
D₃				−3		−3		−3		−3			

a. Since the third finite differences are all the same, the predicted model should be a cubic equation. Choose four points to substitute into the model $y = ax^3 + bx^2 + cx + d$, set up a four-by-four matrix, and solve for a, b, c, and d.

$[A] = \begin{bmatrix} 512 & 64 & 8 & 1 \\ 729 & 81 & 9 & 1 \\ 1000 & 100 & 10 & 1 \\ 1331 & 121 & 11 & 1 \end{bmatrix}$, $[B] = \begin{bmatrix} 600 \\ 860 \\ 980 \\ 936 \end{bmatrix}$, $[A]^{-1}[B] = \begin{bmatrix} -4 \\ 38 \\ 482 \\ -3640 \end{bmatrix}$

$y = -4x^3 + 38x^2 + 482x - 3640$

b. To find the maximum value, graph and trace, look at a table, or use the maximum value function on your calculator if it has one. At $10.25, the maximum profit is $985.

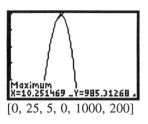

[0, 25, 5, 0, 1000, 200]

c. Look at where the graph crosses the *x*-axis.

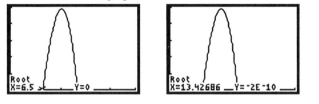

At $6.50 or at $13.43 the profit would be 0.

9.

Time (t)	1	1.5	2	2.5
Liters (L)	38.4	30.0	19.6	7.2
D_1		-8.4	-10.4	-12.4
D_2			-2	-2

a. The model appears to be quadratic. Set up a three-by-three matrix using three points, and solve for the coefficients a, b, and c.

$L = a + b + c$
$L = 2.25a + 1.5b + c$
$L = 6.25a + 2.5b + c$
$L = -4t^2 - 6.8t + 49.2$

$$[A] = \begin{bmatrix} 1 & 1 & 1 \\ 2.25 & 1.5 & 1 \\ 6.25 & 2.5 & 1 \end{bmatrix}, [B] = \begin{bmatrix} 38.4 \\ 30 \\ 7.2 \end{bmatrix}, [A]^{-1}[B] = \begin{bmatrix} -4 \\ -6.8 \\ 49.2 \end{bmatrix}$$

b. At $t = 0$, there were 49.2 L.

c.

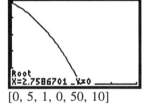

[0, 5, 1, 0, 50, 10]

The tub empties in 2.76 min.

Problem Set 10.6

1. a. $y = x - 4$ **b.** $y = (x - 4)^2$ **c.** $y = (x - 4)^3$

2. a. **b.**

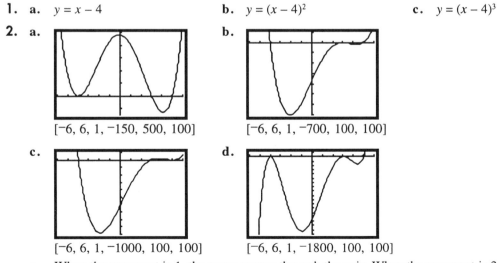

[−6, 6, 1, −150, 500, 100]   [−6, 6, 1, −700, 100, 100]

c. **d.**

[−6, 6, 1, −1000, 100, 100]   [−6, 6, 1, −1800, 100, 100]

e. When the exponent is 1, the curve passes through the axis. When the exponent is 2, the curve appears to bounce off the axis at the intercept or just touch and go back the opposite way.

3. a. There are four x-intercepts. **b.** The smallest possible degree is a fifth-degree polynomial.

   c. $y = Ax(x + 5)^2(x + 1)(x - 4)$. To be sure the point $(1, 216)$ is on the curve, substitute 1 for x, 216 for y, and solve for A: $216 = A(1)(6)^2(2)(-3)$; $216 = -216A$; $A = 1$ so the polynomial is $y = -x(x + 5)^2(x + 1)(x - 4)$.

4. a. Different values of A merely stretch the graph vertically, keeping all x-intercepts the same.

   b. If $A = -2$, the graph will reflect over the x-axis.

   c. They are both "U" shaped, but the quadratic is wider while the fourth-degree graph is flatter at the bottom.

   d. They both go from lower left corner to upper right corner. The first equation is a straight line, while the cubic has a flat spot at the x-intercept of 3.

   e. The graph should start from the upper left corner, bounce off -4, go straight through -1, bounce off 3 from below, "s" through 5, and end up going to the upper right corner.

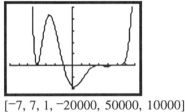

$[-7, 7, 1, -20000, 50000, 10000]$

5. Answers will vary. You should come up with a basic "W" shape, either going up or turned upside down. The points of the W can vary in relative length or be basically the same.

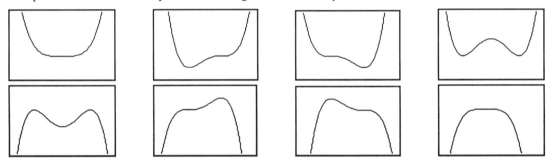

6. False. Answers will vary. Every odd-degree polynomial will have at least one root, but an even polynomial may not have any roots.

7. a. $y = (x + 5)^2(x + 2)(x - 1)$ **b.** $y = -(x + 5)^2(x + 2)(x - 1)$

   c. $y = (x + 5)^2(x + 2)(x - 1)^2$ **d.** $y = -(x + 5)(x + 2)^3(x - 1)$

   e. $\{-5, -5, -2, 1\}$ $\{-5, -5, -2, 1\}$ $\{-5, -5, -2, 1, 1\}$ $\{-5, -2, -2, -2, 1\}$

8. Answers will vary depending on the size of the paper. For the following answers, the paper was 21.6 by 28 cm.

   a. For $x = 3$, $A = 0.5(b)(h) = 0.5(3)(10.6) = 15.9$ cm²; for $x = 6$, $A = 0.5(b)(h) \approx 0.5(6)(10) \approx 30$ cm².

   b. x-values that produce an area of zero are 0 and 21.6 cm

   c. $area = Ax(x - 21.6)(x - R_3)$

   d. $15.9 = A(3)(-18.6)(3 - R_3)$; $15.9 = -55.8A(3 - R_3)$; $30 = A(6)(-15.6)(6 - R_3)$; $30 = -93.6A(6 - R_3)$ Solve the system using substitution: $R_3 = -21.0$ and $A = -0.012$, so the equation for the area, in factored form, is $y = -0.012x(x - 21)(x + 21.6)$.

   e.

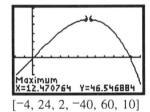

$[-4, 24, 2, -40, 60, 10]$

          The maximum area of 45.3 cm² occurs when $x = 12.5$ cm.

Project: Coefficient of Fit

In order of increasing ρ^2 value the models are as follows:

linear	$y = -0.2202x + 7.5536$	$\rho^2 = 0.1993$
exponential	$y = 7.385(0.9709)^x$	$\rho^2 = 0.2091$
logarithmic	$y = 8.0202 - 1.0997 \ln x$	$\rho^2 = 0.4098$
power	$y = 7.9208x^{-0.1529}$	$\rho^2 = 0.4334$
quadratic	$y = 0.1994x^2 - 2.0149 + 10.544$	$\rho^2 = 0.8531$
cubic	$y = -0.00631x^3 + 0.285x^2 - 2.34x + 10.86$	$\rho^2 = 0.8553$
quartic	$y = -0.01467x^4 + 0.2579x^3 - 1.311x^2 + 1.321x + 8.37$	$\rho^2 = 0.8935$

Based on values for ρ^2 given above, one might choose the quartic model. However, the authors favor the quadratic model because it looks almost identical to the cubic in the given interval and increasing degree will *always* bring increasing ρ^2 values, but not always better models. Simpler is better unless the residuals are improved for the higher degree. In this problem the residuals for all three polynomial models are about equal.

Problem Set 10.7

1. Solve each equation by using the quadratic formula or a calculator program.
   a. complex; $x = 2 \pm i\sqrt{2}$ or $2 \pm 1.414i$ b. complex; $x = \pm i$

   c. complex; $x = \frac{-1 \pm i\sqrt{3}}{2} = -0.5 \pm 0.866i$

2. a. $(x - {}^-3)(x - 5) = 0$; $(x + 3)(x - 5) = x^2 - 2x - 15 = 0$
   b. $(x - {}^-3.5)(x - {}^-3.5) = 0$; $(x + 3.5)^2 = x^2 + 7x + 12.25 = 0$
   c. $(x - 5i)(x - {}^- 5i) = 0$; $(x - 5i)(x + 5i)$; $x^2 - 25i^2 = 0$; $x^2 + 25 = 0$
   d. $(x - (2 + i))(x - (2 - i)) = 0$; $(x - 2 - i)(x - 2 + i) = 0$; $x^2 - 2x + ix - 2x + 4 - 2i - ix + 2i - i^2 = 0$; $x^2 - 4x + 5 = 0$

3. a. $y = A(x + 4)(x - 5)(x + 2)^2$; now substitute $(0, {}^-80)$ into the equation to find A: $-80 = A(4)(-5)(2)^2$; $-80 = -80A$, so $A = 1$. The equation is $y = (x + 4)(x - 5)(x + 2)^2$.
   b. $y = A(x + 4)(x - 5)(x + 2)^2$; $160 = A(4)(-5)(2)^2$; $160 = -80A$, so $A = -2$. The equation is $y = -2(x + 4)(x - 5)(x + 2)^2$.
   c. $y = Ax(3x - 1)(5x + 2)$; $0 = A(0)(-1)(2)$; $0 = 0$. In this case the A-value is not uniquely defined. Any value for A will give the same x-intercepts. The equation is $y = Ax(3x - 1)(5x + 2)$.
   d. $y = A(x + 5i)(x - 5i)(x + 1)^3(x - 4)$; $100 = A(5i)(-5i)(1)^3(-4)$; $100 = 100A$, so $A = 1$. The equation is $y = (x + 5i)(x - 5i)(x + 1)^3(x - 4)$ or $y = (x^2 + 25)(x + 1)^3(x - 4)$.

4. a. $a = 1, b = -10i, c = -9i^2 = 9$; $x = \frac{10i \pm \sqrt{100i^2 - 4(1)(9)}}{2(1)} = \frac{10i \pm \sqrt{-136}}{2} = \frac{10i \pm 11.66i}{2} = 10.83i$ and $-0.83i$

   b. $a = 1, b = -3i, c = -2$; $x = \frac{3i \pm \sqrt{9i^2 - 4(1)(-2)}}{2(1)} = \frac{3i \pm \sqrt{-9 + 8}}{2} = \frac{3i \pm i}{2}$; $x = 2i$ and i

   c. The solutions do not come in conjugate pairs because the coefficients of the equation are imaginary.

5. a. The solutions are nonreal when $b^2 - 4ac < 0$ or when $b^2 < 4ac$.
   b. The solutions are real when $b^2 - 4ac \geq 0$ or when $b^2 \geq 4ac$.
   c. The solutions are equal when $b^2 - 4ac = 0$ or when $b^2 = 4ac$.

6. When $x = {}^-2, 3,$ or 6, the value of y is 50. To find the y-intercept, substitute $x = 0$ into the equation and solve: $-3(2)^2(-3)(-6) + 50 = -166$.

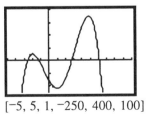

$[-5, 5, 1, -250, 400, 100]$

7. a.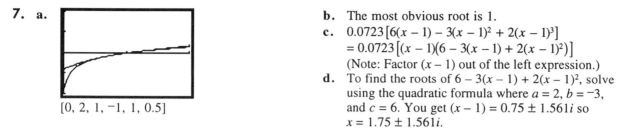

[0, 2, 1, −1, 1, 0.5]

b. The most obvious root is 1.

c. $0.0723[6(x − 1) − 3(x − 1)^2 + 2(x − 1)^3]$
$= 0.0723[(x − 1)(6 − 3(x − 1) + 2(x − 1)^2)]$
(Note: Factor $(x − 1)$ out of the left expression.)

d. To find the roots of $6 − 3(x − 1) + 2(x − 1)^2$, solve using the quadratic formula where $a = 2$, $b = -3$, and $c = 6$. You get $(x − 1) = 0.75 ± 1.561i$ so $x = 1.75 ± 1.561i$.

8. For $y_2 = |y_1|$, every place the function is positive, the graph will be the same, but for each place the function is negative, the graph will reflect over the x-axis.

a.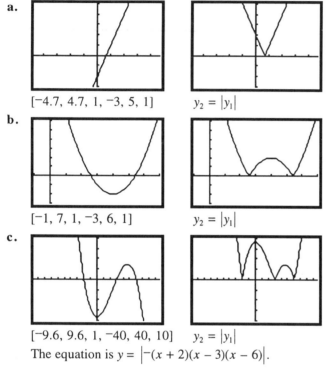

[−4.7, 4.7, 1, −3, 5, 1] $y_2 = |y_1|$

b.

[−1, 7, 1, −3, 6, 1] $y_2 = |y_1|$

c.

[−9.6, 9.6, 1, −40, 40, 10] $y_2 = |y_1|$
The equation is $y = |-(x + 2)(x − 3)(x − 6)|$.

9. See Calculator Note 10B.

Take Another Look 10.7

$i(a + bi) = -b + ai$. Geometrically, this is a rotation around the origin of 90 degrees (counterclockwise).
$i^2(a + bi) = -a − bi$. Geometrically, this is a rotation around the origin of 180 degrees.
$i^3(a + bi) = b − ai$. Geometrically, this is a rotation around the origin of 270 degrees.
$i^4(a + bi) = a + bi$. Geometrically, this is a rotation around the origin of 360 degrees.

The pattern then begins to repeat with n being an integer.
$i^{4n}(a + bi) = a + bi$
$i^{4n+1}(a + bi) = -b + ai$
$i^{4n+2}(a + bi) = -a − bi$
$i^{4n+3}(a + bi) = b − ai$

Project: Least-Squares Polynomial Fit

Sample number	x	x^2	x^3	x^4	y	xy	x^2y
1	1.0	1	1	1	8.5	8.5	8.5
2	2.0	4	8	16	8.0	16	32
3	3.0	9	27	81	6.0	18	54
4	4.0	16	64	256	5.0	20	80
5	5.0	25	125	625	6.0	30	150
6	6.0	36	216	1296	5.5	33	198
7	7.0	49	343	2401	6.5	45.5	318.5
8	8.0	64	512	4096	7.0	56	448
Σ	36	204	1296	8772	52.5	227	1289

$\sum y_i = a\sum x_i^2 + b\sum x_i + cn$

$\sum x_i y_i = a\sum x_i^3 + b\sum x_i^2 + c\sum x_i \Rightarrow$

$\sum x_i^2 y_i = a\sum x_i^4 + b\sum x_i^3 + c\sum x_i^2$

$52.5 = 204a + 36b + 8c$
$227 = 1296a + 204b + 36c$
$1289 = 8772a + 1296b + 204c$

$$\begin{bmatrix} 204 & 36 & 8 \\ 1296 & 204 & 36 \\ 8772 & 1296 & 204 \end{bmatrix}^{-1} \begin{bmatrix} 52.5 \\ 227 \\ 1289 \end{bmatrix} = \begin{bmatrix} 0.1994047619 \\ -2.014880952 \\ 10.54464286 \end{bmatrix}$$

Problem Set 10.8

1. a. $11(4) + 3 = 47$

b. $P(x) = 6x^4 - 5x^3 + 7x^2 - 12x + 15$

$$\begin{array}{r|rrrrr} 1 & 6 & -5 & 7 & -12 & 15 \\ & & 6 & 1 & 8 & -4 \\ \hline & 6 & 1 & 8 & -4 & 11 \end{array}$$

$P(x) = 6x^4 - 5x^3 + 7x^2 - 12x + 15 =$
$(x - 1)(6x^3 + x^2 + 8x - 4) + 11$

c. $P(x) = x^3 - x^2 - 10x + 16$

$$\begin{array}{r|rrrr} 2 & 1 & -1 & -10 & 16 \\ & & 2 & 2 & -16 \\ \hline & 1 & 1 & -8 & 0 \end{array}$$

$P(x) = x^3 - x^2 - 10x + 16 =$
$(x - 2)(x^2 + x - 8)$

2. a. $P(x) = x^5 - 6x^4 + 20x^3 - 60x^2 + 99x - 54$

$$\begin{array}{r|rrrrrr} 1 & 1 & -6 & 20 & -60 & 99 & -54 \\ & & 1 & -5 & 15 & -45 & 54 \\ \hline & 1 & -5 & 15 & -45 & 54 & 0 \end{array}$$

$Q_1 = x^4 - 5x^3 + 15x^2 - 45x + 54$

b.
$$\begin{array}{r|rrrrr} 2 & 1 & -5 & 15 & -45 & 54 \\ & & 2 & -6 & 18 & -54 \\ \hline & 1 & -3 & 9 & -27 & 0 \end{array}$$

$Q_2 = x^3 - 3x^2 + 9x - 27$

c.
$$\begin{array}{r|rrrr} 3 & 1 & -3 & 9 & -27 \\ & & 3 & 0 & 27 \\ \hline & 1 & 0 & 9 & 0 \end{array}$$

$Q_3 = x^2 + 9$

d. $x^2 + 9 = 0$
$a = 1, b = 0, c = 9$
$x = \dfrac{0 \pm \sqrt{0 - 36}}{2}$
$x = \dfrac{6i}{2} = \pm 3i$

e. (Calculator check)

3. a. There are four zeros because the function is a fourth-degree polynomial.

b. $y = x^4 + 3x^3 - 11x^2 - 3x + 10$

$$\begin{array}{r|rrrrr} 1 & 1 & 3 & -11 & -3 & 10 \\ & & 1 & 4 & -7 & -10 \\ \hline 2 & 1 & 4 & -7 & -10 & 0 \\ & & 2 & 12 & 10 \\ \hline & 1 & 6 & 5 & 0 \end{array}$$

$x^2 + 6x + 5 = (x + 5)(x + 1)$

The x-intercepts are $-5, -1, 2,$ and 1.

c. The y-intercept is 10.

d. $x^4 + 3x^3 - 11x^2 - 3x + 10 = (x + 5)(x + 1)(x - 1)(x - 2)$

4. Graph the function and use the method given in Calculator Note 10E to find all the real roots. If there are any imaginary roots (and you would know if there are because the graph crosses the *x*-axis fewer times than the degree of the polynomial), use synthetic division with the roots you found. Then use the quadratic formula.

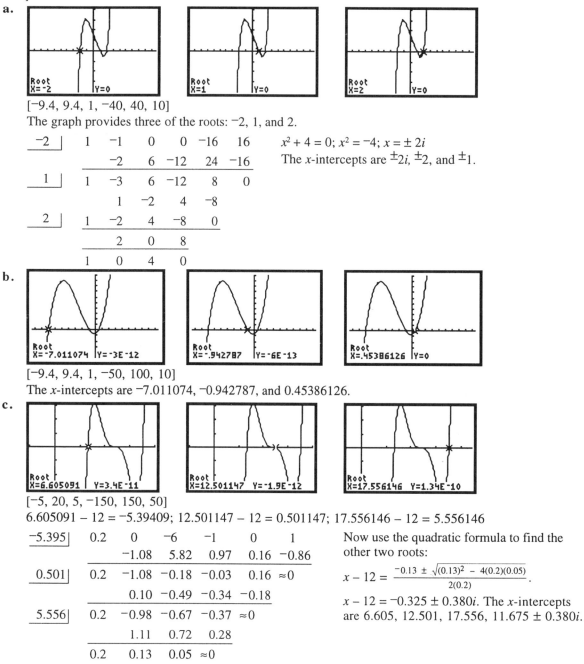

a.

[−9.4, 9.4, 1, −40, 40, 10]

The graph provides three of the roots: −2, 1, and 2.

$$\begin{array}{c|cccccc}
-2 & 1 & -1 & 0 & 0 & -16 & 16 \\
  &   & -2 & 6 & -12 & 24 & -16 \\
\hline
1 & 1 & -3 & 6 & -12 & 8 & 0 \\
  &   & 1 & -2 & 4 & -8 & \\
\hline
2 & 1 & -2 & 4 & -8 & 0 & \\
  &   & 2 & 0 & 8 & & \\
\hline
  & 1 & 0 & 4 & 0 & &
\end{array}$$

$x^2 + 4 = 0$; $x^2 = -4$; $x = \pm 2i$

The *x*-intercepts are $\pm 2i$, ± 2, and ± 1.

b.

[−9.4, 9.4, 1, −50, 100, 10]

The *x*-intercepts are −7.011074, −0.942787, and 0.45386126.

c.

[−5, 20, 5, −150, 150, 50]

$6.605091 - 12 = -5.39409$; $12.501147 - 12 = 0.501147$; $17.556146 - 12 = 5.556146$

$$\begin{array}{c|cccccc}
-5.395 & 0.2 & 0 & -6 & -1 & 0 & 1 \\
  &   & -1.08 & 5.82 & 0.97 & 0.16 & -0.86 \\
\hline
0.501 & 0.2 & -1.08 & -0.18 & -0.03 & 0.16 & \approx 0 \\
  &   & 0.10 & -0.49 & -0.34 & -0.18 & \\
\hline
5.556 & 0.2 & -0.98 & -0.67 & -0.37 & \approx 0 & \\
  &   & 1.11 & 0.72 & 0.28 & & \\
\hline
  & 0.2 & 0.13 & 0.05 & \approx 0 & &
\end{array}$$

Now use the quadratic formula to find the other two roots:

$$x - 12 = \frac{-0.13 \pm \sqrt{(0.13)^2 - 4(0.2)(0.05)}}{2(0.2)}.$$

$x - 12 = -0.325 \pm 0.380i$. The *x*-intercepts are 6.605, 12.501, 17.556, $11.675 \pm 0.380i$.

d.

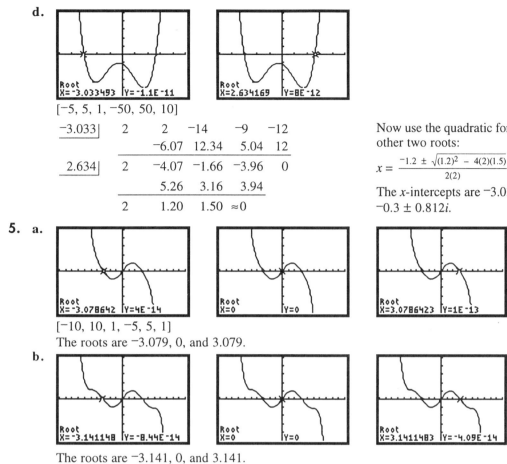

$[-5, 5, 1, -50, 50, 10]$

-3.033	2	2	-14	-9	-12
		-6.07	12.34	5.04	12
2.634	2	-4.07	-1.66	-3.96	0
		5.26	3.16	3.94	
	2	1.20	1.50	≈ 0	

Now use the quadratic formula to find the other two roots:

$$x = \frac{-1.2 \pm \sqrt{(1.2)^2 - 4(2)(1.5)}}{2(2)}.$$

The x-intercepts are -3.033, 2.634, and $-0.3 \pm 0.812i$.

5. a.

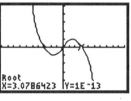

$[-10, 10, 1, -5, 5, 1]$

The roots are -3.079, 0, and 3.079.

b.

The roots are -3.141, 0, and 3.141.

c. As the pattern continues, the real roots approach 0 and $\pm\pi$.

6. Answers will vary.

7. Answers will vary.

Take Another Look 10.8

a. Substitute $A_1 = A_0(1 + r) - P$ into $A_2 = A_1(1 + r) - P$ to get $A_2 = (A_0(1 + r) - P)(1 + r) - P = A_0(1 + r)^2 - P(1 + r) - P$.

b. Substitute $A_2 = A_0(1 + r)^2 - P(1 + r) - P$ into $A_3 = A_2(1 + r) - P$ to get $A_3 = (A_0(1 + r)^2 - P(1 + r) - P)(1 + r) - P = (A_0(1 + r)^3 - P(1 + r)^2 - P)(1 + r) - P$.

c. Substitute $A_3 = A_0(1 + r)^3 - P(1 + r)^2 - P(1 + r) - P$ into $A_4 = A_3(1 + r) - P$ to get $A_4 = (A_0(1 + r)^3 - P(1 + r)^2 - P)(1 + r) - P)(1 + r) - P = A_0(1 + r)^4 - P(1 + r)^3 - P(1 + r)^2 - P(1 + r) - P$. Continue the pattern to get $A_n = A_0(1 + r)^n - P(1 + r)^{n-1} - P(1 + r)^{n-2} - P(1 + r)^{n-3} - \ldots - P(1 + r) - P$.

d. For A_n, factor out P from each term after the first one to get the equation in the text.

e. There are n terms in the series. To use the explicit formula, substitute $u_1 = 1$ and $r = 1 + r$.

f. The sum of the series in part e can be written as $A_n = \frac{1[1 - (1 + r)^n]}{1 - (1 + r)} = \frac{-(1 + r)^n + 1}{-r} = \frac{(1 + r)^n - 1}{r}$.
Substituting this expression in the equation in part d gives the equation given in part f.

g.

$$0 = A_0(1 + r)^n - \frac{P[(1 + r)^n - 1]}{r}$$

$$-A_0(1 + r)^n = -\frac{P[(1 + r)^n - 1]}{r}$$

$$P = A_0(1 + r)^n \left[\frac{r}{P[(1 + r)^n - 1]}\right]$$

$$= \frac{A_0 r(1 + r)^n}{(1 + r)^n - 1}$$

h.
$$P = \frac{11{,}000(0.11/12)(1 + 0.11/12)^{60}}{(1 + 0.11/12)^{60} - 1} = 239.17$$

i.
$$A_0 = \frac{P[(1 + r)^n - 1]}{r(1 + r)^n}$$

$$A_0 = \frac{620[(1 + 0.075/12)^{360} - 1]}{(0.075/12)(1 + 0.075/12)^{360}}$$

$$A_0 \approx 88670.93$$

Project: Mandlebrot Set

If $z_1 = 0$ and $c = 0.25$, then the long-run value will be 0.5, and if $z_1 = 0$ and $c = {}^-0.4 + 0.5i$, then the long-run value will be $^-0.35733919 + 0.29159987i$.

$$\begin{bmatrix} a & -b \\ b & a \end{bmatrix}^2 = \begin{bmatrix} a & -b \\ b & a \end{bmatrix}\begin{bmatrix} a & -b \\ b & a \end{bmatrix} = \begin{bmatrix} a^2 - b^2 & -2ab \\ 2ab & a^2 - b^2 \end{bmatrix}$$

$$(a + bi)^2 = (a + bi)(a + bi) = a^2 + abi + abi + b^2i^2 = a^2 + 2abi - b^2 = (a^2 - b^2) + (2ab)i$$

It is hopeful that in each zoom near the edge of the figure students will find this same "turtle" shape appearing in ever diminishing size.

Chapter Review

Problem Set 10.9

1.

Points	3	4	5	6	7
Triangles	1	4	10	20	35

D_1		3	6	10	15

D_2		3	4	5

D_3		1	1

The model must be cubic. Select 4 points and form a matrix to solve for a, b, c, and d.

$$[A] = \begin{bmatrix} 27 & 9 & 3 & 1 \\ 64 & 16 & 4 & 1 \\ 125 & 25 & 5 & 1 \\ 216 & 36 & 6 & 1 \end{bmatrix}, [B] = \begin{bmatrix} 1 \\ 4 \\ 10 \\ 20 \end{bmatrix}, [A]^{-1}[B] = \begin{bmatrix} 0.1667 \\ 0.5 \\ 0.3333 \\ 0 \end{bmatrix} = \begin{bmatrix} \frac{1}{6} \\ \frac{1}{2} \\ \frac{1}{3} \\ 0 \end{bmatrix}$$

For n points, the equation is $\frac{1}{6}n^3 - \frac{1}{2}n^2 + \frac{1}{3}n$.

2. a. Polynomial form: $y = 2(x - 2)^2 - 16 = 2(x^2 - 4x + 4) - 16 = 2x^2 - 8x + 8 - 16 = 2x^2 - 8x - 8$
   Find the zeros:
$$x = \frac{^-(^-8) \pm \sqrt{(^-8)^2 - 4(2)(^-8)}}{2(2)} = \frac{8 \pm \sqrt{128}}{4} = \frac{8 \pm 8\sqrt{2}}{4} = 2 \pm 2\sqrt{2} = 4.828 \text{ and } ^-0.828$$
   Factored form: $y = 2(x - 4.828)(x + 0.828)$

 b. Polynomial form: $y = ^-3(x - 5)(x + 1) = ^-3(x^2 - 4x - 5) = ^-3x^2 + 12x + 15$
   Vertex form: $y = ^-3(x^2 - 4x) + 15 = ^-3(x - 2)^2 + 27$

 c. Factored form: $y = x^2 + 3x + 2 = (x + 2)(x + 1)$
   Vertex form: $y = (x^2 + 3x) + 2 = (x + 1.5)^2 - 0.25$

 d. Polynomial form: $y = (x + 1)(x - 3)(x + 4) = (x^2 - 2x - 3)(x + 4) = x^3 + 2x^2 - 11x - 12$

 e. $y = 2x^2 + 5x - 6$
   Find the zeros:
$$x = \frac{^-5 \pm \sqrt{5^2 - 4(2)(^-6)}}{2(2)} = \frac{^-5 \pm \sqrt{73}}{4} = 0.886 \text{ and } ^-3.386$$
   Factored form: $2(x + 3.386)(x - 0.886)$
   Vertex form: $y = 2(x^2 + 2.5x) - 6 = 2(x + 1.25)^2 - 9.125$

f. Polynomial form: $y = {}^-(x + 7)^2 - 2 = {}^-(x^2 + 14x + 49) - 2 = {}^-x^2 - 14x - 51$

$$x = \frac{{}^-(^-14) \pm \sqrt{(^-14)^2 - 4(^-1)(^-51)}}{2(^-1)} = \frac{14 \pm \sqrt{196 - 204}}{^-2} = \frac{14 \pm i\sqrt{8}}{^-2} = {}^-7 \pm i\sqrt{2}$$

Factored form: $y = {}^-(x + 7 + 1.414i)(x + 7 - 1.414i)$

3. For parts a.–d., use the information from Problem 2a.–d.

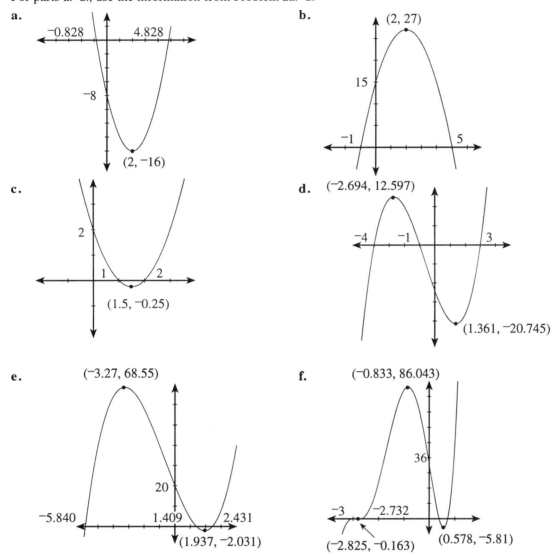

a.

−0.828   4.828

−8

(2, −16)

b.

(2, 27)

15

−1   5

c.

2

1   2

(1.5, −0.25)

d. (−2.694, 12.597)

−4   −1   3

(1.361, −20.745)

e. (−3.27, 68.55)

20

−5.840   1.409   2.431

(1.937, −2.031)

f. (−0.833, 86.043)

36

−3   −2.732

(−2.825, −0.163)   (0.578, −5.81)

4. a. $y = A(x + 1)(x - 4)$. Substitute the y-intercept into the equation to find the multiplier A: $^-8 = A(1)(^-4)$, so $A = 2$; $y = 2(x + 1)(x - 4)$.
  b. $y = A(x + 3)^2 (x - 1)$; $^-18 = A(3)^2(^-1)$, so $A = 2$; $y = 2(x + 3)^2(x - 1)$.
  c. $y = A(x + 2)(x - 3)^3$; $54 = A(2)(^-27)$, so $A = {}^-1$; $y = {}^-(x + 2)(x - 3)^3$.
  d. $y = A(x + 4)(x - 2)(x - 3i)(x + 3i) = A(x + 4)(x - 2)(x^2 + 9)$; $^-36 = A(4)(^-2)(9)$, so $A = 0.5$; $y = 0.5(x + 4)(x - 2)(x^2 + 9)$.

5. Volume $= lwh = yxx = yx^2$. Because the postal regulations restrict the size to $4x + y = 108$, $y = 108 - 4x$. Substitute this y-value into the volume formula. Graph the equation and look for the maximum value: $V = (108 - 4x)x^2$.

The maximum volume of 11,664 in.^{3} occurs when $x = 18$ in. The length is $108 - 4(18) = 36$ in. The dimensions are 18 in. × 18 in. × 36 in.

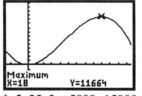

Maximum
X=18   Y=11664

$[^-5, 25, 2, ^-5000, 15000, 1000]$

6. Answers will vary.

7. Answers will vary.

Chapter 11

Problem Set 11.1

1. a. $(8)(7)(6)(5)(4)(3)(2)(1) = 8! = 40,320$ **b.** $(7)(6)(5)(4)(3)(2)(1)(1) = 7! = 5040$

     c. $\frac{5040}{40,320} = \frac{1}{8} = 0.125$ **d.** Answers will vary.

     e. There are four books that can be in the rightmost position. Therefore, the number of ways the books can be arranged is $(7)(6)(5)(4)(3)(2)(1)(4) = 7!(4) = 20,160$. So the probability is $\frac{20,160}{40,320} = \frac{1}{2} = 0.5$.

     f. $(1)(1)(1)(1)(1)(1)(1)(1) = 1$ **g.** $8! - 1 = 40,319$

     h. $\frac{8!-1}{8!} = \frac{40,319}{40,320} = 0.999975$

2. a. $\frac{12(11!)}{11!} = 12$ **b.** $\frac{7(6!)}{6!} = 7$ **c.** $\frac{(n+1)n!}{n!} = n + 1$ **d.** $\frac{n(n-1)!}{(n-1)!} = n$

     e. $\frac{(120)(119)(118!)}{118!} = (120)(119) = 14,280$ **f.** $\frac{n!(n-1)(n-2)!}{(n-2)!} = n(n-1)$

     g. $\frac{(n+1)!}{n} = n + 1; n + 1 = 15; n = 14$

3. a. Answers will vary.

     b. $_7P_3 = \frac{7!}{(7-3)!} = \frac{7!}{4!}$. Answers will vary. The number 7! is the number of ways to arrange all seven objects, and you divide 7! by the number of ways to arrange the last four objects because you are interested only in the first three objects.

     c. Answers will vary.

4. a. $10! = 3,628,800$

     b. If a number is greater than or equal to 7 billion, there must be a 7 in the first digit on the left. The number of arrangements where this happens is $(1)(9)(8)(7)(6)(5)(4)(3)(2)(1) = 9!$. Therefore, the probability of this event happening is $\frac{9!}{10!} = 0.1$.

     c. To be divisible by 5, the digit in the rightmost place must be a 5 or a 0. The number of arrangements where this happens is $(9)(8)(7)(6)(5)(4)(3)(2)(1)(2) = 9!(2)$. The probability of this event happening is $\frac{9!(2)}{10!} = 0.2$.

     d. The other seven numbers can be arranged in $(7)(6)(5)(4)(3)(2)(1) = 7!$ different ways. There are eight positions for the 4, 5, and 6. Therefore, the number of ways the numbers can be arranged with 4, 5, and 6 in that order is $(8)(7)(6)(5)(4)(3)(2)(1) = 8! = 40,320$. So the probability is $\frac{40,320}{3,628,800} \approx 0.01$.

5. $(8)(10)(10)(10)(10)(10)(10) = 8 \cdot 10^6 = 8,000,000$

6. Since $120 \cdot 10^{-6} = 0.00012$, start by multiplying each entry in the table by 10^{-6}. Then divide by 60 to get minutes, divide by 60 again to get hours, divide again by 24 to get hours, and so on.

N	Permutation ($N!$)	Time
5	120	0.00012 sec
10	3,628,800	3.6288 sec
12	479,001,600	$\approx$ 8 min
13	6,227,020,800	$\approx$ 1.7 hr
15	$\approx 1.31 \cdot 10^{12}$	$\approx$ 15 days
20	$\approx 2.43 \cdot 10^{18}$	$\approx$ 771 centuries

7. a. $\left(\frac{46}{50}\right)\left(\frac{45}{49}\right)\left(\frac{4}{48}\right) \approx 0.07$ **b.** $\left(\frac{46}{50}\right)\left(\frac{4}{49}\right)\left(\frac{3}{48}\right) \approx 0.005$

     c. $1 - P(\text{winning nothing}) - P(\text{winning first prize}); 1 - \left(\frac{46}{50} \cdot \frac{45}{49} \cdot \frac{44}{48} + \frac{46}{50} \cdot \frac{45}{49} \cdot \frac{4}{48}\right) \approx 0.16$

     d. $\frac{(4)(3)(2)}{(50)(49)(48)}$ ($\$5 + \$10 + \$25$) $+ \frac{(4)(3)(46)}{(50)(49)(48)}$ ($\$5 + \$10$) $+ \frac{(4)(46)(3)}{(50)(49)(48)}$ ($\$5 + \$25$) $+ \frac{(46)(4)(3)}{(50)(49)(48)}$ ($\$10 + \$25$)

        $+ \frac{(46)(45)(4)}{(50)(49)(48)}$ ($\$25$) $+ \frac{(46)(4)(45)}{(50)(49)(48)}$ ($\$10$) $+ \frac{(46)(45)(4)}{(50)(49)(48)}$ ($\$5$) $+ \frac{(46)(45)(44)}{(50)(49)(48)}$ ($\$0$) $\approx \$3.20$

Take Another Look 11.1

The digits 0 and 1 cannot be used as the first number in an area code, so previously there were $8(2)(10) = 160$ possible area codes. By allowing the middle digit in area codes to be any number between 2 and 9 inclusively, you gain 8(80) or 640 area codes.

Problem Set 11.2

1. a. $_7P_2 = 2 \cdot {}_7C_2$ $(2 = 2!)$ **b.** $_7P_3 = 6 \cdot {}_7C_3$ $(6 = 3!)$ **c.** $_7P_4 = 24 \cdot {}_7C_4$ $(24 = 4!)$
    d. $_7P_7 = 5040 \cdot {}_7C_7$ $(5040 = 7!)$ **e.** $_nC_r = \frac{{}_nP_r}{n!}$

2. a. 120   **b.** 35   **c.** 105   **d.** 1

3. a. 120   **b.** 35   **c.** 105   **d.** 1

4. a. $_{10}C_4 = \frac{10!}{6!4!}$ **b.** $_{10}C_4 = {}_{10}C_6$ **c.** $\frac{10!}{6!4!} = \frac{10!}{4!6!}$ **d.** $_nC_r = \frac{n!}{r!(n-r)!}$

5. a.–d. Answers will vary.

6. a. $_{20}C_6 = 38{,}760$ **b.** $_{18}C_4 = 3060$ **c.** $\frac{3{,}060}{38{,}760} = 0.08$ **d.** Answers will vary.

7. a. $_7C_4 = 35$ **b.** $\frac{{}_6C_3}{{}_7C_4} = \frac{4}{7}$

8. Answers will vary. $_5C_4(0.5)^5 = 0.15625$. There are $_5C_4$ or 5 arrangements of HHHHT, and each has a probability of $0.5^5 = 0.03125$.

9. a. $_7C_5(0.3)^5(0.7)^2 = 0.0250047$ **b.** $_7C_6(0.3)^6(0.7)^1 = 0.0035721$
    c. $_7C_7(0.3)^7(0.7)^0 = 0.0002187$ **d.** $0.0025 + 0.00357 + 0.00022 = 0.2879$

10. Answers will vary. In a "combination" lock, the order in which the numbers are entered does not matter. You could enter the correct three numbers in any order to open the lock.

Problem Set 11.3

1. a. HH, HT, TH, TT   **b.** HH, HT, TH, TT   **c.**
    d. The combination number $_2C_0$ is the number of times you get no tails when two coins are tossed; $_2C_1$ is the number of times you get 1 tail when two coins are tossed; $_2C_2$ is the number of times you get 2 tails when two coins are tossed.
    e. The terms represent the long-range distribution of 2 heads, 1 head, and 0 heads.

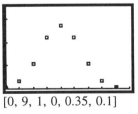

2. a. $(x + y)^4 = {}_4C_0x^4y^0 + {}_4C_1x^3y^1 + {}_4C_2x^2y^2 + {}_4C_3x^1y^3 + {}_4C_4x^0y^4 = x^4 + 4x^3y + 6x^2y^2 + 4xy^3 + y^4$
    b. $(p + q)^5 = {}_5C_0p^5q^0 + {}_5C_1p^4q^1 + {}_5C_2p^3q^2 + {}_5C_3p^2q^3 + {}_5C_4p^1q^4 + {}_5C_5p^0q^5 = p^5 + 5p^4q + 10p^3q^2 + 10p^2q^3 + 5pq^4 + q^5$
    c. $(2x + 3)^3 = {}_3C_0(2x)^3(3)^0 + {}_3C_1(2x)^2(3)^1 + {}_3C_2(2x)^1(3)^2 + {}_3C_3(2x)^0(3)^3 = 1(8x^3)(1) + 3(4x^2)(3) + 3(2x)(9) + 1(27) = 8x^3 + 36x^2 + 54x + 27$
    d. $(3x - 4)^4 = {}_4C_0(3x)^4(-4)^0 + {}_4C_1(3x)^3(-4)^1 + {}_4C_2(3x)^2(-4)^2 + {}_4C_3(3x)^1(-4)^3 + {}_4C_4(3x)^0(-4)^4 = 1(81x^4)(1) + 4(27x^3)(-4) + 6(9x^2)(16) + 4(3x)(-64) + 1(1)(256) = 81x^4 - 432x^3 + 864x^2 - 768x + 256$

3. a. $\{0.00391, 0.03125, 0.10938, 0.21875, 0.27344, 0.21875, 0.10938, 0.03125, 0.00391\}$; 1
    b. Answers will vary. Looking at a table or generating a list works well. On a TI-82, you can enter the sequence $\{0, 1, 2, \ldots, 8\}$ into L_1 and generate the list $y_1(L_1)$ for L_2.

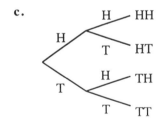

$[0, 9, 1, 0, 0.35, 0.1]$

c. {0.00837, 0.05481, 0.15696, 0.25683, 0.26266, 0.17192, 0.07033, 0.01644, 0.00168}; 1

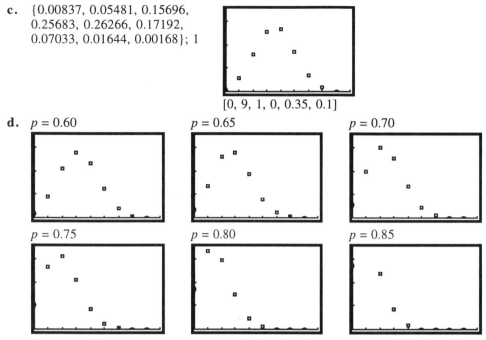

[0, 9, 1, 0, 0.35, 0.1]

d. $p = 0.60$ $p = 0.65$ $p = 0.70$

$p = 0.75$ $p = 0.80$ $p = 0.85$

Answers will vary. As p increases, the distributions lose symmetry and become extremely skewed.

4. a. $0.97^{30} = 0.40$ **b.** $0.97^{30} + {}_{30}C_1(0.97)^{29}(0.03) + {}_{30}C_2(0.97)^{28}(0.03)^2 \approx 0.94$

  c. $y_1 = {}_{30}C_x(0.97)^x(0.03)^{(30-x)}$

  d. $\displaystyle\sum_{J=0}^{2} {}_{30}C_j(0.03)^j(0.97)^{(30-j)} = {}_{30}C_0(0.03)^0(0.97)^{(30-0)} + {}_{30}C_1(0.03)^1(0.97)^{(30-1)} + {}_{30}C_2(0.03)^2(0.97)^{(30-2)}$

      $= {}_{30}C_0(0.03)^0(0.97)^{30} + {}_{30}C_1(0.03)^1(0.97)^{29} + {}_{30}C_2(0.03)^2(0.97)^{28} = 0.94$

5. If $n = 100$, $p = 0.88$, $a = 21$, $b = 100$, then the probability is 0.00727.

6. a. If $n = 100$, $p = 0.88$, $a = 25$, $b = 100$, then the probability is 0.00026.
  b. If $n = 200$, $p = 0.88$, $a = 25$, $b = 200$, then the probability is 0.445888.
  c. If $n = 300$, $p = 0.88$, $a = 25$, $b = 300$, then the probability is 0.98336.

7. ${}_6C_1 + {}_6C_2 + {}_6C_3 + {}_6C_4 + {}_6C_5 + {}_6C_6 = 63$

8. a. Answers will vary.
  b. Answers will vary. The horizontal shift can be found by tracing to the highest point of the binomial curve and finding the x-value. It should be $90(1 - p)$. The y-value of the maximum point should be the value of a in the exponential curve. The value of b will be less than 1, but not much less.

Take Another Look 11.3

Given $x = t$ and $y = {}_5C_t$, $t < 0$ gives errors and $t > 5$ always has a result of 0.

t	${}_5C_t$	${}_5P_t$	${}_5P_t/{}_5C_t$
0	1	1	1
1	5	5	1
2	10	20	2
3	10	60	6
4	5	120	24
5	1	120	120

[0, 5, 1, 0, 5, 1, −2, 10, 1]

To complete the table:
    If $x = t$ and $y = {}_5P_t$, $t < 0$ gives errors and $t > 5$ gives 0.
    If $x = t$ and $y = {}_5P_t/{}_5C_t$, $t < 0$ gives errors and $t > 5$ gives errors.

Graph using window values of approximately [0, 5, 1, 0, 10 , 1, −2, 135, 1]. An alternative to the last column would be T!
Repeat for 12 objects.

t	$_{12}C_t$	$_{12}P_t$	$_{12}C_t/_{12}C_t$
0	1	1	1
1	12	12	1
2	66	132	2
3	220	1,320	6
4	495	11,880	24
5	792	95,040	120
6	924	665,280	720
7	792	3,991,680	5,040
8	495	19,958,400	40,320
9	220	79,833,600	362,880
10	66	239,500,800	3,628,800
11	12	479,001,600	39,916,800
12	1	479,001,600	479,001,600

Problem 3c

Given $y = (8_nC_r x)p^{(8-x)}(1-p)^x$ with $x = 0.8$ and $p = 0.055$,
$x = t$ and $y = (_8C_t)0.55^{(8-t)}(1 - 0.055)^t$ with window values
of $[0, 8, 1, 0, 9, 1, 0, 0.35, 0.1]$, you get the graph shown at
the right.

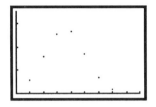

Project: Trinomial Distribution

$(x + y + z)^2 = x^2 + y^2 + z^2 + 2xy + 2xz + 2yz$
$(x + y + z)^3 = x^3 + y^3 + z^3 + 3x^2y + 3x^2z + 3xy^2 + 3xz^2 + 3y^2z + 3yz^2 + 6xyz$
$(x + y + z)^4 = x^4 + y^4 + z^4 + 4x^3y + 4x^3z + 4xy^3 + 4xz^3 + 4y^3z + 4yz^3 + 6x^2y^2 + 6x^2z^2 + 6y^2z^2 + 12x^2yz$
$+ 12xy^2z + 12xyz^2$

$$(x + y + z)^n = \sum_{i=0}^{n} \sum_{j=0}^{n-i} \frac{n!}{i! \cdot j! \cdot (n-i-j)!} x^i y^j z^{(n-i-j)}$$

$\frac{81!}{4! \cdot 6! \cdot 71!} 0.05^4 \cdot 0.08^6 \cdot 0.87^{71} = 0.03283$

We know this value will be small, but you still must add a lot of terms. You will need to sum over 2500 terms to find the value directly and over 700 terms to find it indirectly. The indirect solution comes from summing all the terms where one or both of the sections are not full. When 0.05 is raised from the 0 through 10th power and 0.08 is raised from the 0 through 81st power minus the value to which 0.05 is raised, you will find all the times when first class is not full and both classes are not full. When 0.08 is raised from the 0 through 10th power and 0.05 is raised from the 11th power through the 81st power minus the value to which 0.08 is raised, you will find the probability that only business class is not full. Add these two values together and subtract from 1 and you will find the probability that both sections are overfilled: $1 - 0.9976791 - 0.0022499 = 0.000071$, or a 0.0071% chance.

It is actually easier to find the probability that they are not overfilled then subtract from 1. If you sum all the terms where 0.05 is raised to powers from 0 to 10 and 0.08 is raised to powers from 0 to 10, but skip the term where they are both 0, you will have added 120 terms and get 0.94 for the probability that no section is overfilled. Now subtract from 1 and you will find that 0.06, or 6%, is the chance that one of the sections is too full.

Problem Set 11.4

1. **a.** Answers will vary, but the second set has less spread.
   b. In the first set, the mean is 35 and the standard deviation is 19.99; the mean of the second set is 117 and the standard deviation is 3.16.
   c. Both the mean and the standard deviations are ten times the original numbers.
   d. The mean is ten more than the original mean, and the standard deviation is the same.

2. **a.** The set with the smallest standard deviation is any set with four of the same number, because each member of the set will be equal to the mean.
   b. The set $\{1, 1, 8, 8\}$ has the largest standard deviation; answers will vary.

3. a. The mean for both the French and German tests is the same and lower than that for the German test. However, the larger standard deviation on the French exam indicates that there is a larger variation in scores, meaning that more students did worse (as well as more students doing better).

b. This is clearly the French exam, which has the greatest standard deviation; answers will vary.

c. Determine how many standard deviations each student's score is from the mean.

Pierre: $\frac{88-72}{8.5} = 1.88$ Hans: $\frac{84-72}{5.8} = 2.07$ Juanita: $\frac{91-85}{6.1} = 0.98$

Hans's score is better than the scores of Pierre and Juanita because his score is 2.07 standard deviations above the mean.

4. a. Answers will vary, but $\bar{x}$ should be close to 7, and σ should be close to 2.4.

b. The number of sums within one standard deviation should be close to 67.

c. The percentage of the data within one standard deviation should be close to 68%.

d. The percentage of the data within two standard deviations should be close to 95%.

5. a.–c. Answers will vary. Figure a should have the largest standard deviation and Figure c should have the smallest standard deviation.

6. a. Answers will vary.

b. Presidents: mean = 54.9, σ = 6.21
Vice-presidents: mean = 53.84, σ = 8.42

c.

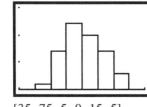 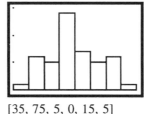

[35, 75, 5, 0, 15, 5]   [35, 75, 5, 0, 15, 5]

d. Calculator procedure

e. For the presidents the range is from ⁻1.92 to 2.27. The range for the vice-presidents is from ⁻2.12 to 2.04.

f.

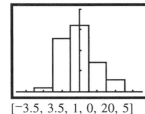 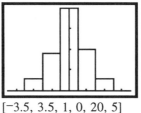

[⁻3.5, 3.5, 1, 0, 20, 5]   [⁻3.5, 3.5, 1, 0, 20, 5]

g. Answers will vary. The graph for the vice-presidents is more symmetrical around the mean than the graph for the presidents.

7. a.

Heads (x)	0	1	2	3	4	5	6	7
P(x)	0.00003	0.00046	0.0032	0.01389	0.04166	0.09164	0.15274	0.19638
Frequency	0.02	0.23	1.6	6.94	20.83	45.82	76.37	98.19

Heads (x)	8	9	10	11	12	13	14	15
P(x)	0.19638	0.15274	0.09164	0.04166	0.01389	0.0032	0.00046	0.00003
Frequency	98.19	76.37	45.82	20.83	6.94	1.6	0.23	0.02

b.

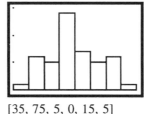

[0, 16, 1, 0, 100, 10, 1]

c. $\bar{x} = 7.5$, $\sigma = 1.94$

d. ≈ 348

e. 69.6%

f. 96.4%

g. 100%

8. Answers will vary.

Take Another Look 11.4

$$(a + b)^9 = {_9C_0}\, a^9 b^0 + {_9C_1}\, a^{9-1}\, b^1 + {_9C_2}\, a^{(9-2)}\, b^2 + \ldots {_9C_9}\, a^{(9-9)} b^9$$

$$(a + b)^n = \sum_{k=0}^{n} {_nC_k}\, a^{(n-k)}\, b^k$$

$$= {_nC_0}\, a^n\, b^0 + {_nC_1}\, a^{(n-1)}\, b^1 + {_nC_2}\, a^{(n-2)}\, b^2 + {_nC_3}\, a^{(n-3)}\, b^3 + \ldots + {_nC_{k-1}}\, a^{(n-2-k)}\, b^{(k-1)} + {_nC_k}\, a^{(n-1-k)}\, b^k$$

Project: Helping Out

This project works best with a good deal of teacher support in finding a project that is within the scope of the students. You will also need to help students design questions that will minimize bias in their results.

Problem Set 11.5

1. a. 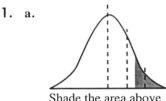   b.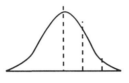

Shade the area above 1.43 standard deviations.

$\frac{72 - 48}{2.8} \approx 1.43$

Answers will vary.

   c. The distribution with the smaller standard deviation will be taller.

2.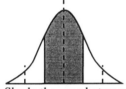

Shade the area between $^-1$ and $^+1$ standard deviations. $\frac{28 - 24}{4} = 1$; $\frac{(24 - 28)}{4} = {^-1}$

3.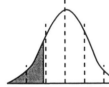

Shade the area below $^-1.14$ standard deviations. $\frac{16 - 16.8}{0.7} = {^-1.14}$

4.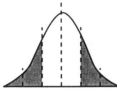

Shade the area greater than or less than one standard deviation.

5. a. $82 - 7.4 \approx 75$; $82 + 7.4 \approx 89$. Using $n = 500$, the area is approximately 256. The probability is $\frac{256}{391} \approx 0.655 = 65.5\%$.

   b. $82 - 2(7.4) \approx 67$; $82 + 2(7.4) \approx 97$. Using $n = 500$, the area is approximately 374. The probability is $\frac{374}{391} \approx 0.9565 = 95.65\%$.

   c. $82 - 3(7.4) \approx 60$; $82 \neq 3(7.4) \approx 104$. Using $n = 500$, the area is approximately 390. The probability is $\frac{390}{391} \approx 0.9974 = 99.74\%$.

6. a. $\frac{21}{391} \approx 0.054$, so the equation is $y = 0.054(0.991)^{(x - 82)^2}$.

 b. For $a = 75$, $b = 89$, $n = 500$, the area is approximately 0.66 or 66%.

 c. For $a = 67$, $b = 97$, $n = 500$, the area is approximately 0.96 or 96%.

 d. For $a = 60$, $b = 104$, $n = 500$, the area is approximately 1.00 or 100%.

7. a. Store the mid-range values for the heights in L1 and the frequencies in L2. To calculate the mean height, multiply L1 by L2 and store the results in L3; mean = $\frac{\text{sum L3}}{\text{sum L2}}$, which is approximately 165. To calculate the standard deviation, store $(L1 - 165)^2(L2)$ in L4; standard deviation = $\sqrt{\frac{\text{sum L4}}{\text{sum L2}}}$, which is approximately 5.82.

 b.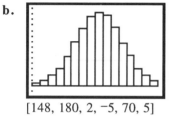

[148, 180, 2, −5, 70, 5]

 c. To find a, use the point representing the mean height, (66, 165).
$$y = ab^{x^2}$$
$$66 = ab^{(165 - 165)^2}$$
$$a = 66$$
To find b, choose another point. The point chosen is (151, 5).
$$5 = 66b^{(151 - 165)^2}$$
$$b = \sqrt[1/256]{\frac{5}{66}}$$
$$b \approx 0.99$$
So the equation is $y = 66(0.99)^{(x - 165)^2}$.

 d. Use the Area program to estimate the area under the curve between $165 - 4(5.82) \approx 142$ and $165 + 4(5.82) \approx 188$. For $n = 500$, this area is approximately 1163. The quotient $\frac{66}{1163}$ provides the new a-value of 0.0567. So the normalizing equation is $y = 0.0567(0.99)^{(x - 165)^2}$.

8. a. $\bar{x} = 79.1$, $\sigma \approx 7.49$

 b.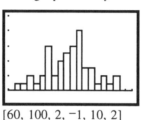

[60, 100, 2, −1, 10, 2]

 c. To find the frequency for a mean of 79, do a trace on the histogram. The frequency is 5 for pulse rates greater than or equal to 78 and less than 80. Use the point (5, 79) to find the a-value.
$$5 = ab^{(79 - 79)^2}$$
$$a = 5$$
Choose a point to use to find b. The point chosen is (85, 3).
$$3 = 5b^{(85 - 79)^2}$$
$$b = \sqrt[1/36]{\frac{3}{5}} \approx 0.9859$$
So the equation is $y = 5(0.9859)^{(x - 79)^2}$.

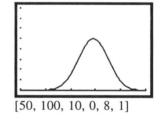

[50, 100, 10, 0, 8, 1]

 d. Use the Area program to estimate the area under the curve between $79 - 4(7.49) \approx 49$ and $79 + 4(7.49) \approx 109$. For $n = 500$, this area is approximately 74. The quotient $\frac{5}{75}$ provides the new a-value of 0.0667. So the normalizing equation is $y = 0.0676(0.9859)^{(x - 165)^2}$.

 e. Answers will vary. The data does not appear to be normally distributed. It seems to be evenly distributed with several peaks.

9.

`:Prompt A,B,N`	Input values for the left endpoint, the right endpoint, and the number of divisions.
`:(B−A)/N→D`	Take the difference between the left and right endpoint, divide this difference by the number of divisions, and store this result in D.
`:0→S`	Store 0 in S.
`:For(J,0,N)`	For values of J from 0 to N (J is a counter).
`:S+Y₁(A+JD)→S`	Compute the value of the function, Y_1, at the endpoint of each interval, and add this result to the previous sum of function values. This sum represents the sum of the heights of all of the intervals.
`:End`	End the loop when $J = N$.
`:Disp (B−A)S/(N+1)`	$(B - A)$ represents the length of the interval. $S/(N + 1)$ represents the average height of an interval. So the entire expression computes the area under the curve by multiplying the length of the interval by the average height.

Take Another Look 11.5

Answers will vary. Consider:

a. Random sampling in the classroom, lunchroom, hallway, and so on.

b. Results will be more significant with a somewhat larger number.

c. Choose close to equal numbers of people from each sex, race, grade, and so on.

d. Answers will vary.

Problem Set 11.6

1. Use the Area program with the equation $y_1 = \frac{1}{4.1\sqrt{2\pi}}\left(1 - \frac{1}{2(4.1)^2}\right)^{(x-23)^2}$ to find the area between 23 and 25. Then subtract this area and the area below the mean (0.5) from 1 to find the probability that it will take her more than 25 min: $1 - (0.5 + 0.187) = 0.313$ or 31%.

2. a. Use the Area2 program. For $m = 75.3$, $s = 4.7$, and $p = 0.2$, the leftmost endpoint is approximately 71.352. The weight of each candy bar should be at least 71.4 g.

    b. Use the Area2 program. For $m = 75.3$, $s = 4.7$, and $p = 0.1$, the leftmost endpoint is approximately 69.284. The weight of each candy bar should be at least 69.3 g.

    c. Use the Area2 program. For $m = 75.3$, $s = 4.7$, and $p = 0.05$, the leftmost endpoint is approximately 66.592. The weight of each candy bar should be at least 66.6g.

3. a. Use the Area program with the equation $y_1 = \frac{1}{20\sqrt{2\pi}}\left(1 - \frac{1}{2(20)^2}\right)^{x^2}$ to find the area between −50 and 50. Then subtract this result from 1. $1 - 0.9855 = 0.0145$ or 1.45%.

    b. Repeat the procedure used for part a to find the area between −75 and 75. Then subtract this result from 1. $1 - 0.9975 = 0.0025$ or 0.25%.

4. $\frac{225}{300} = 0.75$, which means that 75% of the samples were between 5.5 and 6.5. The standard deviation must be greater than 2 for the Area2 program to work. Because of the percentage given, you know that 5.5 is less than one standard deviation from the mean, so for the program to work, you can multiply the mean by 10. Use a mean of 60 and guess-and-check to find a standard deviation that will provide a leftmost endpoint of 55 (5.5 • 10). The percentage you would enter is $\frac{1-0.75}{2} = 0.125$. The standard deviation is $0.439\left(\frac{4.39}{10}\right)$.

5. a. Because the standard deviation is less than 2, multiply 0.75 by 10 to get a standard deviation of 7.5. You will also have to multiply your guess for the mean by 10. Use the Area2 program, a probability value of 0.10 $(1 - 0.90)$, and guess-and-check to find the mean that will provide a leftmost endpoint of 12. The mean is 12.96 oz $\left(\frac{129.6}{10}\right)$.

    b. Use the Area program with the equation $y_1 = \frac{1}{7.5\sqrt{2\pi}}\left(1 - \frac{1}{2(7.5)^2}\right)^{(x-129.6)^2}$ to find the area between 129.6 and 135. Subtract this result from 0.5. $0.5 - 0.267 = 0.233$ or 23.3%.

6. a. $_{95}C_{25}(0.28)^{25}(1 - 0.28)^{70} = 0.08655$ b. $0.08655(1000) = 86.55$; 86 or 87 groups

    c. Create a list of x-values of 0 to 95 inclusive in L1. Then place $_{L1}C_{95} \cdot 0.28^{L1} \cdot 0.72^{(95-L1)}$ in L2. Next place round $(1000\ L2, 0)$ in L3.

    d. To calculate the standard deviation, use L1 and L3. (1-Var Stats L1, L3). The standard deviation is 4.363.

    e. 4.363 is close to $\sqrt{95(0.28)(0.72)} \approx 4.376$.

7. a.

N	47	64	150	Your choice	Your choice
P	0.3	0.8	0.18	0.61	Your choice
M	14.1	51.2	27	Answers will vary.	Answers will vary.
S	3.14	3.2	4.7	Answers will vary.	Answers will vary.

b. You can look at the table to see how close the values are for each of the functions. They are the same graph.

$N = 47, P = 0.3$

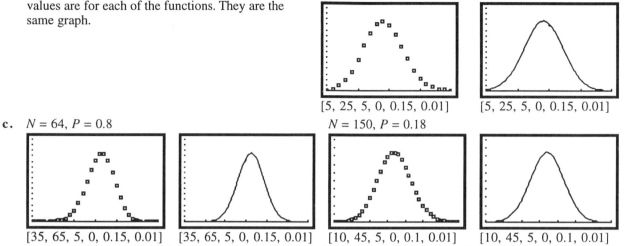

[5, 25, 5, 0, 0.15, 0.01]   [5, 25, 5, 0, 0.15, 0.01]

c. $N = 64, P = 0.8$ $N = 150, P = 0.18$

[35, 65, 5, 0, 0.15, 0.01]   [35, 65, 5, 0, 0.15, 0.01]   [10, 45, 5, 0, 0.1, 0.01]   [10, 45, 5, 0, 0.1, 0.01]

Answers will vary. The values for the discrete function (y_1) are very close to the values for the continuous function (y_2).

Take Another Look 11.6

1. Using the series $f(x) = 1 + \frac{x}{1} + \frac{x2}{2!} + \frac{x3}{3!} + \frac{x4}{4!} + \cdots$ with $x = 1$, the values of the terms are those shown in the table below.

1	2	3	4	5	6	7	. . .
1	2	2.5	2.666 . . .	2.7083 . . .	2.7166 . . .	2.718055 . . .	. . .

The limit of the series is Euler's number e. If you replace x with 2, 3, and so on, you will discover that the limit becomes e^x. For example, when $x = 2$, $e^2 = 7.389056$; when $x = 3$, $e^3 = 20.08553692$; and so on.

2. Use $(a + b)^n = \sum_{k=0}^{n} {}_nC_k \, a^{(n-k)} b^k$ to find the sum when $a = 1$, $b = \frac{1}{n}$, and $n = 1, 2, 3$, and so on.

For $n = 2$: ${}_2C_0 \, (1)^2 \left(\frac{1}{2}\right)^0 + {}_2C_1 \, (1)^1 \left(\frac{1}{2}\right)^1 + {}_2C_2 \, (1)^0 \left(\frac{1}{2}\right)^2 = 1 + 1 + 0.25 = 2.25$

For $n = 3$: ${}_3C_0 \, (1)^3 \left(\frac{1}{3}\right)^0 + {}_3C_1 \, (1)^2 \left(\frac{1}{3}\right)^1 + {}_3C_2 \, (1)^1 \left(\frac{1}{3}\right)^2 + {}_3C_3 \, (1)^0 \left(\frac{1}{3}\right)^3 = 1 + 1 + \frac{1}{3} + \frac{1}{27} = 2.37037037$

For $n = 4$, proceed as above. The sum is approximately 2.44140625.
For $n = 5$, the sum is approximately 2.48832.
As n approaches infinity, the sum approaches e.

Project: Normal Curves and e

When the standard deviation is 10, the curves are nearly identical. When the standard deviation is 3, you can begin to see a slight difference in the two graphs. When the standard deviation is 1.1, the curves are much different. The formula given in the chapter does not work when the standard deviation is less than 0.7. When properly scaled, the approximate formula should give very close results for all problems.

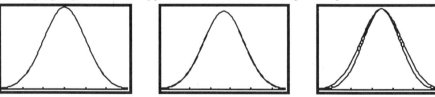

Chapter Review

Problem Set 11.7

1. a. $12! = 479,001,600$

   b. $\frac{5!\,7!}{12!} = 0.00126$ or 0.13%

2. $\frac{(_{26}C_{10})(_{26}C_3)}{_{52}C_{13}} \approx 0.0217 = 2.17\%$

3. $\sum\limits_{i=17}^{20} {}_{20}C_i (0.65)^i (0.35)^{(20-i)} \approx 0.044 = 4.4\%$

4. a. $100(_8C_0 x^0 - {}_8C_1 x^1 + {}_8C_2 x^2 - {}_8C_3 x^3 + {}_8C_4 x^4 - {}_8C_5 x^5 + {}_8C_6 x^6 - {}_8C_7 x^7 + {}_8C_8 x^8)$
$100(1 - 8x^1 + 28x^2 - 56x^3 + 70x^4 - 56x^5 + 28x^6 - 8x^7 + 1x^8)$
$100 - 800x^1 + 2800x^2 - 5600x^3 + 7000x^4 - 5600x^5 + 2800x^6 - 800x^7 + 100x^8$

   b. $600(_5C_0(1)^5(x/12)^0 + {}_5C_1(1)^4(x/12)^1 + {}_5C_2(1)^3(x/12)^2 + {}_5C_3(1)^2(x/12)^3 + {}_5C_4(1)^1(x/12)^4 + {}_5C_5(1)^0(x/12)^5) =$
$600(1(1)(1) + 5(1)(x/12) + 10(1)(x^2/144) + 10(1)(x^3/1728) + 5(1)(x^4/20736) + 1(1)(x^5/248,832)) =$
$600 + 250x + 41.667x^2 + 3.4722x^3 + 0.14468x^4 + 0.002411x^5$

5. Store the heights in L1 and the frequencies in L2. Calculate the 1-Var Stats for L1 and L2. The mean is approximately 67.8 in. The standard deviation is approximately 3.6 in. Approximately 67% of the adults in Normalville are between 64 in. and 71 in. tall.

6. $y = \frac{1}{8.5\sqrt{2\pi}}\left(1 - \frac{1}{2(8.5)^2}\right)^{(x-167)^2}$

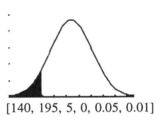

[140, 195, 5, 0, 0.05, 0.01]

7. $_{10}C_6(0.5)^6(0.5)^4 = {}_{10}C_6(0.5)^{10} = 0.205$

8. $_nC_r = \frac{n!}{r!(n-r)!}; \quad {}_nP_r = \frac{n!}{(n-r)!}$

9. $\sum\limits_{i=7}^{10} {}_{10}C_i (0.20)^i (0.80)^{10-i} \approx 0.00086 = 0.086\%$

10. a. $y = \frac{1}{14\sqrt{2\pi}}\left(1 - \frac{1}{2(14)^2}\right)^{(x-175)^2}$

   b. Use the Area program to find the percentage between 160 lb and 175 lb. Then subtract this result from 0.50 to find the percentage less than 160 lb: $0.50 - 0.36 = 0.14$ or 14%.

   c. To find the leftmost endpoint, use a percentage of $\frac{100 - 0.90}{2} = 0.05$. The leftmost endpoint is 152. Because of the symmetry of the normal curve, the rightmost endpoint is $175 + (175 - 152) = 198$, so 90% of the males weigh between 152 lb and 198 lb.

   d. 0.32 or 32%.

Chapter 12

Problem Set 12.1

1. a. $f(x) = \frac{1}{x} + 2$

   b. $f(x) = \frac{1}{x - 3}$

   c. $f(x) = \frac{1}{x + 4} - 1$

d. $f(x) = \frac{1}{x/2}$ or $\frac{2}{x}$

e. $f(x) = \frac{1}{x/3} + 1$ or $\frac{3}{x} + 1$

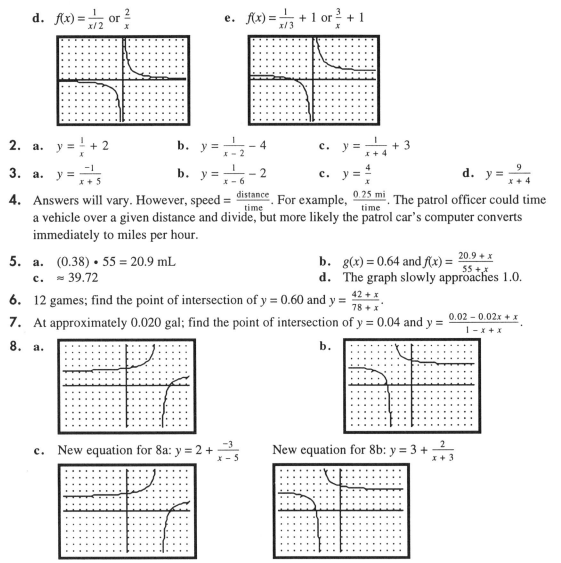

2. a. $y = \frac{1}{x} + 2$ **b.** $y = \frac{1}{x-2} - 4$ **c.** $y = \frac{1}{x+4} + 3$

3. a. $y = \frac{-1}{x+5}$ **b.** $y = \frac{1}{x-6} - 2$ **c.** $y = \frac{4}{x}$ **d.** $y = \frac{9}{x+4}$

4. Answers will vary. However, speed $= \frac{\text{distance}}{\text{time}}$. For example, $\frac{0.25 \text{ mi}}{\text{time}}$. The patrol officer could time a vehicle over a given distance and divide, but more likely the patrol car's computer converts immediately to miles per hour.

5. a. $(0.38) \cdot 55 = 20.9$ mL   **b.** $g(x) = 0.64$ and $f(x) = \frac{20.9 + x}{55 + x}$
  c. ≈ 39.72 **d.** The graph slowly approaches 1.0.

6. 12 games; find the point of intersection of $y = 0.60$ and $y = \frac{42 + x}{78 + x}$.

7. At approximately 0.020 gal; find the point of intersection of $y = 0.04$ and $y = \frac{0.02 - 0.02x + x}{1 - x + x}$.

8. a.

b.

  c. New equation for 8a: $y = 2 + \frac{-3}{x - 5}$ New equation for 8b: $y = 3 + \frac{2}{x + 3}$

  d. Graphs 8a and 8c: these equations are equivalent. Graphs 8b and 8c: these equations are equivalent.

  e. Graph 8a: the transformations alter $y = \frac{1}{x}$ by a vertical stretch of $^-3$, a horizontal slide 5 units right, and a vertical slide 2 units up. Graph 8b: the transformations alter $y = \frac{1}{x}$ by a vertical stretch of 2, a horizontal slide 3 units left, and a vertical slide 3 units up.

Problem Set 12.2

1. a. The graph has a slant asymptote at $y = x - 2$.

b. The graph is stretched vertically by a factor of 2 and has a slant asymptote at $y = ^-2x + 3$.

c. The graph is a horizontal line at $y = 4$ with a hole at (2, 4).

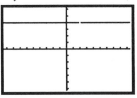

d. The first graph has a slant asymptote of $y = x - 2$, because for large absolute values of x, the term $\frac{1}{x}$ becomes insignificant and the equation is very nearly $y = x - 2$.

The second graph has a slant asymptote of $y = -2x + 3$, because for large absolute values of x, the term $\frac{2}{x}$ becomes insignificant and the equation is very nearly $y = -2x + 3$.

The third graph has a hole at $x = 2$, because the function is undefined there. For all other x-values, however, the equation is equivalent to $y = 3 + 1$ or $y = 4$.

2. a.

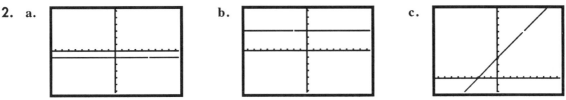

d. Graph 2a has a hole at $x = 5$ because the function is undefined at that point. Graph 2b has a hole at $x = -2$ because the function is undefined at that point. Graph 2c has a hole at $x = 4$ because the function is undefined at that point.

3. a. $y = \frac{x + 2}{x + 2}$ **b.** $y = -3 + \frac{x - 3}{x - 3}$ or $y = \frac{-2(x - 3)}{x - 3}$ **c.** $y = \frac{(x + 2)(x + 1)}{x + 1}$

4. a. The graph of $y = \frac{4}{x}$ is translated 3 units right. This means it has a vertical asymptote at $x = 3$. The graph has a slant asymptote at $y = -x$.

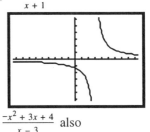

b. As you zoom out, the graph looks more and more like the line $y = -x$.
c. The graph gets closer and closer to both sides of the vertical line $x = 3$.
d. $-x + \frac{4}{x - 3} = \frac{-x(x - 3)}{x - 3} + \frac{4}{x - 3} = \frac{-x^2 + 3x + 4}{x - 3}$
e. $x^2 - 3x - 4 = (x - 4)(x + 1)$, so the roots are $x = 4$ and $x = -1$. The equation $\frac{-x^2 + 3x + 4}{x - 3}$ also has the roots 4 and -1.

5. a. The graph has a slant asymptote of $y = x$, has a vertical asymptote at $x = -2$, and has been vertically stretched by -3.
b. $y = x$
c. Answers will vary. One possibility is $y = \frac{1}{x + 2}$.
d. Answers will vary. One possibility is $y = (x + 3)(x - 1)$.
e. $y = x + \frac{-3}{x + 2}$ or $\frac{(x + 3)(x - 1)}{x + 2}$

6. $y = \frac{-(x + 2)(x - 6)}{3(x - 2)}$

7. a. The graph has x-intercepts at 1 and -4 and vertical asymptotes at $x = 2$ and $x = -3$, and a y-intercept at $\frac{2}{3}$.
b. The graph has a horizontal asymptote at $y = 1$.
c.

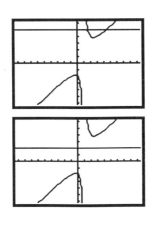

8. a. The solutions are $x \approx 1.586$ and $x \approx 4.414$. (See the graphs of $y = 5$ and $y = \frac{2}{x - 1} + x$.)

b. There are no solutions. (See the graphs of $y = 2$ and $y = \frac{2}{x - 1} + x$.)

c. The solutions are $-7 \le x < -2$.
   (See the graphs of $y = 2$ and
   $y = \frac{x-3}{x+2}$.)

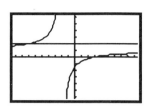

9. a.

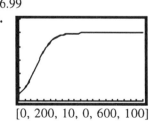

[2, 7, 1, 0, 60, 10]

b. If the volume is fixed, the height gets larger as the radius gets smaller. The radius $x > 2$.

c. $V = \pi x^2 h - 4\pi h$

d. $h = \frac{V}{\pi(x^2 - 4)}$, a graph with vertical asymptote at $x = 2$.

e. Volume ≈ 400 in.^{3}

Project: Going Downhill Fast

There are many ways to set up this experiment. One that works well is to use a carpet tube. The heavy cardboard tube that carpet is rolled on can be obtained from most carpet stores. It is long and bends very little. Attach a protractor with a weight and string (VAMD) to measure the angle. You can even drill holes through the side of the tube and set up photogates to increase the accuracy of the measurement.

Time will decrease as the angle increases. The angle will range between 0° and 90°. There will be no intercepts. An x-intercept would mean that at some angle the time would be zero. The ball may go fast, but it will always take some time to travel the length of the tube. A y-intercept would be the amount of time at an angle of zero. If the tube were laid perfectly flat, the ball would not roll from one end to the other.

Now the physics. If we ignore friction, then the ball on the incline will accelerate at the sine of the angle times the acceleration due to gravity. This means that a ball going from rest would travel a distance equal to $0.5g \sin\theta \cdot t^2$. Since the distance is constant, say 8 feet, then $8 = 0.5(16)t^2 \sin\theta$. Solving this equation for t, you would get $t = \sqrt{\csc\theta}$.

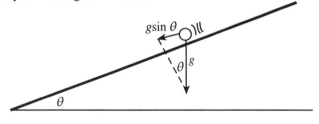

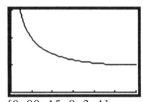

[0, 90, 15, 0, 3, 1]

Problem Set 12.3

1. a. The unrestricted growth rate is 8% and the population limit is 500.

   b. $50 + 0.08\left(1 - \frac{50}{500}\right)50 = 53.6$

   c. 70.38, 131.75, 220.44, . . . , 476.99

   d. 500

   e.

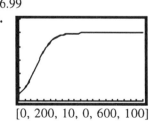

[0, 200, 10, 0, 600, 100]

2. $u_{(n-1)} + 1.25\left(1 - \frac{u_{(n-1)}}{5000}\right)u_{(n-1)}$; uStart = 50. After 20 weeks, the bacteria population will be 5000.

The net rate increase is $\sqrt[10]{\frac{5000}{50}} \approx 1.26$, which is a 26% net growth rate.

3. Answers will vary, but the arguments should fit the information pictured in this table, where n is the number of elapsed time periods and u_n is the number of daisies. The limit for the number of daisies is 750 over the interval described by this expression. The model used in the table and the graph is $u_{(n-1)} + 0.35\left(1 - \frac{u_{(n-1)}}{750}\right)u_{(n-1)}$.

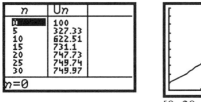

n	Un
0	100
5	327.33
10	622.51
15	731.1
20	747.73
25	749.74
30	749.97

$n=0$

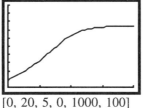

[0, 20, 5, 0, 1000, 100]

4. Answers will vary. This graph and model are based on 48% unrestricted growth per year and a limiting population of 11,000 grasshoppers. The model used for the graph is $u_{(n-1)} + 0.47\left(1 - \frac{u_{(n-1)}}{11,000}\right)u_{(n-1)}$.

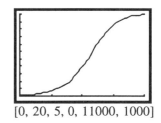

[0, 20, 5, 0, 11000, 1000]

5. a. The deer population will disappear within 35 yr.

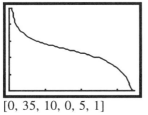

[0, 35, 10, 0, 5, 1]

b.

Harvest (millions)	0	0.1	0.2	0.3	0.4	0.5
Level (millions)	5	4.8274	4.6409	4.4365	4.2078	3.9434

Harvest (millions)	0.6	0.7	0.75	0.76	0.8
Level (millions)	3.618	3.1455	2.5	0	0

Answers will vary. A sample of possible results is in the table above. As the harvest value increases from 0 to 0.75, the long-term deer population decreases from 5 million to 2.5 million along a square root curve. (The equation graphed is $y = 2.5 + \frac{5}{\sqrt{3}}\sqrt{0.75 - x}$.)

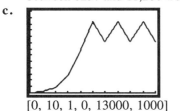

6. a. $u_{(n-1)} + 2.10\left(1 - \frac{u_{(n-1)}}{10,000}\right)u_{(n-1)}$. After 6 years, there are 8074 weeds.

b. 8237.3, 11286, 8237.3, 11286, 8237.3, 11286. After about 5 yr, the weed population vacillates between 8237 and 11,286 weeds.

c.

[0, 10, 1, 0, 13000, 1000]

d. Answers will vary. The high growth rate sends the population above the limit, which then causes many dandelions to die. This in turn causes another surge in population, and this process continues to repeat.

7. Answers will vary. The frog population fluctuates and seems quite unpredictable without using the equation $u_{(n-1)} + 2.95\left(1 - \frac{u_{(n-1)}}{470}\right)u_{(n-1)}$.

8. a. $u_n = u_{(n-1)}(1 + 0.04 - 0.02v_{(n-1)})$;
$v_n = v_{(n-1)}(1 + 0.001u_{(n-1)} - 0.03)$;
$_uStart = 38$, $_vStart = 15$

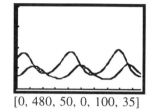

[0, 480, 50, 0, 100, 35]

b. Answers will vary. A steady state exists if there are 30 rabbits and 20 foxes. You can determine this result by solving the system $r = r(1 + 0.04 - 0.02f)$ and $f = f(1 + 0.001r - 0.03)$.

Take Another Look 12.3

An improved population model might be

new population = old population + net growth rate • old population

$$u_n = u_{(n-1)} + 0.03\left(1 - \frac{u_{(n-1)}}{25,000,000}\right)u_{(n-1)}$$

Using a starting value of 10,000,000 when $n = 0$ gives $u_{200} = 24,910,414$.

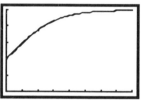

[0, 200, 25, 0, 25000000, 5000000]

Answers will vary, but this model includes the limiting value of the population. The graph of (*time, population*) shows a slower growth as the population approaches the limiting number. The growth is related to the present population.

Problem Set 12.4

1. a. The shortest possible distance occurs when the boat travels directly to point D.

b. The boat would travel $\sqrt{15^2 + 98^2} \approx 99.1$ mi and the ambulance 0 mi.

c. Time (boat) = $\frac{\sqrt{15^2 + x^2}}{23}$; time (ambulance) = $\frac{98 - x}{70}$.

So total time = $\frac{\sqrt{15^2 + x^2}}{23} + \frac{98 - x}{70}$. Graph this equation or look at a table to find the point where the minimum occurs.

The shortest time (2.016 hr) occurs when $x \approx 5.218$. Using this point the boat travels 15.88 mi and the ambulance $98 - 5.218 = 92.782$ mi.

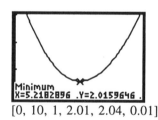

Minimum
X=5.2182896 .Y=2.0159646 .
[0, 10, 1, 2.01, 2.04, 0.01]

2. a. $y = \sqrt{(10^2 + x^2)} + \sqrt{(20 - x)^2 + 13^2}$

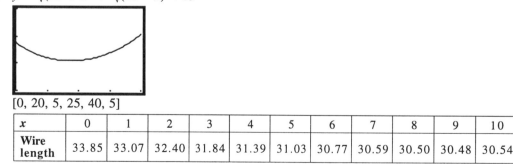

[0, 20, 5, 25, 40, 5]

x	0	1	2	3	4	5	6	7	8	9	10
Wire length	33.85	33.07	32.40	31.84	31.39	31.03	30.77	30.59	30.50	30.48	30.54

b. $0 \le x \le 20$, $30 \le y \le 43$

c. The wire should be fastened at $x \approx 8.696$ m. The minimum length of the wire is about 30.48 m.

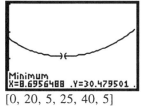

[0, 20, 5, 25, 40, 5]

3. a. $d = rt$; $24 = 2t$; $t = 12$ sec

b. $x_{1t} = t$; $y_{1t} = \sqrt{24^2 - (2t)^2}$

Time (sec)	0	1	2	3	4	5	6
Height (ft)	24	23.92	23.66	23.24	22.63	21.82	20.78

Time (sec)	7	8	9	10	11	12
Height (ft)	19.49	17.89	15.87	13.27	9.59	0

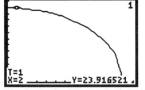

[0, 2, 1, 0, 12, 1, 0, 24, 2]

c. No; the table and graph indicate that the rate of the ladder top moving down increases as you pull steadily at the bottom of the ladder.

d. i. The location of the foot of the ladder: $x_{1t} = 2t$.

ii. The location of the top of the ladder: $y_{1t} = \sqrt{24^2 - (2t)^2}$.

e. Answers will vary.

4. a. To determine the rate in miles per second: $\frac{450 \text{ mi}}{\text{hr}} \cdot \frac{1 \text{ hr}}{60 \text{ min}} \cdot \frac{1 \text{ min}}{60 \text{ sec}} = \frac{450 \text{ mi}}{60 \cdot 60} = 0.125$ mi/sec $= \frac{1}{8}$ mi/sec

It will be 64 sec before the plane is directly overhead.

b. $d = \sqrt{7^2 + (8 - 0.125t)^2}$

c.

Time (sec)	0	1	5	10	20	30	64
Ground distance (mi) $(8 - 0.125t)^2$	8	7.875	7.375	6.75	5.5	4.25	0
Actual distance (mi) $\sqrt{7^2 + (8 - 0.125t)^2}$	10.63	10.536	10.168	9.7243	8.9022	8.1892	7

d.

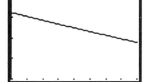

[0, 8, 1, 9 11, 0.5]

5. a. $y = \sqrt{(5 - x)^2 + (0.5x^2 + 1 + 3)^2}$

b.

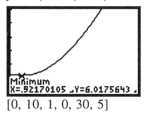

The minimum distance of about 6.02 units occurs at about (0.92, 1.42).

[0, 10, 1, 0, 30, 5]

6. a. Because the Ferris wheel makes one revolution in 30 sec, the rate is $\frac{360°}{30 \text{ sec}} = 12°/\text{sec}$. If one revolution on the Ferris wheel takes 30 sec, then it takes $\frac{1}{8} \cdot 30 = 3.75$ sec to move one-fourth the way up. The parametric equations are $x = 50 \cos 12(t - 3.75)$ and $y = 50 \sin 12(t - 3.75) + 55$. (Add 55 to the y-equation since the center of the Ferris wheel is 55 ft above the ground.) To plot the point where Ann is standing, enter the coordinates into two lists, and use a scatter plot.

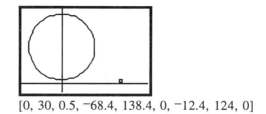

$[0, 30, 0.5, {}^-68.4, 138.4, 0, {}^-12.4, 124, 0]$

b. The parametric equations used to model the motion of the keys are $x = {}^-55t \cos 70 + 90$ and $y = 55t \sin 70 + 4 - 16t^2$. It appears that Sandra can catch the keys.

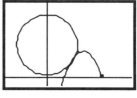

c. The distance equations are $x = t$ and $y = \sqrt{(x_{1t} - x_{2t})^2 + (y_{1t} - y_{2t})^2}$. She should be able to catch the keys because they are only 1.7 ft from her at 2.2 sec. They get as close as 0.253 ft at the 2.246 sec mark.

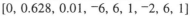
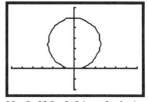

7. a. If the tire moves at 25 ft/sec, then $\frac{25 \text{ ft}}{\text{sec}}\left(\frac{1 \text{ rev}}{5\pi \text{ ft}}\right) = \frac{5}{\pi} \frac{\text{rev}}{\text{sec}}$ or $\frac{\pi}{5} \frac{\text{sec}}{\text{rev}} \approx \frac{0.628 \text{ sec}}{\text{rev}}$. Because $t = 0.628$ sec is the time for one revolution and $Bt = 360°$, $B = \frac{360}{0.628}$ or $\frac{360}{\frac{\pi}{5}} = \frac{1800}{\pi}$. To start the tack at the bottom,

replace t with $\left(t - \frac{0.628}{4}\right)$ or $(t - 0.157)$. The radius of the tire is 2.5 ft, and it needs to be negative so that the tire will rotate correctly to move forward. Therefore, the parametric equations are $x = {}^-2.5 \cos \frac{1800(t - 0.157)}{\pi}$ and $y = 2.5 + 2.5 \sin \frac{1800(t - 0.157)}{\pi}$. You can graph these equations and watch the tack move around through one revolution.

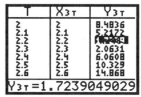

$[0, 0.628, 0.01, {}^-6, 6, 1, {}^-2, 6, 1]$

b. To graph (*time, height*), be sure the equations in part a are entered in x_{1t} and y_{1t}. Turn these equations off, and graph $x_{2t} = t$ and $y_{2t} = y_{1t}$.

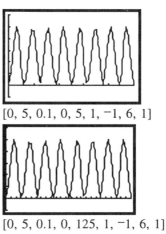

$[0, 5, 0.1, 0, 5, 1, {}^-1, 6, 1]$

c. To graph (*horizontal distance, height of tack*), enter $x_{2t} = 25t$ and $y_{2t} = y_{1t}$.

$[0, 5, 0.1, 0, 125, 1, {}^-1, 6, 1]$

Take Another Look 12.4

Problem 5, Section 12.3:

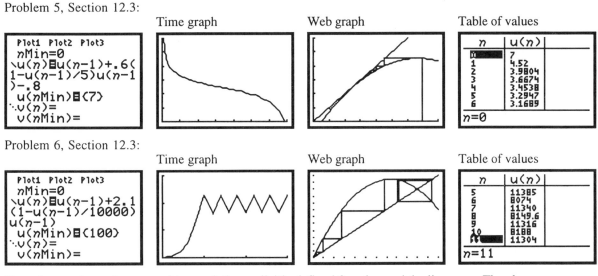

| | Time graph | Web graph | Table of values |

Problem 6, Section 12.3:

| | Time graph | Web graph | Table of values |

To make a web graph you need to graph the explicitly defined function and the line $y = x$. Then by drawing horizontal and vertical lines between the two graphs you can observe long-run behavior. A time graph plots a sequence as a function of n. A web graph calculates u_n as a function of $u_{(n-1)}$ and plots $u_{(n-1)}$ on the horizontal axis and u_n on the vertical axis.

Project: Basketball

Answers will vary.

Problem Set 12.5

1. a. $y = \pm\sqrt{4 - x^2}$
Center at $(0, 0)$ and radius 2.

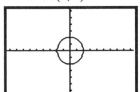

b. $y = \pm\sqrt{1 - (x - 3)^2}$
Center at $(3, 0)$ and radius 1.

c. $y = \pm\sqrt{9 - (x + 1)^2} + 2$
Center at $(-1, 2)$ and radius 3.

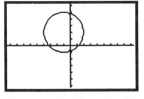

d. $y = \pm\sqrt{0.25 - x^2} + 1.5$
Center at $(0, 1.5)$ and radius 0.5.

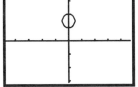

e. Center at $(1, 2)$ and radius 2.

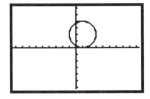

f. Center at $(-3, 0)$ and radius 4.

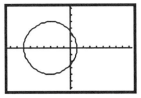

2. a. $x = 5 \cos t + 3$ and $y = 5 \sin t$ or $(x - 3)^2 + y^2 = 25$

    b. $x = 3 \cos t - 1$ and $y = 3 \sin t + 2$ or $(x + 1)^2 + (y - 2)^2 = 9$

    c. $x = 4 \cos t + 2.5$ and $y = 4 \sin t + 0.75$ or $(x - 2.5)^2 + (y - 0.75)^2 = 16$

    d. $x = 0.5 \cos t + 2.5$ and $y = 0.5 \sin t + 2.5$ or $(x - 2.5)^2 + (y - 2.5)^2 = 0.25$

3. a. (2, 0), (−2, 0), (0, 4), (0, −4)   **b.** (5, −2), (−1, −2), (2, −1), (2, −3)

c. (1, 1), (7, 1), (4, 4), (4, −2)   **d.** (−5, −1), (1, −1), (−2, 1), (−2, −3)

e. (−5, 3), (3, 3), (−1, 5), (−1, 1)   **f.** (0, 0), (6, 0), (3, 5), (3, −5)

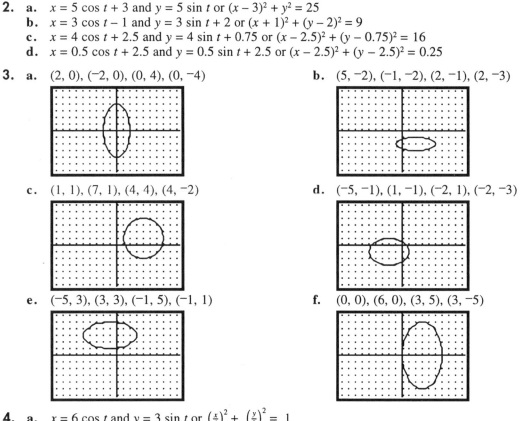

4. a. $x = 6 \cos t$ and $y = 3 \sin t$ or $\left(\frac{x}{6}\right)^2 + \left(\frac{y}{3}\right)^2 = 1$

    b. $x = 2 \cos t + 3$ and $y = 5 \sin t$ or $\left(\frac{x - 3}{2}\right)^2 + \left(\frac{y}{5}\right)^2 = 1$

    c. $x = 4 \cos t - 1$ and $y = 3 \sin t + 2$ or $\left(\frac{x + 1}{4}\right)^2 + \left(\frac{y - 2}{3}\right)^2 = 1$

    d. $x = 6 \cos t + 3$ and $y = 3 \sin t - 1$ or $\left(\frac{x - 3}{6}\right)^2 + \left(\frac{y + 1}{3}\right)^2 = 1$

5. a. Answers will vary. Enter the data and draw and graph. Use the cursor to estimate the x-intercepts. For estimates of (990, 0) and (4, 0), the center is at (493, 0). The equation of the ellipse is $\left(\frac{x - 493}{497}\right)^2 + \left(\frac{y}{63}\right)^2 = 1$. Graph the two equations, $y = \pm 63 \sqrt{1 - \left(\frac{x - 493}{497}\right)^2}$.

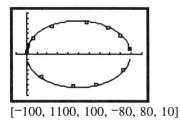

[−100, 1100, 100, −80, 80, 10]

    b. Substitute $x = 493$ into the equation in part a: $y \approx \pm 63$ AU.

    c. The furthest distance is 990 AU.

    d. The x-coordinate of the sun would be at 990 − 4 = 986 AU, so the coordinates are (986, 0).

6. a. Answers will vary. The 16 cm string is tacked to the cardboard at F_1 and F_2. A pencil traces out an ellipse as it moves against the stretched string.

    b. The distance between F_1 and F_2 is 10 cm. Since the length of the string is 16 cm, the distance from one of the foci to the opposite vertex is 13 cm (10 + 3 + 3 = 16). Therefore, the coordinates of the vertices are (8, 0) and (−8, 0).

    c. $\sqrt{8^2 - 5^2} = \sqrt{39}$, so the vertices at the ends of the shorter axis are $\left(0, \sqrt{39}\right)$ and $\left(0, -\sqrt{39}\right)$.

    d. $\left(\frac{x}{8}\right)^2 + \left(\frac{y}{\sqrt{39}}\right)^2 = 1$

e. The distance relation is $y = \sqrt{(x-5)^2 + 39\left(1 - \left(\frac{x}{8}\right)\right)^2} + \sqrt{(x+5)^2 + 39\left(1 - \left(\frac{x}{8}\right)\right)^2}$

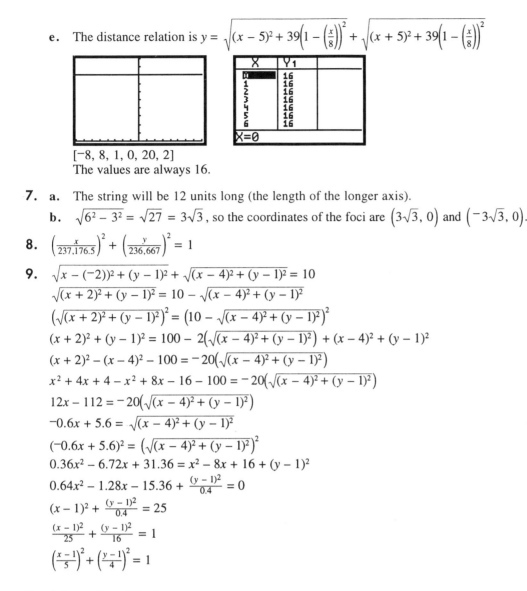

[−8, 8, 1, 0, 20, 2]
The values are always 16.

7. a. The string will be 12 units long (the length of the longer axis).

 b. $\sqrt{6^2 - 3^2} = \sqrt{27} = 3\sqrt{3}$, so the coordinates of the foci are $\left(3\sqrt{3}, 0\right)$ and $\left(^-3\sqrt{3}, 0\right)$.

8. $\left(\frac{x}{237,176.5}\right)^2 + \left(\frac{y}{236,667}\right)^2 = 1$

9. $\sqrt{x - (-2))^2 + (y - 1)^2} + \sqrt{(x - 4)^2 + (y - 1)^2} = 10$

$\sqrt{(x + 2)^2 + (y - 1)^2} = 10 - \sqrt{(x - 4)^2 + (y - 1)^2}$

$\left(\sqrt{(x + 2)^2 + (y - 1)^2}\right)^2 = \left(10 - \sqrt{(x - 4)^2 + (y - 1)^2}\right)^2$

$(x + 2)^2 + (y - 1)^2 = 100 - 2\left(\sqrt{(x - 4)^2 + (y - 1)^2}\right) + (x - 4)^2 + (y - 1)^2$

$(x + 2)^2 - (x - 4)^2 - 100 = ^-20\left(\sqrt{(x - 4)^2 + (y - 1)^2}\right)$

$x^2 + 4x + 4 - x^2 + 8x - 16 - 100 = ^-20\left(\sqrt{(x - 4)^2 + (y - 1)^2}\right)$

$12x - 112 = ^-20\left(\sqrt{(x - 4)^2 + (y - 1)^2}\right)$

$^-0.6x + 5.6 = \sqrt{(x - 4)^2 + (y - 1)^2}$

$(^-0.6x + 5.6)^2 = \left(\sqrt{(x - 4)^2 + (y - 1)^2}\right)^2$

$0.36x^2 - 6.72x + 31.36 = x^2 - 8x + 16 + (y - 1)^2$

$0.64x^2 - 1.28x - 15.36 + \frac{(y - 1)^2}{0.4} = 0$

$(x - 1)^2 + \frac{(y - 1)^2}{0.4} = 25$

$\frac{(x - 1)^2}{25} + \frac{(y - 1)^2}{16} = 1$

$\left(\frac{x - 1}{5}\right)^2 + \left(\frac{y - 1}{4}\right)^2 = 1$

Problem Set 12.6

1. a. $\left(\frac{x}{2}\right)^2 + 5 = y$; $x^2 + 20 = 4y$. The coefficient of the linear variable is 4, so the distance from the vertex to the focus and from the vertex to the directrix are each $\frac{4}{4} = 1$. The vertex is (0, 5). Add 1 to the y-coordinate of the vertex to get the focus, (0, 6). Subtract 1 from the y-coordinate of the vertex to get the equation of the directrix, $y = 4$.

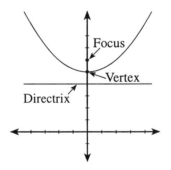

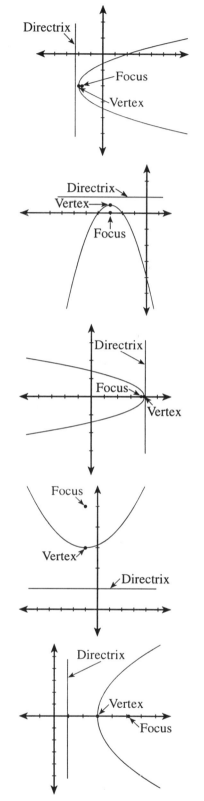

b. $(y + 2)^2 - 2 = x$; $(y + 2)^2 = x + 2$. The coefficient of the linear variable is 1, so the distance from the vertex to the focus and from the vertex to the directrix are each $\frac{1}{4} = 0.25$. The vertex is $(-2, -2)$. Add 0.25 to the x-coordinate of the vertex to get the focus, $(-1.75, -2)$. Subtract 0.25 from the x-coordinate of the vertex to get the equation of the directrix, $x = -2.25$.

c. $-(x + 3)^2 + 1 = 2y$; $-(x + 3)^2 = 2y - 1$; $-(x + 3)^2 = 2\left(y - \frac{1}{2}\right)$.
The coefficient of the linear variable is 2, so the distance from the vertex to the focus and from the vertex to the directrix are each 0.5. The vertex is $(-3, 0.5)$. Subtract 0.5 from the y-coordinate of the vertex to get the focus, $(-3, 0)$. Add 0.5 to the y-coordinate of the vertex to get the equation of the directrix, $y = 1$.

d. $2y^2 = -x + 4$; $y^2 = -\frac{1}{2}x + 2$. The coefficient of the linear variable is 0.5, so the distance from the vertex to the focus and from the vertex to the directrix are each $\frac{0.5}{4} = 0.125$ or $\frac{1}{8}$. The vertex is $(4, 0)$. Subtract 0.125 from the x-coordinate of the vertex to get the focus, $(3.875, 0)$. Add 0.125 to the x-coordinate of the vertex to get the equation of the directrix, $x = 4.125$.

e. $\begin{cases} x(t) = 4t - 1 \\ y(t) = 2t^2 + 3 \end{cases}$; $\frac{y - 3}{2} = \left(\frac{x + 1}{4}\right)^2$
The coefficient of the linear variable is 8, so the distance from the vertex to the focus and from the vertex to the directrix are each $\frac{8}{4} = 2$. The vertex is $(-1, 3)$. Add 2 to the y-coordinate of the vertex to get the focus, $(-1, 5)$. Subtract 2 from the y-coordinate of the vertex to get the equation of the directrix, $y = 1$.

f. $\begin{cases} x(t) = 3t^2 + 3 \\ y(t) = 5t \end{cases}$; $\left(\frac{y}{5}\right)^2 = \frac{x - 3}{3}$
The coefficient of the linear variable is $\frac{25}{3}$, so the distance from the vertex to the focus and from the vertex to the directrix are each $\frac{25}{3} \div 4 = \frac{25}{12}$. The vertex is $(3, 0)$. Add $\frac{25}{12}$ to the x-coordinate of the vertex to get the focus, $\left(\frac{61}{12}, 0\right)$. Subtract $\frac{25}{12}$ from the x-coordinate of the vertex to get the equation of the directrix, $x = \frac{11}{12}$.

2. a. $x = t^2$ and $y = t + 2$ or $x = (y - 2)^2$; vertex $(0, 2)$, focus $(0.25, 2)$, and directrix $x = -0.25$

b. $x = t$ and $y = -t^2 + 4$ or $y = -x^2 + 4$; vertex $(0, 4)$, focus $(0, 3.75)$, and directrix $y = 4.25$

c. $x = 2t + 3$ and $y = t^2 - 1$ or $y = \left(\frac{x - 3}{2}\right)^2 - 1$; vertex $(3, -1)$, focus $(3, 0)$, and directrix $y = -2$

d. $x = -t^2 - 6$ and $y = 3t + 2$ or $y = \pm 3\sqrt{-x - 6} + 2$ or $x = -\frac{1}{9}(y - 2)^2 - 6$; vertex $(-6, 2)$, focus $(-8.25, 2)$, and directrix $x = -3.75$

3. The path will be parabolic. The rock is the focus and the shoreline is the directrix.

4. **a.** The graph is a parabola with vertex (0, 1), focus (0, 3), and directrix $y = -1$.

   b. $y = \frac{x^2}{8} + 1$ or $y = 0.125x^2 + 1$

   c.

5. **a.** The graph is a parabola with vertex (3, 4), focus (3.5, 4), and directrix $x = 2.5$.

   b. $y = \pm 2\sqrt{x - 3} + 4$

   c.

6. Substitute the x- and y-values in the general form of the quadratic equation and use matrices to solve for a, b, and c.

   $0.764 = a(3.6)^2 + b(3.6) + c$
   $1.436 = a(5)^2 + b(5) + c$
   $-2.404 = a(5.8)^2 + b(5.8) + c$

   $[A] = \begin{bmatrix} 12.96 & 3.6 & 1 \\ 25 & 5 & 1 \\ 33.64 & 5.8 & 1 \end{bmatrix}$, $[B] = \begin{bmatrix} 0.764 \\ 1.436 \\ -2.404 \end{bmatrix}$, $[A]^{-1}[B] = \begin{bmatrix} -2.4 \\ 21.12 \\ -44.164 \end{bmatrix}$

   $y = -2.4x^2 + 21.12x - 44.164$

7. If you graph the three points in a "friendly window," you can see that they appear to be three vertices of a square or an isosceles right triangle. (You can verify this by finding the slopes of the two segments that appear to be perpendicular.) The center of the circle will be the midpoint of the hypotenuse. Thus the center of the circle is $(-2, 1)$. The distance from the center to the point (2, 4) is $\sqrt{(-2 - 2)^2 + (1 - 4)^2} = 5$. So the equation of the circle is $x^2 + y^2 + 4x - 2y - 20 = 0$ or $(x + 2)^2 + (y - 1)^2 = 25$.

Problem Set 12.7

1. **a.** The center of the hyperbola is at (0, 0). The upper corners of the box are (2, 4) and (−2, 4). So the slopes of the asymptotes are 2 and −2. The vertices are (−2, 0) and (2, 0). The equations of the asymptotes are $y = \pm 2x$.

   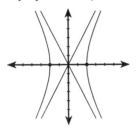

   b. The center of the hyperbola is at (2, −2). The upper corners of the box are (5, −1) and (−1, −1). So the slopes of the asymptotes are $\frac{1}{3}$ and $-\frac{1}{3}$. The vertices are (2, −1) and (2, −3). The equations of the asymptotes are $y = \pm\frac{1}{3}(x - 2) - 2$ or $y = \frac{1}{3}x - \frac{8}{3}$ and $y = -\frac{1}{3}x - \frac{4}{3}$.

   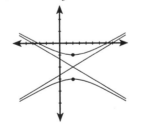

c. The center of the hyperbola is at (4, 1). The upper corners of the box are (1, 4) and (7, 4). So the slopes of the asymptotes are 1 and −1. The vertices are (1, 1) and (7, 1). The equations of the asymptotes are $y = \pm(x - 4) + 1$ or $y = x - 3$ and $y = {}^-x + 5$.

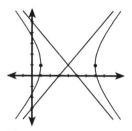

d. The center of the hyperbola is at (−2, −1). The rightmost corners of the box are (1, 1) and (1, −3). So the slopes of the asymptotes are $\frac{2}{3}$ and $-\frac{2}{3}$. The vertices are (−2, 1) and (−2, −3). The equations of the asymptotes are $y = \pm\frac{2}{3}(x + 2) - 1$ or $y = \frac{2}{3}x + \frac{1}{3}$ and $y = -\frac{2}{3}x - \frac{7}{3}$.

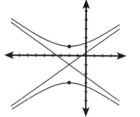

e. The center of the hyperbola is at (−1, 3). The rightmost corners of the box are (3, 5) and (3, 1). The slopes of the asymptotes are 0.5 and −0.5. The vertices are (−5, 3) and (3, 3). The equations of the asymptotes are $y = \pm 0.5(x + 1) + 3$ or $y = 0.5x + 3.5$ and $y = {}^-0.5x + 2.5$.

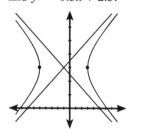

f. The center of the hyperbola is at (3, 0). The upper corners of the box are (0, 5) and (6, 5). The slopes of the asymptotes are $\pm\frac{5}{3}$. The vertices are (3, 5) and (3, −5). The equations of the asymptotes are $y = \pm\frac{5}{3}(x - 3)$ or $y = \frac{5}{3}x - 5$ and $y = -\frac{5}{3}x + 5$.

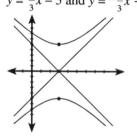

2. a. The parametric equations are $x = \frac{2}{\cos t}$ and $y = \tan t$. The nonparametric equation is $\left(\frac{x}{2}\right)^2 - \left(\frac{y}{1}\right)^2 = 1$. The asymptotes are $y = \pm 0.5x$.

b. The parametric equations are $x = 2 \tan t + 3$ and $y = \frac{2}{\cos t} - 3$. The nonparametric equation is $\left(\frac{y + 3}{2}\right)^2 - \left(\frac{x - 3}{2}\right)^2 = 1$. The asymptotes are $y = \pm(x - 3) - 3$ or $y = x - 6$ and $y = {}^-x$.

c. The parametric equations are $x = \frac{3}{\cos t} - 2$ and $y = 4 \tan t + 1$. The nonparametric equation is $\left(\frac{x + 2}{3}\right)^2 - \left(\frac{y - 1}{4}\right)^2 = 1$. The asymptotes are $y = \pm\frac{4}{3}(x + 2) + 1$ or $y = \frac{4}{3}x + \frac{11}{3}$ and $y = -\frac{4}{3}x - \frac{5}{3}$.

d. The parametric equations are $x = 3 \tan t - 2$ and $y = \frac{4}{\cos t} + 1$. The nonparametric equation is $\left(\frac{y - 1}{4}\right)^2 - \left(\frac{x + 2}{3}\right)^2 = 1$. The asymptotes are $y = \pm\frac{4}{3}(x + 2) + 1$ or $y = \frac{4}{3}x + \frac{11}{3}$ and $y = -\frac{4}{3}x - \frac{5}{3}$.

3. a. The center of the hyperbola is (0, 0). One-half the length of one of the box diagonals is $\sqrt{1^2 + 1^2} = \sqrt{2}$. So the coordinates of the foci are $\left(\pm\sqrt{2}, 0\right)$.

b. The center of the hyperbola is (2, −2). The length of the x-radius is 3 and the length of the y-radius is 1. The length of the diagonal is $\sqrt{1^2 + 3^2} = \sqrt{10}$. So the coordinates of the foci are $\left(2, -2 + \sqrt{10}\right)$ and $\left(2, -2 - \sqrt{10}\right)$ or (2, 1.16) and (2, −5.16).

4. $\left| \sqrt{(x + 2)^2 + (y - 1)^2} - \sqrt{(x - 4)^2 + (y - 1)^2} \right| = 10$

5. To find the *x*-coordinate of the upper right corner of the box, substitute the *y*-value of the vertex into the equation of the asymptote: $1.46 = 1.5x + 1.035$; $x = 0.2833$. The distance from the point $(0.2833, 1.46)$ to the vertex, or the *x*-radius, is $|0.2833 - {}^-2.35| = 2.633$. Substituting the *x*-coordinate of the vertex into the equation for the asymptote provides the *y*-coordinate of the center of the hyperbola: $y = 1.5({}^-2.35) + 1.035 = {}^-2.49$. So the coordinates of the center are $({}^-2.35, {}^-2.49)$. The vertical distance from the center to the vertex, or the *y*-radius, is $|{}^-2.49 - 1.46| = 3.95$. Use this information to write the equation of the hyperbola: $\left(\frac{y + 2.49}{3.95}\right)^2 - \left(\frac{x + 2.35}{2.63}\right)^2 = 1$.

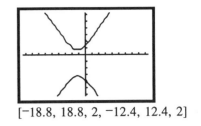

$[{}^-18.8, 18.8, 2, {}^-12.4, 12.4, 2]$

6. First you need to find the equation of the asymptote. The center of the hyperbola is $({}^-2, {}^-1)$. The upper right corner of the box is $(1, 1)$, so the slope of the asymptote with a positive slope is $\frac{2}{3}$. The equation of the asymptote is $y = \frac{2}{3}(x + 2) - 1$. The equation that represents the distance between the hyperbola and the asymptote is $y = \left| \pm 2\sqrt{1 + \left(\frac{x + 2}{3}\right)^2} - 1 - \left(\frac{2}{3}(x + 2) - 1\right) \right|$. Evaluate this function for each value of *x* to complete the table.

x-value	5	10	20	40
Distance	0.41	0.25	0.14	0.07

7. **a.** A possible equation is $\left(\frac{y}{2.5}\right)^2 - \left(\frac{x - 9.5}{2.5}\right)^2 = 1$.
 b. The center is $(9.5, 0)$.
 c. One explanation is that when the car has traveled 9.5 mi it is still 2.5 mi from the transmitter, and this is as close as the car will get.

8. Answers will vary.

Take Another Look 12.7

1. Foci $(2, 0)$ and $({}^-2, 0)$
 The constant difference between the points and the foci is 2.

$\sqrt{(x + 2)^2 + y^2} - \sqrt{(x - 2)^2 + y^2} = 2$	(Assuming the difference is positive.)
$\sqrt{(x + 2)^2 + y^2} = 2 + \sqrt{(x - 2)^2 + y^2}$	Isolate one radical.
$\left(\sqrt{(x + 2)^2 + y^2}\right)^2 = \left(2 + \sqrt{(x - 2)^2 + y^2}\right)^2$	Square each side to remove radical.
$(x + 2)^2 + y^2 = 4 + 4\sqrt{(x - 2)^2 + y^2} + (x - 2)^2 + y^2$	Expand.
$x^2 + 4x + 4 + y^2 = 4 + x^2 - 4x + 4 + y^2 + 4\sqrt{(x - 2)^2 + y^2}$	Expand and rearrange.
$8x - 4 = 4\sqrt{(x - 2)^2 + y^2}$	Simplify.
$2x - 1 = \sqrt{(x - 2)^2 + y^2}$	Divide by 4.
$(2x - 1)^2 = \left(\sqrt{(x - 2)^2 + y^2}\right)^2$	Square both sides.
$4x^2 - 4x + 1 = (x - 2)^2 + y^2$	Remove the radical.
$4x^2 - 4x + 1 = x^2 - 4x + 4 + y^2$	Expand.
$3x^2 = 3 + y^2$	Simplify.
$3x^2 - y^2 = 3$	Correct form.
$\frac{x^2}{1} - \frac{y^2}{3} = 1$	Done!

The x-intercepts are $(1, 0)$ and $(-1, 0)$. There are no y-intercepts.

Solve $\frac{x^2}{1} - \frac{y^2}{3} = 1$ for y.

$\frac{y^2}{3} = x^2 - 1$

$y = \pm\sqrt{3}\sqrt{x^2 - 1}$ or

$y = \pm\sqrt{3}\left(1 - \frac{1}{x^2}\right)$

When x is large $\left(1 - \frac{1}{x^2}\right)$ is near 1.

The asymptotes are $y = \pm\sqrt{3}$.

The rectangle is formed by lines perpendicular to the x-axis drawn through $x = \pm 1$ and perpendicular to the y-axis drawn through $y = \pm\sqrt{3}$ on the y-axis. The diagonals of the rectangle are the asymptotes. The length of the diagonal is $\left(2\sqrt{3}\right)^2 + 2^2 = 4$. When the rectangle is rotated about its center, the distance from the origin to a focus is one half the length of the diagonal, or 2 units.

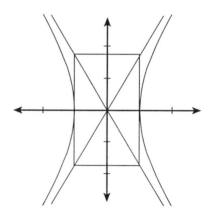

2. $\sqrt{(x + 3)^2 + y^2} + \sqrt{(x - 3)^2 + y^2} = 10$

$\sqrt{(x + 3)^2 + y^2} = 10 - \sqrt{(x - 3)^2 + y^2}$ Isolate one radical.

$\left(\sqrt{(x + 3)^2 + y^2}\right)^2 = \left(10 - \sqrt{(x - 3)^2 + y^2}\right)^2$ Square each side to remove radical.

$(x + 3)^2 + y^2 = 100 - 20\sqrt{(x - 3)^2 + y^2} + (x - 3)^2 + y^2$ Expand.

$x^2 + 6x + 9 + y^2 = 100 + x^2 - 6x + 9 + y^2 - 20\sqrt{(x - 3)^2 + y^2}$ Expand and rearrange.

$12x - 100 = {}^-20\sqrt{(x - 3)^2 + y^2}$ Simplify.

$3x - 25 = {}^-5\sqrt{(x - 3)^2 + y^2}$ Divide by 4.

$(3x - 25)^2 = {}^-5\left(\sqrt{(x - 3)^2 + y^2}\right)^2$ Square both sides.

$9x^2 - 150x + 625 = 25(x - 3)^2 + y^2$ Remove radical.

$9x^2 - 150x + 625 - 25x^2 - 150x + 225 + 25y^2$ Expand.

${}^-16x^2 = {}^-400 + 25y^2$ Simplify.

$16x^2 + 25y^2 = 400$ Correct form.

$\frac{x^2}{25} + \frac{y^2}{16} = 1$ Done!

The final equation represents an ellipses with x-intercepts of 5 and -5, and y-intercepts of 4 and -4.

Project: Piston Pressure

You can locate the syringes needed for this project at a farm-animal feed store as these syringes are often used to give medicine to animals. The end of the syringe can be capped by drilling a hole partway into a rubber stopper that is 50% smaller than the opening at the end of the syringe. Then fill the hole with epoxy glue before you force the syringe into the hole. Because there is a great deal of weight going on this device, you may wish to design some support system. Clamping the syringe to a heavy ring stand works.

As an option you can also collect this data using a pressure-monitoring probe such as the device available from Vernier, which interfaces with the TI-CBL and the Casio EA-100. Check with your chemistry and physics teachers to help you set up this project with whatever equipment your school may have.

This function should be a strict inverse function $y = \frac{a}{x}$ when it is converted correctly. When it is not converted correctly, it is a horizontal shift of the same function. There are no intercepts. If the x-value or the pressure were zero, then the volume would be infinite because pressure is the collision of air molecules. No pressure means the molecules have spread so far apart that they do not collide. If the y-value or the volume were zero, then all the molecules of air would be pressed into nothing. This might make a very big explosion as the molecules are changed from matter into energy.

Problem Set 12.8

1. a. $(x + 7)^2 = 9(y - 11)$
$x^2 + 14x + 49 = 9y - 99$
$x^2 + 14x - 9y + 148 = 0$
$1x^2 + 0xy + 0y^2 + 14x - 9y + 148 = 0$

b. $\frac{(x - 7)^2}{9} + \frac{(y + 1)^2}{1} = 1$
$(x - 7)^2 + 9(y + 1)^2 = 9$
$x^2 - 14x + 49 + 9(y^2 + 22y + 121) = 9$
$x^2 - 14x + 49 + 9y^2 + 198y + 1089 = 9$
$1x^2 + 0xy + 9y^2 - 14x + 198y + 1129 = 0$

2. a. $a = \frac{21}{15} = \frac{7}{5} = 1.4$ **b.** $2b = 1.4; b = 0.7$ **c.** $(0.7)^2 = 0.49$ **d.** $15(0.49) = 7.35$
   e. $\sqrt{0.49} = 0.7$

3. a. False; one correction is $y^2 + 22y + 121 = (y + 11)^2$.
   b. True   **c.** True   **d.** False; one correction is $4x^2 + 48x + 144 = 4(x + 6)^2$.

4. a. iv   **b.** ii   **c.** iii   **d.** i

5. a. $25x^2 - 4y^2 + 100 = 0$
$25x^2 - 4y^2 = -100$
$4y^2 - 25x^2 = 100$
$\frac{y^2}{25} - \frac{x^2}{4} = 1$
$\left(\frac{y}{5}\right)^2 - \left(\frac{x}{2}\right)^2 = 1$
The graph of the equation is a hyperbola.

b. $4y^2 - 10x + 16y + 36 = 0$
$4(y^2 + 4y) = 10x - 36$
$y^2 + 4y = \frac{10}{4}x - 9$
$(y + 2)^2 - 4 = \frac{5}{2}x - 9$
$(y + 2)^2 = \frac{5}{2}x - 5$
$(y + 2)^2 = \frac{5}{2}(x - 2)$
The graph of the equation is a parabola.

c. $4x^2 + 4y^2 + 24x - 8y + 39 = 0$
$4(x^2 + 6x) + 4(y^2 - 2y) = -39$
$4(x^2 + 6x + 9) + 4(y^2 - 2y + 1) - 36 - 4 = -39$
$4(x + 3)^2 + 4(y - 1)^2 = 1$
$\left(\frac{x + 3}{\frac{1}{2}}\right)^2 + \left(\frac{y - 1}{\frac{1}{2}}\right)^2 = 1$
The graph of the equation is a circle.

d. $3x^2 + 5y^2 - 12x + 20y + 8 = 0$
$3x^2 - 12x + 5y^2 + 20y = -8$
$3(x^2 - 4x + 4) + 5(y^2 + 4y + 4) - 12 - 20 = -8$
$3(x - 2)^2 + 5(y - 2)^2 = 24$
$\frac{(x - 2)^2}{8} + \frac{5(y - 2)^2}{24} = 1$
$\left(\frac{x + 2}{\sqrt{8}}\right)^2 + \left(\frac{y + 2}{\sqrt{4.8}}\right)^2 = 1$
$\left(\frac{x - 2}{2.83}\right)^2 + \left(\frac{y + 2}{2.19}\right)^2 = 1$
The graph of the equation is an ellipse.

6. a. $25x^2 - 4y^2 + 100 = 0$
$-4y^2 + 0y + 25x^2 + 100 = 0$
$a = -4; b = 0; c = 25x^2 + 100$

$$y = \frac{0 \pm \sqrt{0^2 - 4(-4)(25x^2 + 100)}}{2(-4)}$$

$$y = \frac{\pm\sqrt{400x^2 + 1600}}{-8}$$

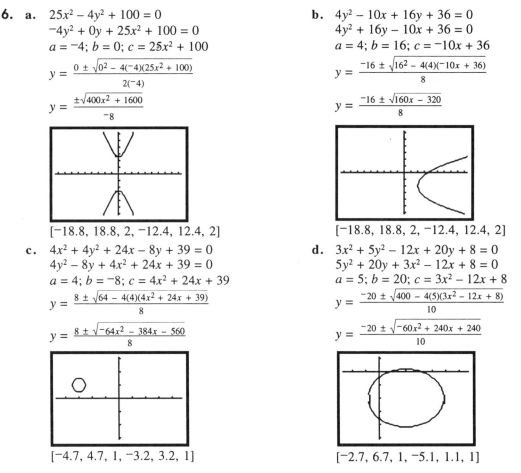

$[-18.8, 18.8, 2, -12.4, 12.4, 2]$

b. $4y^2 - 10x + 16y + 36 = 0$
$4y^2 + 16y - 10x + 36 = 0$
$a = 4; b = 16; c = -10x + 36$

$$y = \frac{-16 \pm \sqrt{16^2 - 4(4)(-10x + 36)}}{8}$$

$$y = \frac{-16 \pm \sqrt{160x - 320}}{8}$$

$[-18.8, 18.8, 2, -12.4, 12.4, 2]$

c. $4x^2 + 4y^2 + 24x - 8y + 39 = 0$
$4y^2 - 8y + 4x^2 + 24x + 39 = 0$
$a = 4; b = -8; c = 4x^2 + 24x + 39$

$$y = \frac{8 \pm \sqrt{64 - 4(4)(4x^2 + 24x + 39)}}{8}$$

$$y = \frac{8 \pm \sqrt{-64x^2 - 384x - 560}}{8}$$

$[-4.7, 4.7, 1, -3.2, 3.2, 1]$

d. $3x^2 + 5y^2 - 12x + 20y + 8 = 0$
$5y^2 + 20y + 3x^2 - 12x + 8 = 0$
$a = 5; b = 20; c = 3x^2 - 12x + 8$

$$y = \frac{-20 \pm \sqrt{400 - 4(5)(3x^2 - 12x + 8)}}{10}$$

$$y = \frac{-20 \pm \sqrt{-60x^2 + 240x + 240}}{10}$$

$[-2.7, 6.7, 1, -5.1, 1.1, 1]$

7. You can identify three points on the curve: $(-200, 50)$, $(200, 50)$, and $(0, 4)$. Use these three points to write three equations.

$a(-200)2 + b(-200) + c = 50$
$a(200)2 + b(200) + c = 50$
$a(0)2 + b(0) + c = 4$

Use matrices to find values for a, b, and c.

$$[A] = \begin{bmatrix} 40{,}000 & -200 & 1 \\ 40{,}000 & 200 & 1 \\ 0 & 0 & 1 \end{bmatrix}, [B] = \begin{bmatrix} 50 \\ 50 \\ 4 \end{bmatrix}, [A]^{-1}[B] = \begin{bmatrix} 0.00115 \\ 0 \\ 4 \end{bmatrix}$$

So, $y = 0.00115x^2 + 4$.
Or as an alternate method, you can identify the vertex as $(0, 4)$. So the equation, in vertex form, is $y = ax^2 + 4$. Use one of the other known points, for example $(200, 50)$, to find the value of a.
$50 = a(200)^2 + 4$
$\frac{46}{200^2} = a; a = 0.00115$
So the equation is $y = 0.00115x^2 + 4$.

8. Answers will vary.

Take Another Look 12.8

To investigate the graph you could solve the equation $\left(\frac{x}{a}\right)^n + \left(\frac{y}{b}\right)^n = 1$ for y. Enter $Y_1 = b\sqrt[n]{1 - \left(\frac{x}{a}\right)^n}$ and $Y_2 = {}^-Y_1$. Then on the HOME screen, store values for a, b, and n.

Some generalizations that students may find are listed below.

For $a = 3$, $b = 2$, and $n = 1$, the graph is two intersecting lines.

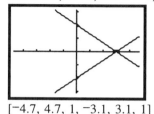

$[{}^-4.7, 4.7, 1, {}^-3.1, 3.1, 1]$

If n is 2, the graph of the equation is an ellipse with x-intercepts of a and ${}^-a$, and y-intercepts of b and ${}^-b$. As the even powers of n get larger, the ellipse-like graph gets closer to becoming a rectangle-like curve.

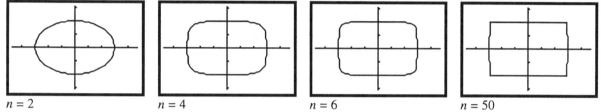

$n = 2$ $n = 4$ $n = 6$ $n = 50$

When $n > 2$ and odd, the graphs are similar to the ones shown below. As n gets larger, the curve has "sharper" corners.

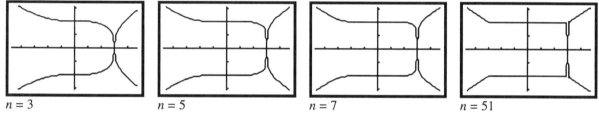

$n = 3$ $n = 5$ $n = 7$ $n = 51$

Problem Set 12.9

1. a. $\begin{bmatrix} \cos 30° & {}^-\sin 30° \\ \sin 30° & \cos 30° \end{bmatrix} = \begin{bmatrix} 0.866 & {}^-0.5 \\ 0.5 & 0.866 \end{bmatrix}$ **b.** $\begin{bmatrix} \cos 147° & {}^-\sin 147° \\ \sin 147° & \cos 147° \end{bmatrix} = \begin{bmatrix} {}^-0.839 & {}^-0.545 \\ 0.545 & {}^-0.839 \end{bmatrix}$

c. $\begin{bmatrix} \cos 270° & {}^-\sin 270° \\ \sin 270° & \cos 270° \end{bmatrix} = \begin{bmatrix} 0 & 1 \\ {}^-1 & 0 \end{bmatrix}$

d. $\begin{bmatrix} \cos(360 - 213)° & {}^-\sin(360 - 213)° \\ \sin(360 - 213)° & \cos(360 - 213)° \end{bmatrix} = \begin{bmatrix} \cos 147° & {}^-\sin 147° \\ \sin 147° & \cos 147° \end{bmatrix} = \begin{bmatrix} {}^-0.839 & {}^-0.545 \\ 0.545 & {}^-0.839 \end{bmatrix}$

2. $\begin{bmatrix} \cos 90° & {}^-\sin 90° \\ \sin 90° & \cos 90° \end{bmatrix} = \begin{bmatrix} 0 & {}^-1 \\ 1 & 0 \end{bmatrix}$

$\begin{bmatrix} 0 & {}^-1 \\ 1 & 0 \end{bmatrix}\begin{bmatrix} 1 \\ {}^-2 \end{bmatrix} = \begin{bmatrix} 2 \\ 1 \end{bmatrix}$; $\begin{bmatrix} 0 & {}^-1 \\ 1 & 0 \end{bmatrix}\begin{bmatrix} 4 \\ {}^-5 \end{bmatrix} = \begin{bmatrix} {}^-5 \\ 4 \end{bmatrix}$; $\begin{bmatrix} 0 & {}^-1 \\ 1 & 0 \end{bmatrix}\begin{bmatrix} 7 \\ {}^-2 \end{bmatrix} = \begin{bmatrix} 2 \\ 7 \end{bmatrix}$

or $\begin{bmatrix} 0 & 1 \\ {}^-1 & 0 \end{bmatrix}\begin{bmatrix} 1 & 4 & 7 \\ {}^-2 & 5 & {}^-2 \end{bmatrix} = \begin{bmatrix} 2 & {}^-5 & 2 \\ 1 & 4 & 7 \end{bmatrix}$

The vertices of the rotated triangle are $(2, 1)$, $({}^-5, 4)$, and $(2, 7)$.

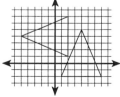

3. a.

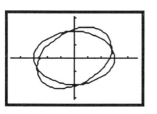

b. $x_{1t} = 3 \cos t$; $y_{1t} = 2 \sin t$
$x_{2t} = x_{1t} \cos 30° - y_{1t} \sin 30°$
$y_{2t} = x_{1t} \sin 30° + y_{1t} \cos 30°$

4. a. The rotation matrix is $\begin{bmatrix} \cos 180° & -\sin 180° \\ \sin 180° & \cos 180° \end{bmatrix} = \begin{bmatrix} -1 & 0 \\ 0 & -1 \end{bmatrix}$.

$\begin{bmatrix} -1 & 0 \\ 0 & -1 \end{bmatrix}\begin{bmatrix} 1 & 7 & 4 \\ 4 & 2 & -1 \end{bmatrix} = \begin{bmatrix} -1 & -7 & -4 \\ -4 & -2 & 1 \end{bmatrix}$

The vertices of the rotated triangle are (−1, −4), (−7, −2), and (−4, 1).

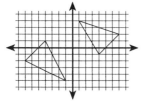

b. A reflection over the x-axis followed by a reflection over the y-axis (or vice versa).

5. a. $[A][B] = \begin{bmatrix} 3 & 6 & 6 & 3 \\ -1 & -1 & -3 & -3 \end{bmatrix}$

Reflection over x

b. $[A][B] = \begin{bmatrix} -3 & -6 & -6 & -3 \\ 1 & 1 & 3 & 3 \end{bmatrix}$

Reflection over y

c. $[A][B] = \begin{bmatrix} -1 & -1 & -3 & -3 \\ 3 & 6 & 6 & 3 \end{bmatrix}$

Rotate 90° counterclockwise

d. $[A][B] = \begin{bmatrix} -3 & -6 & -6 & -3 \\ -1 & -1 & -3 & -3 \end{bmatrix}$

Rotate 180°

e. $[A][B] = \begin{bmatrix} 1 & 1 & 3 & 3 \\ 3 & 6 & 6 & 3 \end{bmatrix}$

Reflect over $y = x$

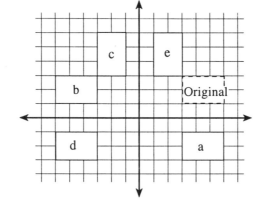

6. a. The graph is a unit hyperbola that opens vertically.
b. The equations for x_2 and y_2 rotate the original hyperbola 50° clockwise.

c.

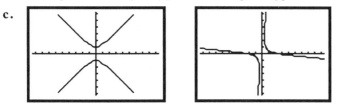

7. Graph $y = \frac{4}{x}$

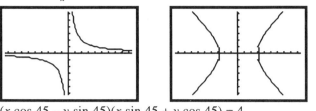

$(x \cos 45 - y \sin 45)(x \sin 45 + y \cos 45) = 4$

$x^2 \sin 45 \cos 45 - xy \sin^2 45 + xy \cos^2 45 - y^2 \sin 45 \cos 45 = 4$

$0.5x^2 - 0.5xy + 0.5xy - 0.5y^2 = 4$

$x^2 - y^2 = \frac{4}{0.5}$

$x^2 - y^2 = 8$

8. **a.–b.** Answers will vary, but here is one possibility.

$x_1 = 2 \cos t$; $y_1 = 2 \sin t$; $x_2 = 0.5(x_1 \cos 60 - y_1 \sin 60)$; $y_2 = 0.5(x_1 \sin 60 + y_1 \cos 60)$ with parameters of Tmin = 90, Tmax = 450, and Tstep = 120.

Chapter Review
Problem Set 12.10

1. $\frac{2.4 + x}{20 + x} = \frac{42}{100}$

$240 + 100x = 840 + 42x$

$58x = 600$

$x \approx 10.34$ oz

2. **a.** The slice is perpendicular to the axis of rotation.
b. The slice intersects only one branch of the cone. The angle is not perpendicular to the axis of rotation.
c. The slice intersects only one branch of the cone and is parallel to an edge.
d. The slice intersects both branches of the cone but does not contain the vertex.
e. The slice intersects at the vertex.
f. The slice is along an edge.
g. The axis of rotation is contained in the slice.

3. **a.** $\left(\frac{x-5}{3}\right)^2 + \left(\frac{y+2}{4}\right)^2 = 1$
b. $x = 3 \cos t + 5$ and $y = 4 \sin t - 2$
c. The center is $(5, -2)$. The foci are $\left(5, -2 + \sqrt{7}\right)$ and $\left(5, -2 - \sqrt{7}\right)$.

(right triangle with legs labeled $\sqrt{7}$, 3 and hypotenuse 4)

d. $\left(\frac{x-5}{9}\right)^2 + \left(\frac{y+2}{4}\right)^2 = 1$

$\frac{(x-5)^2}{5} + \frac{(y+2)^2}{16} = 1$

$16(x^2 - 10x + 25) + 9(y^2 + 4y + 4) = 144$

$16x^2 - 160x + 400 + 9y^2 + 36y + 36 = 144$

$16x^2 + 9y^2 - 160x + 36y + 292 = 0$

e. $x = (3 \cos t + 5) \cos 75 - (4 \sin t - 2) \sin 75$; $y = (3 \cos t + 5) \sin 75 + (4 \sin t - 2) \cos 75$
f. $16(x \cos 75 - y \sin 75)^2 + 9(x \sin 75 + y \cos 75)^2 - 160(x \cos 75 - y \sin 75) + 36(x \sin 75 + y \cos 75)$
$+ 292 = 9.47x^2 + 12.5xy + 15.53y^2 + 34.77x + 9.32y + 292 = 0$.

4. **a.** $y = \pm 0.5x$
b. $\frac{x^2}{4} - \frac{y^2}{1} = 1$

$x^2 - 4y^2 = 4$

$x^2 - 4y^2 - 4 = 0$

c. Solve the general quadratic equation in part b for y.

$$-4y^2 = 4 - x^2$$
$$y^2 = \frac{x^2}{4} - 1$$
$$y = \pm\sqrt{\frac{x^2}{4} - 1}$$

Distance $= 0.5x - \sqrt{\frac{x^2}{4} - 1}$

d.

x	0	1	2	10	20
Distance	None	None	1	0.101	0.050

5. a.
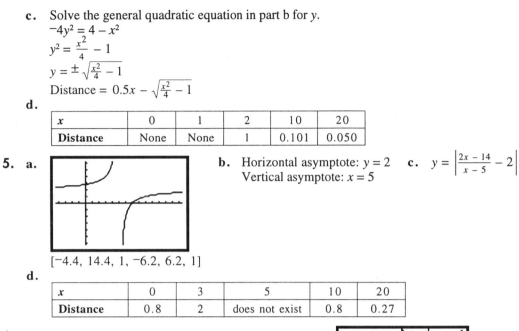

$[^-4.4, 14.4, 1, ^-6.2, 6.2, 1]$

b. Horizontal asymptote: $y = 2$
Vertical asymptote: $x = 5$

c. $y = \left| \frac{2x - 14}{x - 5} - 2 \right|$

d.

x	0	3	5	10	20
Distance	0.8	2	does not exist	0.8	0.27

6. Include $(x + 3)$ as a factor in both the numerator and denominator of the fraction. $y = \frac{(2x - 14)(x + 3)}{(x - 5)(x + 3)}$

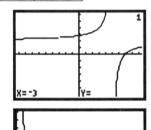

7. About 23.3 mi/hr and 43.3 mi/hr. One approach is to find the intersection of the two times represented by y_1 and y_2. (x is the rate during the first 2 mi.)

$y_1 = \frac{2}{x} + \frac{3.5}{x + 20}$ and $y_2 = \frac{10}{60}$

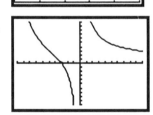

8. a. $y_1 = \frac{34}{x + 11} + \frac{13}{x}$

c. Answers will vary depending on how fast you think Eric can run
(perhaps $2 < x < 10$ and $3 < y < 9$).

d. About 4.6 mi/hr

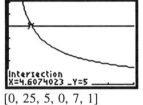

$[0, 25, 5, 0, 7, 1]$

b.

There is a vertical asymptote at $x = ^-1$.
There is a horizontal asymptote at $y = 0$.

$[^-10, 10, 1, ^-10, 10, 1]$

9. Answers will vary.

Chapter 13

Problem Set 13.1

1. a. sin 85° = 0.9962
reference angle = 85°

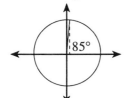

b. cos 147° = ⁻0.8387
reference angle = 33°

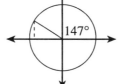

c. sin 280° = ⁻0.9848
reference angle = 80°

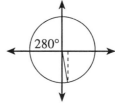

d. cos 310° = 0.6428
reference angle = 50°

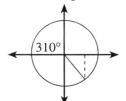

e. sin ⁻47° = ⁻0.7314
reference angle = 47°

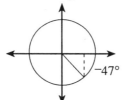

2. a. $y = \sin x$

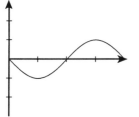

b. The graph will shift up 2 units.

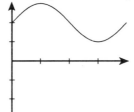

c. The graph will shift right 180°.

d. The graph will be stretched vertically by a factor of 2, shifted up 3 units, and shifted to the right 180°.

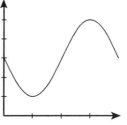

3. a.–b.

Angle A	0°	30°	60°	90°	120°	150°	180°
x-coordinate	1	0.8660	0.5	0	−0.5	−0.8660	−1
y-coordinate	0	0.5	0.8660	1	0.8660	0.5	0
Slope	0	0.5774	1.7321	Undefined	−1.7321	−0.5774	0
tan A	0	0.5774	1.7321	Undefined	−1.7321	−0.5774	0

Angle A	210°	240°	270°	300°	315°	330°	360°
x-coordinate	−0.8660	−0.5	0	0.5	0.7071	0.8660	1
y-coordinate	−0.5	−0.8660	−1	−0.8660	−0.7071	−0.5	0
Slope	0.5774	1.7321	Undefined	−1.7321	−1	−0.5774	0
tan A	0.5774	1.7321	Undefined	−1.7321	−1	−0.5774	0

c. The lengths of the legs of the reference triangle form the same ratio as the ratio of the x- and y-coordinates because lengths of the sides are the same as the coordinates, so the definition of a slope, $\frac{\text{rise}}{\text{run}}$, can be translated to $\frac{y\text{-coordinate}}{x\text{-coordinate}}$. Another name for the ratio of the legs is the tangent.

d. The tangents of the angles in the table in part a are the same as the slopes for the angles in the table.

e. $\tan A = \dfrac{\text{height of lily pad}}{\text{horizontal distance of lily pad from center}}$

4. a.

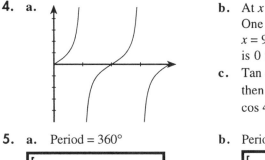

b. At $x = 90°$ the function does not exist. Answers will vary. One explanation involves looking at the paddle wheel; at $x = 90°$ the vertical leg is 1 unit long and the horizontal leg is 0 units long. The tangent is then $\frac{1}{0}$, which is undefined.

c. Tan $40° =$ tan $220°$ because if $\cos A° = y$ and $\sin A° = x$, then the slope equals $\frac{y}{x}$. In the case of $40°$ and $220°$, $\cos 40° = {}^{-}\cos 220°$ and $\sin 40° = {}^{-}\sin 220°$, so $\frac{y}{x} = \frac{{}^{-}y}{{}^{-}x} = \frac{y}{x}$.

5. a. Period $= 360°$

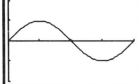

b. Period $= 360°$

c. Period $= 180°$

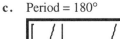

d. Period $= 180°$

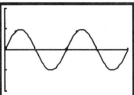

e. Period $= 60°$

6. a. The value of a determines the period such that as a increases the period decreases.

sin x sin $2x$ sin $3x$

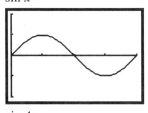

sin $4x$ sin $5x$

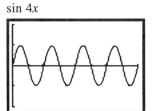

b. Period $= \dfrac{360}{a}$

7. a. $90°$

b. $540°$

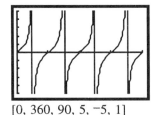

[0, 360, 90, 5, ${}^{-}$5, 1]   [0, 540, 90, 5, ${}^{-}$5, 1]

c. The change in period is similar to a horizontal stretch.

8. Answers will vary for the equations. Two possibilities are given for each.

   a. Period = 180°; 360/a = 180, a = 2; vertical shift of 1 for sine and cosine; horizontal shift of 45° for cosine; $y = \sin(2x) + 1$ or $y = \cos 2(x - 45) + 1$

   b. Period = 360°; there is no vertical stretch factor; reflection over x-axis for cosine; no vertical shift; horizontal shift of 90° for sine; $y = {}^-\cos x$ or $y = \sin(x - 90)$

   c. Period = 90°; 180/a = 90, a = 2; vertical stretch factor of 2; vertical shift of $^-1$; could be horizontal shift of $^-90°$; $y = \tan(2x) - 1$ or $y = \tan 2(x + 90) - 1$

   d. Period = 180°; 360/a = 180, a = 2; vertical stretch factor of 2; reflection over the x-axis; no vertical shift; horizontal shift of $^-45$ for cosine; $y = {}^-2\sin 2x$ or $y = 2\cos 2(x + 45)$

9. **a.** 15 min; $\frac{360}{15} = 24$ **b.** 10 mi   **c.** + 300 mi   **d.** $y = 10\sin 24x + 300$

Project: Design a Picnic Table

In order to get a start on this project, students may wish to measure some real picnic tables to determine standard heights, widths, and lengths of both the benches and table top. A visit or call to the lumber yard may be in order to learn the dimensions of available lumber. Once the basic measurements are decided, the figuring begins.

First the angle between the legs at the end of the table needs to be decided. Then use right triangles to determine the lengths of the boards and the angles.

The values of h and w are decided upon, and the values of l and θ are calculated using the Pythagorean theorem and right triangle trigonometric relationships. The legs can now be cut.

The values of a and b are decided upon, and the values of c and α are calculated. The supports can now be cut.

Students should make a scale model of cardboard or balsa wood to verify their calculations.

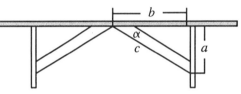

Problem Set 13.2

1. **a.**

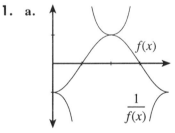

   b. $y_1 = \sin(x - 90)$ or $y_1 = {}^-\cos x$

   $y_2 = \dfrac{1}{\sin(x-90)}$ or $y_2 = \dfrac{1}{-\cos x}$

2. **a.** $y = 0.5\csc(x) + 1$ or $y = 0.5\sec(x - 90) + 1$

   b. $y = {}^-\cot\left(\frac{1}{3}(x + 270)\right)$ or $y = \left(\tan\frac{1}{3}x\right)$

   c. $y = \cot(x + 90) + 1$ or $y = {}^-\tan(x) + 1$

   d. $y = \sin 2(x - 45) - 0.5$ or $y = {}^-\cos(2x) - 0.5$

3. **a.** The d-value shifts the graph of the function up or down; a positive d-value shifts the function up, and a negative d-value shifts the function down.

   b. The a-value represents the amplitude. A value of 1 for a gives an amplitude of 1, and a value of 5 gives an amplitude of 5.

   c. The b-value determines the period such that as b increases the period decreases; $\frac{360}{b}$ = period.

   d. The c-value shifts the graph; a positive c-value shifts the graph to the left, and a negative c-value shifts the graph to the right.

e.

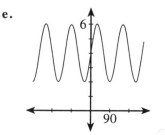

4. **a.** The radius of the rim is 7.5 in., so the amplitude of the function is 7.5. The 12 in. radius of the tire shifts the graph vertically. The period is $\frac{360}{4} = 90$ because the bug does one-fourth of a revolution in a minute. To show 20 min you will need 5 revolutions, so Xmax needs to be 5(4) = 20.

Equation: $y = 7.5 \cos(90x) + 12$

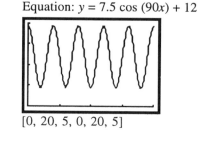

[0, 20, 5, 0, 20, 5]

b.

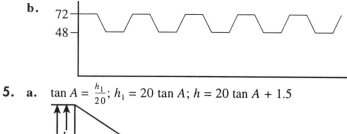

5. **a.** $\tan A = \frac{h_1}{20}$; $h_1 = 20 \tan A$; $h = 20 \tan A + 1.5$

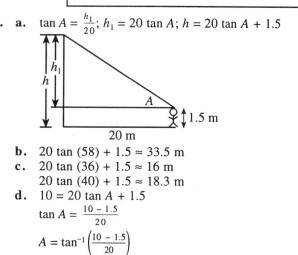

b. $20 \tan(58) + 1.5 \approx 33.5$ m

c. $20 \tan(36) + 1.5 \approx 16$ m
$20 \tan(40) + 1.5 \approx 18.3$ m

d. $10 = 20 \tan A + 1.5$

$\tan A = \frac{10 - 1.5}{20}$

$A = \tan^{-1}\left(\frac{10 - 1.5}{20}\right)$

$A \approx 23°$

6. **a.** The equation should be similar to $y = 3.25 \sin \frac{360}{365}(x - 80) + 12.15$.

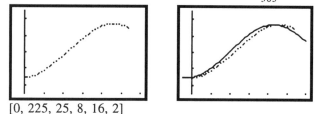

[0, 225, 25, 8, 16, 2]

b. According to the equation, the least amount of daylight (8.9 hr) occurs when $x = -11.5$, which is 11 or 12 days before January 1, or around December 20.

c. The graph should be similar in shape but with a greater amplitude.

7. a.

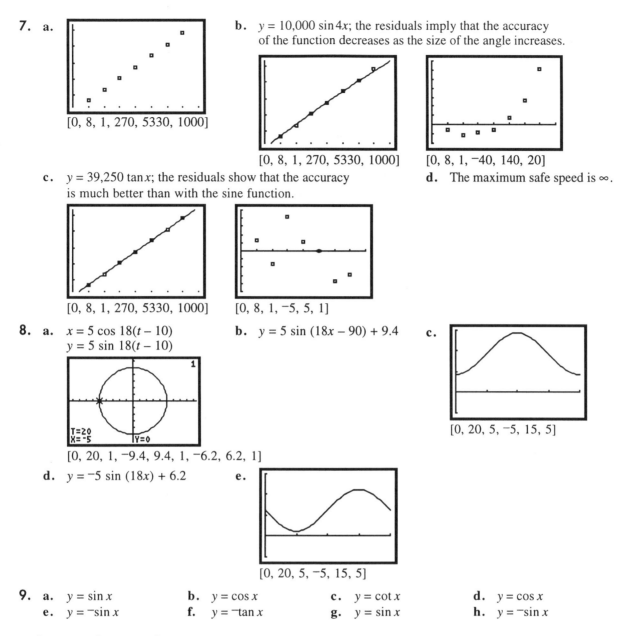

[0, 8, 1, 270, 5330, 1000]

b. $y = 10,000 \sin 4x$; the residuals imply that the accuracy of the function decreases as the size of the angle increases.

[0, 8, 1, 270, 5330, 1000]   [0, 8, 1, −40, 140, 20]

c. $y = 39,250 \tan x$; the residuals show that the accuracy is much better than with the sine function.

d. The maximum safe speed is ∞.

[0, 8, 1, 270, 5330, 1000]   [0, 8, 1, −5, 5, 1]

8. a. $x = 5 \cos 18(t - 10)$
$y = 5 \sin 18(t - 10)$

b. $y = 5 \sin (18x - 90) + 9.4$

c.

[0, 20, 5, −5, 15, 5]

[0, 20, 1, −9.4, 9.4, 1, −6.2, 6.2, 1]

d. $y = {}^-5 \sin (18x) + 6.2$ **e.**

[0, 20, 5, −5, 15, 5]

9. a. $y = \sin x$ **b.** $y = \cos x$ **c.** $y = \cot x$ **d.** $y = \cos x$
    e. $y = {}^-\sin x$ **f.** $y = {}^-\tan x$ **g.** $y = \sin x$ **h.** $y = {}^-\sin x$

Take Another Look 13.2

Answers may vary. Angles can be measured in radians rather than degrees. Radians can be determined using arc length and radius. If θ represents a complete revolution, $s = 2\pi r$. Therefore, $\theta = 2\pi r/r = 2\pi$. In degrees, θ would be 360. Therefore, $180 = \pi$ radians.
    1 degree $= \pi/180$ radians
    1 radian $= 180/\pi = 57.3$ degrees
To draw a circle parametrically using radians, enter the equations
$X_{1T} = 1 \cos (t)$ and $Y_{1T} = 1 \sin (t)$. Use window values of
$[0, 2\pi, (1/8)\pi, −4.7, 4.7, 1, −3.1, 3.1, 1]$.

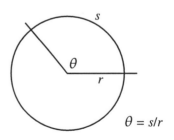

$\theta = s/r$

Problem Set 13.3

1. $360/45 = 8$; $y = \sin 8x$; $0° \leq x \leq 45°$, $−1 \leq y \leq 1$

2. a. Answers will vary.

b. Physical: 365/23 = 15.8695; $y = \sin 15.8695x$: emotional: 365/28 = 13.0357; $y = \sin 13.0357x$: intellectual: 365/33 = 11.0606; $y = \sin 11.0606x$

c. The plot depends on where your cycles are starting today.

d. (23)(28)(33) = 21,252 days; $\frac{21,252 \text{ days}}{365} \approx 58.22$ yr

3. a.

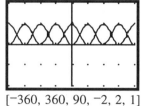

$[-360, 360, 90, -2, 2, 1]$

b.

x	0°	30°	60°	120°	150°	180°
$\cos^2 x + \sin^2 x$	1	1	1	1	1	1

A plot of all of these points would look like the line, $y = 1$.

c. $\cos^2 x + \sin^2 x = 1$

d. The function equation of a circle is $x^2 + y^2 = 1$. The parametric substitutions for x and y are $x = \cos t$ and $y = \sin t$. Substituting these expressions into the function equation, you get $(\cos t)^2 + (\sin t)^2 = 1$.

4. a. The period is 360/20 = 18. The height of the center causes a vertical shift of 12. The amplitude is 10, which is the radius of the wheel. Since she begins her ride at the lowest point, you need a horizontal shift of -15 sec. The equation is $y = 10 \sin 18(x + 15) + 12$.

b. The period is 360/30 = 12. The amplitude is the distance between the lower wheel and the center of rotation, which is 11. The vertical shift is the height of the center from the ground plus the radius of rotation, which is 23. Since the rotation begins at the lowest point, you need a horizontal shift of -22.5. The equation is $y = 11 \sin 12(x + 22.5) + 23$.

c. $y = (10 \sin 18(x + 15) + 12) + (11 \sin 12(x + 22.5) + 23) - 12$

Note: The term "-12" is needed because the total height is 23 not 34.

d. 10 times; you can graph the equation and graph $y = 6$ to see when Sandra is within 6 feet of the ground.

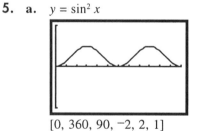

$[0, 300, 30, -2, 40, 5]$

5. a. $y = \sin^2 x$ $y = \cos^2 x$

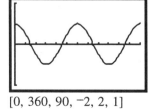

$[0, 360, 90, -2, 2, 1]$ $[0, 360, 90, -2, 2, 1]$

b.

x	0°	30°	60°	90°	120°	150°
$\cos^2 x - \sin^2 x$	1	0.5	-0.5	-1	-0.5	0.5

c. $y = \cos 2x$

d. $\cos^2 x - \sin^2 x = \cos 2x$

When plotted the points resemble a periodic function.

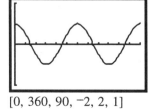

$[0, 360, 90, -2, 2, 1]$

6. $\sin 2x = 2 \cos x \sin x$

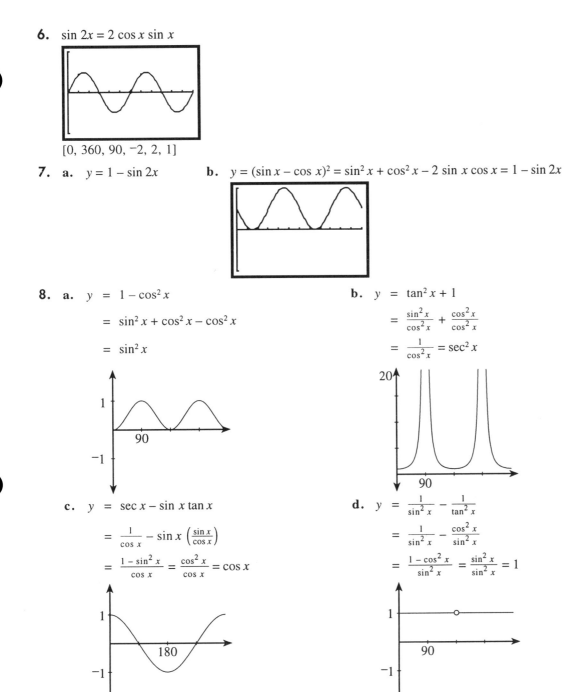

[0, 360, 90, −2, 2, 1]

7. a. $y = 1 - \sin 2x$

b. $y = (\sin x - \cos x)^2 = \sin^2 x + \cos^2 x - 2 \sin x \cos x = 1 - \sin 2x$

8. a. $y = 1 - \cos^2 x$

$= \sin^2 x + \cos^2 x - \cos^2 x$

$= \sin^2 x$

b. $y = \tan^2 x + 1$

$= \dfrac{\sin^2 x}{\cos^2 x} + \dfrac{\cos^2 x}{\cos^2 x}$

$= \dfrac{1}{\cos^2 x} = \sec^2 x$

c. $y = \sec x - \sin x \tan x$

$= \dfrac{1}{\cos x} - \sin x \left(\dfrac{\sin x}{\cos x} \right)$

$= \dfrac{1 - \sin^2 x}{\cos x} = \dfrac{\cos^2 x}{\cos x} = \cos x$

d. $y = \dfrac{1}{\sin^2 x} - \dfrac{1}{\tan^2 x}$

$= \dfrac{1}{\sin^2 x} - \dfrac{\cos^2 x}{\sin^2 x}$

$= \dfrac{1 - \cos^2 x}{\sin^2 x} = \dfrac{\sin^2 x}{\sin^2 x} = 1$

9. 2 Hz: Graph $y = \sin 440x + \sin 442x$ over the interval [0, 360]. You will see two cycles of a pattern. These are the beats.

[0, 360, 0, −1, 1, 1]

Take Another Look 13.3

a. Answers will vary depending on the day.

b. The variable x represents the number of days since January 1, 365 days is the number of days in a year, 360 is the number of degrees for the rotation of the earth, 80 represents the number of days until the sun crosses the equator, 12 represents the number of hours of daylight at the equator, a sine curve plots the position of the sun in the sky, and the constant 2.4 depends on the latitude and longitude of the city.

c. i. 12; ii. 12.86; iii. 12.6; iv. 9.6

d. $D(x) = 24 - 12 + 2.4 \cdot \sin\left(\frac{360°(x - 80)}{365}\right)$

e. Answers will vary.

Problem Set 13.4

1. a. $m\angle B = 180 - 107.5 - 47 = 25.5$; $\frac{\sin 47°}{BC} = \frac{\sin 25.5°}{3.77}$, $BC = \frac{3.77(\sin 47°)}{\sin 25.5} \approx 6.4$; $\frac{\sin 107.5°}{AB} = \frac{\sin 25.5°}{3.77}$, $AB = \frac{3.77(\sin 107.5°)}{\sin 25.5°} \approx 8.35$

b. $DF = \sqrt{8.86^2 + 7.13^2 - 2(8.86)(7.13)\cos 46.1°} \approx 6.46$; $\frac{\sin F}{7.13} = \frac{\sin 46.1°}{6.46}$, $m\angle F = \sin^{-1}\left(\frac{7.13 \sin 46.1°}{6.46}\right) \approx 52.68°$; $m\angle D = 180 - 52.68 - 46.1 = 81.22°$

c. $m\angle I = \cos^{-1}\left(\frac{3.16^2 - 5.96^2 - 6.48^2}{-2(5.96)(6.48)}\right) \approx 29.05°$; $m\angle H = \cos^{-1}\left(\frac{6.48^2 - 5.96^2 - 3.16^2}{-2(5.96)(3.16)}\right) \approx 84.64°$; $m\angle G \approx 180 - 29.05 - 84.64 = 66.31°$

d. $\frac{\sin 107.9°}{8.26} = \frac{\sin J}{5.44}$, $m\angle J = \sin^{-1}\left(\frac{5.44 \sin 107.9°}{8.26}\right) \approx 38.81°$; $m\angle L = 180 - 107.9 - 38.81 = 33.29°$; $\frac{\sin 33.29°}{KJ} = \frac{\sin 107.9°}{8.26}$, $KJ = \frac{8.26 \sin 33.29°}{\sin 107.9°} \approx 4.76$

2. If the known parts include SAS or SSS, use the Law of Cosines. If the known parts include AAS, use the Law of Sines. If the known parts are SSA, you can use either law, but be careful if you use the Law of Sines to check whether you want an acute or obtuse angle.

3. $d = \sqrt{900^2 + 800^2 - 2(900)(800)\cos 155°} \approx 1659.8$ mi

4. $m\angle B = \cos^{-1}\left(\frac{7^2 - 5^2 - 3^2}{-2(5)(3)}\right) = 120°$

$m\angle C = \cos^{-1}\left(\frac{5^2 - 3^2 - 7^2}{-2(3)(7)}\right) \approx 38.21°$

$m\angle A = 180 - 120 - 38.21 \approx 21.79°$

5. $d = \sqrt{55^2 + 75^2 - 2(55)(75)\cos 50°} \approx 57.85$ cm

6. $\frac{\sin 47°}{d} = \frac{\sin 26°}{1.5}$, distance ≈ 2.5 km; heading $= 180 - 107 - 47 = 34°$

7. $m\angle CAD = \cos^{-1}\left(\frac{25^2 - 26^2 - 15^2}{-2(26)(15)}\right) \approx 69.3°$

$80 + 69.3 = 149.3°$ from north

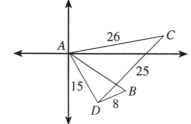

8. $\frac{\sin 0.00022}{3.13 \cdot 10^{-5}} = \frac{\sin 42.13204}{x}$; $x = 5.46845$ light-years from first position

$\frac{\sin 0.00022}{3.13 \cdot 10^{-5}} = \frac{\sin 137.86774}{x}$; $x = 5.46847$ light-years from second position

Project: Sum and Difference Identities

Deriving the identity:

$d = \sqrt{(\cos A - \cos B)^2 + (\sin A - \sin B)^2}$, $d = \sqrt{1 + 1 - 2 \cos C}$

$(\cos A - \cos B)^2 + (\sin A - \sin B)^2 = 2 - 2 \cos C$

$\cos^2 A - 2 \cos A \cos B + \cos^2 B + \sin^2 A - 2 \sin A \sin B + \sin^2 B = 2 - 2 \cos C$

$\cos^2 A + \cos^2 B + \sin^2 A + \sin^2 B - 2 \cos A \cos B - 2 \sin A \sin B = 2 - 2 \cos C$

$1 + 1 - 2 \cos A \cos B - 2 \sin A \sin B = 2 - 2 \cos C$

$-2 \cos A \cos B - 2 \sin A \sin B = -2 \cos C$

$\cos A \cos B + \sin A \sin B = \cos C$

$\cos A \cos B + \sin A \sin B = \cos (A - B)$

$\cos (110° - 30°) = \cos 110° \cos 30° + \sin 110° \sin 30°$

$0.1736 = (-0.3420)(0.8660) + (0.9397)(0.5)$

$0.1736 = -0.2962 + 0.4699$

$0.1736 = 0.1736$

a. $\cos (A - {}^-B) = \cos A \cos ({}^-B) + \sin A \sin ({}^-B)$

$\cos ({}^-B) = \cos B$, $\sin ({}^-B) = {}^-\sin B$

$\cos (A + B) = \cos A \cos B - \sin A \sin B$

b. $\sin (A - B) = \cos (90 - (A - B)) = \cos ((90 - A) + B)$

$= \cos (90 - A) \cos B - \sin (90 - A) \sin B$

$\sin (90 - A) = \cos A$

$\sin (A - B) = \sin A \cos B - \sin A \cos B$

c. $\sin (A + B) = \cos (90 - (A + B)) = \cos ((90 - A) - B)$

$= \cos (90 - A) \cos B + \sin (90 - A) \sin B$

$\sin (A + B) = \sin A \cos B + \sin A \cos B$

d. $\cos 75° = \cos (30° + 45°) = \cos 30° \cos 45° - \sin 30° \sin 45°$

$= \frac{\sqrt{3}}{2} \frac{\sqrt{2}}{2} - \frac{1}{2} \frac{\sqrt{2}}{2} = \frac{\sqrt{6} - \sqrt{2}}{4}$

$\sin 15° = \sin (45° - 30°) = \sin 45° \cos 30° - \sin 30° \cos 45°$

$= \frac{\sqrt{2}}{2} \left(\frac{\sqrt{3}}{2} \right) - \frac{1}{2} \left(\frac{\sqrt{2}}{2} \right) = \frac{\sqrt{6} - \sqrt{2}}{4}$

Problem Set 13.5

1. a. $\frac{\sin 40°}{4.7} = \frac{\sin A}{7}$; $m\angle A = \sin^{-1} \left(\frac{7 \sin 40°}{4.7} \right) \approx 73.2°$. Since angle A is obtuse, $m\angle A = 180 - 73.2 = 106.8°$.

b. $\frac{\sin 16.7°}{2.5} = \frac{\sin B}{7.5}$; $m\angle B = \sin^{-1} \left(\frac{7.5 \sin 16.7°}{2.5} \right) \approx 59.6°$. Since angle A is obtuse, $m\angle A = 180 - 59.6 = 120.4°$.

2. a. $x = t$; $y = \sin t$ $x = \sin t$; $y = t$
    $0 \le t \le 360$ $-90 \le t \le 90$

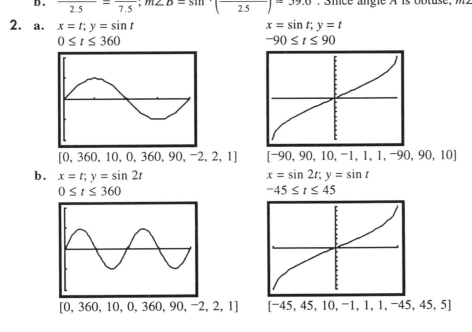

[0, 360, 10, 0, 360, 90, -2, 2, 1]   [-90, 90, 10, -1, 1, 1, -90, 90, 10]

b. $x = t$; $y = \sin 2t$ $x = \sin 2t$; $y = \sin t$
    $0 \le t \le 360$ $-45 \le t \le 45$

[0, 360, 10, 0, 360, 90, -2, 2, 1]   [-45, 45, 10, -1, 1, 1, -45, 45, 5]

c. $x = t; y = \sin \frac{1}{2}t$　　　　　　　　$x = \sin \frac{1}{2}t; y = t$

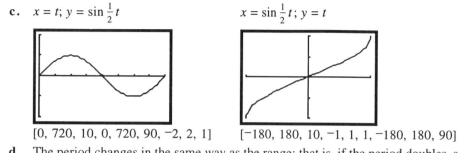

[0, 720, 10, 0, 720, 90, −2, 2, 1]　　[−180, 180, 10, −1, 1, 1, −180, 180, 90]

d. The period changes in the same way as the range; that is, if the period doubles, so does the range.

3. Graph $y_1 = 7.5 \sin 30t + 15$ and $y_2 = 11.5$, and look for the points of intersection of the two graphs. The intervals are $0 \le t \le 6.927$, $11.073 \le t \le 18.927$, $23.073 \le t \le 30.927$, $35.073 \le t \le 42.927$, and $47.073 \le t \le 48$.

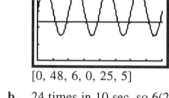

[0, 48, 6, 0, 25, 5]

4. a. Period $= \frac{10}{12}$; $y = \sin \frac{360(12)}{10}x = \sin 432x$　　　**b.** 24 times in 10 sec, so 6(24) = 144 times in 60 sec

5. The amplitude of the spring is 2. The period is $\frac{10}{12}$. Because the spring is released at its lowest position, use a flipped cosine curve. The equation is $y_1 = {}^-2 \cos 432x$. To find at what time the mass is 0.5 cm below its resting position, graph $y = {}^-0.5$. Find the points of intersection of y_1 and y_2, or graph $y_3 = y_2 - y_1$ and find where the graph crosses the x-axis.

y_1 and y_2　　　　　　　　$y_2 - y_1$

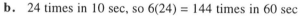

$t = \{0.17, 0.66, 1.01, 1.49, 1.84, 2.33, 2.67\}$

[0, 3, 1, −3, 2, 1]　　　　[0, 3, 1, −3, 3, 1]

6. a. First spring: amplitude = 2.5, period 1, $y_1 = {}^-2.5 \cos 360x$

Second spring: amplitude = 2.5, period $= \frac{8}{10} = 0.8$, $y_2 = {}^-2.5 \cos 450x$

Graph $y_3 = y_2 - y_1$ and count the number of times $y_3 = 0$.

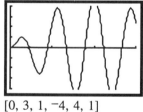

Not including $t = 0$, the two springs are at the same height 6 times.

[0, 3, 1, −4, 4, 1]

b. Graph $y_4 = |y^2 - y^1| - 1$ and find the sum of the interval lengths where $y_4 < 0$. (0.52 + 0.09 + 0.07 + 0.06 + 0.06 + 0.07) = 0.87; $\frac{0.8}{3} \approx 0.29$ or 29% of the time.

7. a. Graph $y_1 = \frac{1}{\cos x}$ and $y_2 = {}^-2.5$, or graph $y_2 - y_1$, and look for the x-intercepts.

y_1 and y_2　　　　　　$y_2 - y_1$

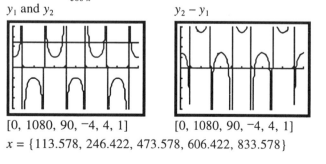

[0, 1080, 90, −4, 4, 1]　　[0, 1080, 90, −4, 4, 1]

$x = \{113.578, 246.422, 473.578, 606.422, 833.578\}$

b. Graph $y_1 = \left(\dfrac{1}{\sin x} - \dfrac{1}{\tan x}\right)\left(\dfrac{1}{\cos x} + 1\right)$ and $y_2 = 0.8$, or graph $y_2 - y_1$, and look for the x-intercepts.

y_1 and y_2 $y_2 - y_1$

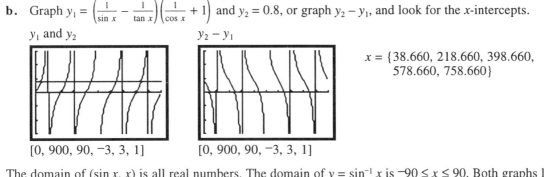

$x = \{38.660,\ 218.660,\ 398.660,$
$\phantom{x = \{}578.660,\ 758.660\}$

[0, 900, 90, −3, 3, 1]   [0, 900, 90, −3, 3, 1]

8. The domain of $(\sin x, x)$ is all real numbers. The domain of $y = \sin^{-1} x$ is $-90 \le x \le 90$. Both graphs look exactly the same for $-90 \le x \le 90$.

9. a. period $= \dfrac{1}{60} = 21{,}600$;
amplitude $= 110$;
the equation is
$y = 110 \sin 21600x$.

    b.

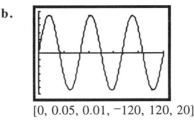

[0, 0.05, 0.01, −120, 120, 20]

10. a. The amplitude is $16 - 11 = 5$. The period for one complete cycle is 14. The first maximum value needs to occur when $x = 12$, so shift the graph of the cosine 12 units to the right:
$y_1 = 5 \cos 25.7(x - 12) + 11$.

    b. Graph $y_2 = 9$. Look at the next two time periods when the sine curve is below this graph. $16.42 \le x \le 21.58$ and $30.42 \le x \le 35.58$ or between 4:25 and 9:35 p.m. and again between 6:25 and 11:35 a.m. the next morning.

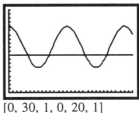

[0, 30, 1, 0, 20, 1]

Project: A Dampened Sine Curve

The equation that models the decay of the amplitude of the sine curve will most likely be an exponential one. Careful measurement and experimental techniques will make this an easier analysis. Shorter strings decay quite fast, but they make it more difficult to measure the angle; long strings make the angle measuring easier, but the decaying action is slower. Have students vary the length of the string until they are content with the accuracy and range of their data. It may be possible to use photogates to get more accurate data.

Because the time of the swing does not vary, the data of (*swing number, angle*) can be quickly converted to (*time, angle*). And with a little right triangle trigonometry, you can find data for (*time, height*). It may likely be in the form of $y = ab^x \sin fx + h$, with $a + h$ the initial height and $h - a$ the at-rest height, with the value of b equal to 1 minus the decay rate ($b \approx 0.94$ depending on the length of the string), and with f equal to the frequency of the pendulum.

Problem Set 13.6

1. $(2, 390°)$ and $(-2, -510°)$

2. $(3, 240°)$, $(-3, 300°)$ and $(3, -120°)$

3. a.

θ	0°	5°	10°	15°	20°	25°	30°	35°	40°	45°	50°	55°
r	3	2.90	2.60	2.12	1.5	0.78	0	−0.78	−1.5	−2.12	−2.60	−2.9

θ	60°	65°	70°	75°	80°	85°	90°	95°	100°	105°	110°	115°	120°
r	−3	−2.90	−2.60	−2.12	−1.5	−0.78	0	0.78	1.5	2.12	2.60	2.90	3

θ	125°	130°	135°	140°	145°	150°	155°	160°	165°	170°	175°	180°	185°
r	2.90	2.60	2.12	1.5	0.78	0	−0.78	−1.5	−2.12	−2.60	−2.90	−3	−2.90

θ	190°	195°	200°	205°	210°	215°	220°	225°	230°	235°	240°	245°	250°
r	−2.60	−2.12	−1.5	−0.78	0	0.78	1.5	2.12	2.60	2.90	3	2.90	2.60

θ	255°	260°	265°	270°	275°	280°	285°	290°	295°	300°	305°	310°	315°
r	2.12	1.5	0.78	0	−0.78	−1.5	−2.12	−2.60	−2.9	−3	−2.9	−2.60	−2.12

θ	320°	325°	330°	335°	340°	345°	350°	355°	360°
r	−1.5	−0.78	0	0.78	1.5	2.12	2.60	2.90	3

b.

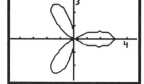

[0, 360, 10, −4.7, 4.7, 1, −3.1, 3.1, 1]

4. a.

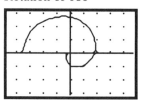

b. The graph is flipped over the x-axis.

c. Rotation of 180°

d. The spiral is stretched in all directions by a factor of 2.

5. a. The final graphs are exactly the same. The difference is in where the graph begins. The graph of $r = \cos\theta + 1$ begins at the point (2, 0°), whereas the equation of $r = \cos\theta - 1$ begins at the origin.

$r = \cos\theta + 1$ $r = \cos\theta - 1$

b. The graph is the same image rotated 90° counterclockwise.

c. The width at $y = 0$ is $2a$. The distances from the origin are all multiplied by the coefficient a.

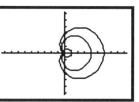

6. a. Notice that all of the cardioids drawn extend very little on the dimple side. This means that sound on stage, around the large curve, is picked up just as well as sound only very close to the microphone on the audience side. The microphone will pick up sound from all over the stage much better that it will sound from even the first few rows of the audience.

b. The equation graphed is $r = 2(\cos\theta + 1)$. For $\theta = 0°$, $r = 4$. The player on either edge is 3 units from the microphone. The other two players are each 3.732 units away.

7. a. $r = 3\cos\theta$: $0° \le \theta \le 180°$

b. $r = 3\cos 2\theta$, $r = 2\sin 2\theta$: $0° \le \theta \le 360°$

c. $r = {}^-2(\cos\theta + 1)$: $0° \le \theta \le 360°$

d. $r = {}^\pm2(\cos\theta + 1)$, $r = 2$: $0° \le \theta \le 360°$

8. a. $0° \le \theta \le 720°$ **b.** $0° \le \theta \le 720°$

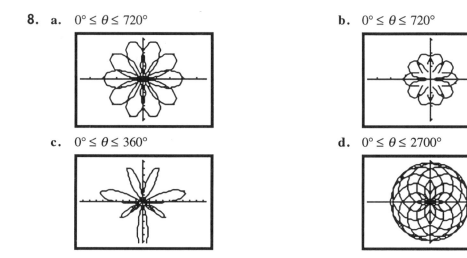

c. $0° \le \theta \le 360°$ **d.** $0° \le \theta \le 2700°$

Take Another Look 13.6

Answers will vary. A Lissajous figure is a combination of two harmonic motions in two directions at right angles. If the periods are equal, the curve is an ellipse.

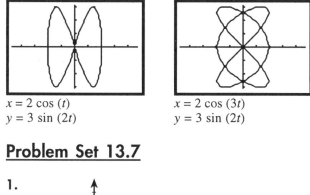

$x = 2 \cos (t)$
$y = 3 \sin (2t)$

$x = 2 \cos (3t)$
$y = 3 \sin (2t)$

Problem Set 13.7

1.

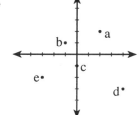

2. Answers will vary with different choices for θ.

a. $r = \sqrt{2^2 + 2^2} \approx 2.828$; $\theta = \tan^{-1}\frac{2}{2} = 45°$; $2.828(\cos 45° + i \sin 45°)$

b. $r = \sqrt{(-1)^2 + 1^2} \approx 1.414$; $\theta = \tan^{-1}\frac{1}{-1} = -45°$; the point is in the second quadrant, so $\theta = 135°$; $1.414(\cos 135° + i \sin 135°)$

c. $r = \sqrt{0^2 + (-1)^2} = 1$; $\theta = \tan^{-1}\frac{-1}{0}$, which is undefined, so $\theta = -90°$ since the point is located on the negative y-axis; $1(\cos {-90°} + i \sin {-90°})$

d. $r = \sqrt{4^2 + (-3)^2} = 5$; $\theta = \tan^{-1}\frac{-3}{4} \approx -36.87°$; the point is in the fourth quadrant; $5(\cos {-36.87°} + i \sin {-36.87°})$

e. $r = \sqrt{(-3)^2 + (-2)^2} \approx 3.606$; $\theta = \tan^{-1}\frac{-2}{-3} \approx 33.69°$; the point is in the third quadrant, so $\theta = -146.31°$; $3.606(\cos {-146.31°} + i \sin {-146.31°})$

3. $8 = 8 + 0i$

$8^{1/3}\left(\cos\frac{1}{3}(0°) + i\sin\frac{1}{3}(0°)\right); 2(1 + 0i) = 2 + 0i$

$8^{1/3}\left(\cos\frac{1}{3}(360°) + i\sin\frac{1}{3}(360°)\right); 2(\cos 120° + i\sin 120°) =$
$2(-0.5 + 0.8660i) = -1 + 1.732i$

$8^{1/3}\left(\cos\frac{1}{3}(720°) + i\sin\frac{1}{3}(720°)\right); 2(\cos 240° + i\sin 240°) =$
$2(-0.5 + -0.8660i) = -1 - 1.732i$

4. $1 = 1 + 0i$

$1^{1/5}\left(\cos\frac{1}{5}(0°) + i\sin\frac{1}{5}(0°)\right) = 1(1 + 0i) = 1 + 0i$

$1^{1/5}\left(\cos\frac{1}{5}(360°) + i\sin\frac{1}{5}(360°)\right) = 1(\cos 72° + i\sin 72°) = 0.309 + 0.951i$

$1^{1/5}\left(\cos\frac{1}{5}(720°) + i\sin\frac{1}{5}(720°)\right) = 1(\cos 144° + i\sin 144°) = -0.809 + 0.588i$

$1^{1/5}\left(\cos\frac{1}{5}(1080°) + i\sin\frac{1}{5}(1080°)\right) = 1(\cos 216° + i\sin 216°) = 0.809 - 0.588i$

$1^{1/5}\left(\cos\frac{1}{5}(1440°) + i\sin\frac{1}{5}(1440°)\right) = 1(\cos 288° + i\sin 288°) = 0.309 + -0.951i$

5. a. $(3 - 5i) + (2 + 7i) = 5 + 2i$

b. $\left(2 + i\sqrt{12}\right)^3; r = \sqrt{2^2 + 12} = \sqrt{16} = 4; \tan^{-1}\frac{\sqrt{12}}{2} = 60°$

$[4(\cos 60° + i\sin 60°)]^3 = 4^3(\cos 3(60°) + i\sin 3(60°)) = 64(\cos 180° + i\sin 180°) = 64(-1 + 0i) = -64 + 0i$

c. $(4(\cos 27° + i\sin 27°)^{-1} = 4^{-1}(\cos(-1)27° + i\sin(-1)27°) = 0.25(\cos -27° + i\sin -27°) =$
$0.25(0.891 + -0.454i) = 0.223 - 0.114i$

d. $(4 + 4i)(3 - 3i)^{-1}$

$4 + 4i = \sqrt{32}(\cos 45° + i\sin 45°)$

$(3 + 3i)^{-1} = \left(\sqrt{18}(\cos 45° + i\sin 45°)\right)^{-1} = \left(\sqrt{18}\right)^{-1}(\cos -45° + i\sin -45°)$

$(4 + 4i)(3 - 3i)^{-1} = \sqrt{32}(\cos 45° + i\sin 45°)\frac{1}{\sqrt{18}}(\cos -45° + i\sin -45°) = \frac{\sqrt{32}}{\sqrt{18}}(\cos 0° + i\sin 0°) =$
$\frac{4}{3}(1 + 0i) = \frac{4}{3} + 0i$

e. $\frac{1}{-4 + 4i} = (-4 + 4i)^{-1} = \left[\sqrt{32}(\cos 135° + i\sin 135°)\right]^{-1} = \left(\sqrt{32}\right)^{-1}(-0.707 - 0.707i) = -0.125 - 0.125i$

f. $6(\cos 36° + i\sin 36°) \cdot 2(\cos 54° + i\sin 54°) = 12(\cos 90° + i\sin 90°) = 12(0 + i) = 0 + 12i = 12i$

6. a. Points continue to spiral out.

$(1, 1), (0, 2), (-2, 2), (-4, 0),$
$(-4, -4), (0, 8), (8, -8)$

$(1 + i) = \sqrt{2}(\cos 45° + i\sin 45°)^6 = 1 + i$

$(1 + i)^2 = \left[\sqrt{2}(\cos 45° + i\sin 45°)\right]^2 = 2(\cos 90° + i\sin 90°) = 2(0 + i) = 0 + 2i$

$(1 + i)^3 = \left[\sqrt{2}(\cos 45° + i\sin 45°)\right]^3 = \sqrt{8}(\cos 135° + i\sin 135°) = -2 + 2i$

$(1 + i)^4 = \left[\sqrt{2}(\cos 45° + i\sin 45°)\right]^4 = 4(\cos 180° + i\sin 180°) = -4 + 0i$

$(1 + i)^5 = \left[\sqrt{2}(\cos 45° + i\sin 45°)\right]^5 = \sqrt{32}(\cos 225° + i\sin 225°) = -4 - 4i$

$(1 + i)^6 = \left[\sqrt{2}(\cos 45° + i\sin 45°)\right]^6 = 8(\cos 270° + i\sin 270°) = 0 - 8i$

$(1 + i)^7 = \left[\sqrt{2}(\cos 45° + i\sin 45°)\right]^7 = \sqrt{128}(\cos 315° + i\sin 315°) = 8 - 8i$

b. Points spiral in to origin.

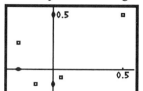

(0.5, 0.5), (0, 0.5), (−0.25, 0.25),
(−0.25, 0), (−0.125, 0.125), (0, −0.125),
(0.0625, −0.0625)

$(0.5 + 0.5i) = \frac{2}{\sqrt{2}}(\cos 45° + i\sin 45°)$

$(0.5 + 0.5i)^2 = \left[\frac{2}{\sqrt{2}}(\cos 45° + i\sin 45°)\right]^2 = \frac{1}{2}(\cos 90° + i\sin 90°) = 0 + \frac{1}{2}i = 0 + 0.5i$

$(0.5 + 0.5i)^3 = \left[\frac{2}{\sqrt{2}}(\cos 45° + i\sin 45°)\right]^3 = \frac{1}{\sqrt{8}}(\cos 135° + i\sin 135°) = -\frac{1}{4} + \frac{1}{4}i = -0.25 + 0.25i$

$(0.5 + 0.5i)^4 = \left[\frac{2}{\sqrt{2}}(\cos 45° + i\sin 45°)\right]^4 = \frac{1}{4}(\cos 180° + i\sin 180°) = -\frac{1}{4} + 0i = -0.25 + 0i$

$(0.5 + 0.5i)^5 = \left[\frac{2}{\sqrt{2}}(\cos 45° + i\sin 45°)\right]^5 = \frac{1}{\sqrt{32}}(\cos 225° + i\sin 225°) = -\frac{1}{8} - \frac{1}{8}i = -0.125 - 0.125i$

$(0.5 + 0.5i)^6 = \left[\frac{2}{\sqrt{2}}(\cos 45° + i\sin 45°)\right]^6 = \frac{1}{8}(\cos 270° + i\sin 270°) = 0 - \frac{1}{8}i = 0 - 0.125i$

$(0.5 + 0.5i)^7 \left[\frac{2}{\sqrt{2}}(\cos 45° + i\sin 45°)\right]^7 = \frac{1}{\sqrt{28}}(\cos 315° + i\sin 315°) = \frac{1}{16} - \frac{1}{16}i = 0.0625 - 0.0625i$

c. Because the modulus of $1 + i$ is more than 1, raising it to increasing powers will make each result larger. Because the modulus of $0.5 + 0.5i$ is less than 1, raising it to increasing powers will make each result smaller.

7. a. $r = \sqrt{1^2 + 1^2} = \sqrt{2} \approx 1.414$; $\tan^{-1}\left(\frac{-1}{-1}\right) = \tan^{-1} 1 = 45°$; the point $(-1, -1)$ indicates that the point is in the third quadrant, so $\theta = -135°$ or $225°$.

b. $(-1 - i)^t = \left(\sqrt{2}\right)^t(\cos 225t - i\sin 225t)$

c. $x = \left(\sqrt{2}\right)^t\cos 225t$; $y = \left(\sqrt{2}\right)^t\sin 225t$

t	0	1	2	3	4	5	6	7	8	9	10
x	1	−1	0	2	−4	4	0	−8	16	−16	0
y	0	−1	2	−2	0	4	−8	0	−16	32	32

d.

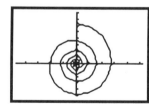

[0, 10, 0.1, −47, 52, 10, −25, 40, 5]

The graph is a spiral that is expanding exponentially. (This is a model of a static warp shell, but it is only theoretical.)

8. a. For Problem 7a.–d.

a. $r = \sqrt{(0.5)^2 + (0.866)^2} = 1$; $\theta = \tan^{-1}\left(\frac{0.866}{0.5}\right) = 60°$; $1(\cos 60° + i\sin 60°)$

b. $(0.5 + 0.866i)^t = 1^t(\cos 60t + i\sin 60t)$

c. $x = \cos 60t$; $y = \sin 60t$

t	0	1	2	3	4	5	6
x	1	0.5	−0.5	−1	−0.5	0.5	1
y	0	0.866	0.866	0	−0.866	−0.866	0

t	7	8	9	10	11	12
x	0.5	−0.5	−1	−0.5	0.5	1
y	0.866	0.866	0	−0.866	−0.866	0

d.

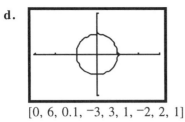

[0, 6, 0.1, −3, 3, 1, −2, 2, 1]

This number is one of the sixth roots of 1. All powers have a modulus of 1, and the pattern repeats every six.

b. (0.5, 0.866); Since $(0.5 + 0.866i)^{463} = 0.5 + 0.866i$ because 463 is equivalent to 1 and 6, the point is (0.5, 0.866).

9. a. The table values repeat in groups of 5. The five points in the table represent the five roots of 32. The five roots are $2 + 0i, 0 + 1.902i, {}^{-}1.618 + 1.176i, {}^{-}1.618 - 1.176i, 0.618 - 1.902i$.

t	0	1	2	3	4
x	2	0.618	⁻1.618	⁻1.618	0.618
y	0	1.902	1.176	⁻1.176	⁻1.902

b. $x = 32^{1/6} \cos\left(\frac{360t}{6}\right); y = 32^{1/6} \sin\left(\frac{360t}{6}\right)$

t	0	1	2	3	4	5
x	1.782	0.891	⁻0.891	⁻1.782	⁻0.891	0.891
y	0	1.543	1.543	0	⁻1.543	⁻1.543

The six roots of 32 are $1.782 + 0i, 0.891 + 1.543i, {}^{-}0.891 + 1.543i, {}^{-}1.782 + 0i, {}^{-}0.891 - 1.543i, 0.981 - 1.543i$.

10. a. Goes to (1, 0)   **b.** Goes to (1, 0)   **c.** Goes to (1, 0)   **d.** All points go to (1, 0)

11. The points iterate as shown below. Those colored black iterate to (1, 0). Those left white iterate to (⁻0.5, 0.866). The others iterate to (⁻0.5, ⁻0.866). If you try to find the point where it switches from one color to another, you will always find a point that goes to the other point. For example, while $^{-}1.6 + 0i$ iterates to (1, 0) and $^{-}1.6 + 0i$ iterates to (⁻0.5, 0.866), if you iterate $^{-}1.6 + 0.0999i$, it goes to (⁻0.5, ⁻0.866).

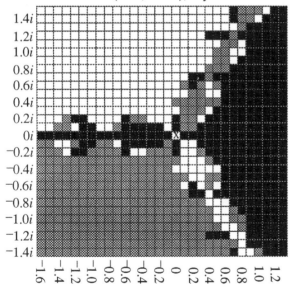

Project: More on Julia Sets

The graph of the Julia set for $c = -0.5 + 0.5i$ is shown at right. When coloring the grid, you should end up with a black region that appears to fill the interior of the Julia set. The second graph is the Julia set for $c = -1 + 0i$. Again the prisoner set will be the interior of the region.

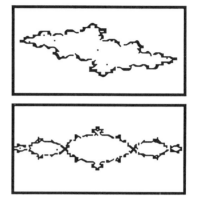

The two equations used are inverses of each other. When the program is used to plot the Julia set, this method is known as inverse iteration. The program takes the initial point and by sending it through the inverse of the actual equation, it causes the point to go back to the boundary of the set rather than escape or remain trapped.

Experimenting with various choices for c will yield everything from near circles to sets of dustlike points. Some interesting choices are $c = 0.25 + 0i$, $-0.9 + 0.12i$, and $0 + i$.

Chapter Review

Problem Set 13.8

1. **a.** Period $= 360/3 = 120°$, $y = -2 \cos 3(x - 120°)$ **b.** Period $= 360/4 = 90°$, $y = 3 \sin 4(x - 22.5°)$
    c. Period $= 360/2 = 180°$, $y = \csc 2(x + 45°)$ **d.** Period $= \frac{180}{2} = 90$, $y = \cot 2(x - 45°) + 1$

2. **a.** $y = -2 \sin 2x - 1$ **b.** $y = \sin 0.5x + 1.5$ **c.** $y = 0.5 \tan(x - 45)$ **d.** $y = 0.5 \sec 2x$

3. **a.** The equation should be similar to $y = 1.92 \sin \frac{360}{365}(x - 80) + 12.13$.

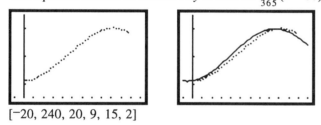

[-20, 240, 20, 9, 15, 2]

   b. According to the equation, the maximum amount of daylight (14.05 hr) occurs on the 171st day after January 1, or about June 19.
   c. By tracing the graph, you will find that $y = 12$ when $x \approx 77$ days and when $x \approx 266$ days, so the dates are approximately March 17 and September 22.

4. **a.**

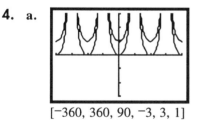

[-360, 360, 90, -3, 3, 1]

   b. $\sec^2 x = \tan^2 x + 1$

5. **a.** Use the Law of Cosines to calculate AB: $AB^2 = 12.2^2 + 13.8^2 - 2(12.2)(13.8)\cos 47.1° \approx 10.49$ cm.
    Use the Law of Sines to calculate $m\angle A$ or $m\angle B$: $\frac{\sin A}{13.8} = \frac{\sin 47.1}{10.49}$; $\sin^{-1} A = \frac{13.8 \sin 47.1}{10.49} \approx 74.51°$.
    $m\angle A \approx 74.5°$; $m\angle B \approx 180 - 74.5 - 47.1 \approx 58.4°$
   b. Use the Law of Sines to find the measure of angle E: $\frac{\sin 110}{17.4} = \frac{\sin E}{14.7}$; $\sin^{-1} E = \frac{14.7 \sin 110}{17.4} \approx 52.55°$.
    $m\angle E = 52.55°$; $m\angle F = 180 - 110 - 52.55 = 17.45°$
    Use the Law of Sines to find DE: $\frac{\sin 17.45}{DE} = \frac{\sin 110}{17.4}$; $DE = \frac{17.4 \sin 17.45}{\sin 110} \approx 5.55$ cm.

6. If the known parts include SAS or SSS, use the Law of Cosines. If the known parts include AAS, use the Law of Sines. If the known parts are SSA, you can use either law, but be careful if you use the Law of Sines to check whether you want an acute or obtuse angle.

7. $y = 100 \cos \frac{360}{105}(x - 10)$; $y = 100 \cos \frac{360}{105}(0 - 10) \approx 82.6$ mi from the equator. The spaceship passes over the launch site 41 times in 3 days. (3 days • 24 hr • 60 min = 4320 min; $\frac{4320}{105} = 41$ times)

8. $(5, {-}320°)$, $(5, 400°)$

9. **a.** $r = {-}2(\cos \theta + 1)$

    b. $r = 2(\sin \theta + 1)$

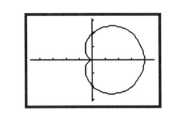

10. **a.** $(3, 4)$

    b. $({-}2, {-}1)$

    c. $(1.732, 1)$

    d. $(15, {-}8)$

    e. $i^6 = (0 + i)^6 = [1(\cos 90° + i \sin 90°)]^6 = 1(\cos 540° + i \sin 540°) = 1(\cos 180° + i \sin 180°) = {-}1 + 0i$, which graphs as the point $({-}1, 0)$.

    f. $(4(\cos 48° + i \sin 48°))^{1/4} = 4^{1/4}(\cos 12 + i \sin 12) =$ $\sqrt{2}(\text{cis } 12) = 1.38 + 0.294i$

    $(4(\cos 102° + i \sin 102°))^{1/4} = 4^{1/4}(\cos 102° + i \sin 102°) =$ $\sqrt{2}(\text{cis } 102°) = {-}0.294 + 1.38i$

    $(4(\cos 192° + i \sin 192°))^{1/4} = 4^{1/4}(\cos 192° + i \sin 192°) =$ $\sqrt{2}(\text{cis } 192°) = {-}1.38 + {-}0.294i$

    $(4(\cos 282° + i \sin 102°))^{1/4} = 4^{1/4}(\cos 282° + i \sin 282°) =$ $\sqrt{2}(\text{cis } 282°) = 0.294 - 1.38i$

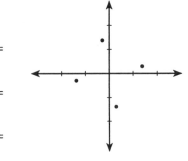

11. Points inside a circle of radius 1 centered at the origin iterate to $(0, 0)$. Points outside the circle become further and further away from the origin as they are iterated. Points on the circle stay on the circle. Some, such as $1 + i$, iterate to a single point. Others, such as $\left(\sqrt{0.3}, \sqrt{0.7}\right)$, keep bouncing around the circle hitting various points on the circle.